ESSENTIALS
OF
HUMAN GENETICS

ESSENTIALS
OF
HUMAN GENETICS

S. M. BHATNAGAR
Professor, Department of Anatomy
M. G. M. Medical College, Navi Mumbai

M. L. KOTHARI
Professor, Department of Anatomy
Seth G. S. Medical College, Mumbai

LOPA A. MEHTA
Professor & Head, Department of Anatomy
Seth G. S. Medical College, Mumbai

Orient Longman

Dedicated to
that marvel of all marvels
THE GENE

The greatest single achievement of Nature to date was surely the invention of the molecule of DNA. We have had it from the very beginning, built into the first cell to emerge, membranes and all, somewhere in the soupy water of the cooling planet three thousand million years ago. All of today's DNA, strung through all the cells of the earth, is simply an extension and elaboration of that first molecule. In a fundamental sense we cannot claim to have made progress, since the method used for growth and replication is essentially unchanged.

Lewis Thomas
in 'The Wonderful Mistake'
from *Notes of a Biology Watcher*

ORIENT LONGMAN PRIVATE LIMITED

Registered Office :

3-6-752 Himayatnagar, Hyderabad 500 029 (A.P.), INDIA
e-mail : cogeneral@orientlongman.com

Other Offices :

Bangalore/Bhopal/Bhubaneshwar/Chennai/
Ernakulam/Guwahati/Hyderabad/Jaipur/Kolkatta/
Lucknow/Mumbai/New Delhi/Patna

ISBN13 : 978 81 250 1426 3
ISBN10 : 81 250 1426 8

Typeset in Garamond by
Trendz Phototypesetters
Vaju Kotak Marg, Fort
Mumbai 400 001

Printed in India by
Novena Offset Printing Co.,
Chennai 600 005

Published by
Orient Longman Private Ltd
160 Anna Salai
Chennai 600 002.
e-mail: chegeneral@orientlongman.com

Preface

This new edition (fourth edition) brings with it a number of changes. It is thoroughly revised, updated, enlarged, and is broadly divided into two parts—**Principles of Genetics** and **Applications of Genetics**. We have endeavoured to make the text compact and readable. All the current advances in clinical and laboratory genetics have been given due attention.

The authors would like to express their appreciation and heartfelt thanks to Dr. K. Shyamkishore, Lecturer, Anatomy, Seth G.S. Medical College, for contributing the chapter on Cytology and for providing other valuable suggestions in bringing out this edition.

Our sincere thanks are due to Dr. Anirudha Chaphekar and Dr. Anirban Chatterjee for their kind help in many ways. We are also indebted to our publishers Orient Longman for their unstinted support. We are indeed most grateful to all the readers whose criticism and comments have greatly assisted the revision of this book.

S. M. Bhatnagar
M. L. Kothari
Lopa A. Mehta

Mumbai
1999

Preface to the third edition

Genetics has become an integral part of medical teaching at undergraduate and postgraduate levels. Our interest in the subject coupled with the absence of any suitably compact text encouraged us to write one that covers most of the essentials of human genetics.

For aspiring medical students, who are forever burdened with a heavy load of study, genetics is an interesting but a difficult discipline. It is a science where conceptual and terminological changes occur every day. Any text on medical genetics should be brief, simple, comprehensive and yet interesting enough to sustain a student's keenness for studying it. The authors are happy that in this regard their attempt has met with some success— as demonstrated by the fact that this is the third edition of the book.

The response from students and teachers alike, for the first two editions, has been spontaneous and heartening, and we have received some useful suggestions from them—many of which have been incorporated in this new edition.

This edition is new in more ways than one:
* The entire text has been revised, rewritten and substantially added to.
* The illustrations, which are easy to comprehend and reproduce, have been redrawn and changed at many places.
* A two-column format has been adopted.
* An introductory section has been added at the beginning of each chapter.
* A summary has been added at the end of every chapter.
* Each chapter carries a set of questions that will act as exercises in self-assessment for the student.
* The glossary has been updated.

We have made a small attempt to encompass, in brief, the vast and growing field of genetics and the consequent explosion in its literature. This book could provide a starting point in the introduction to a course in human genetics, and we feel that it will play a useful role in today's medical education. We do, however, feel that given the fact that, in advanced countries, genetic disorders are receiving ever-increasing attention, perhaps in India too Chairs in medical genetics could be instituted in all medical colleges.

Orient Longman and Vinay Masurekar and Hemang Shah deserve our thanks for, as it were, co-authoring the book. Orient Longman are responsible for giving the book a new shape and a more attractive layout; Mr. Masurekar has laboured, artistically, over the illustrations. Our renewed thanks are due to Messrs. Kothari Medical Publishing House for their cooperation in the publication of the earlier editions. To colleagues in the teaching fraternity, and to students, we are grateful for providing us with feedback that has assisted the revisions.

Surendra Bhatnagar
Manu Kothari
Lopa Mehta

Mumbai

CONTENTS

1 AN INTRODUCTION TO HUMAN GENETICS

The twentieth century has been the century of the study of genetics, the science of heredity and variation. This field, the youngest among the biological sciences, has expanded and grown so rapidly that it has (justly) appropriated a significant proportion of time, money and recognition. A scrutiny of the Nobel Prizes in Medicine over the last fifty years reveals that a substantial number have been conferred on geneticists. The expanded frontiers of genetics in general, and human genetics in particular, have totally changed the face of medical practice. The highest application of human genetics has been in the field of medical genetics.

Laboratory research has advanced so rapidly that it has made the biologist's dream of knowing human structure and function, at molecular and sub-molecular levels come true. This has further revealed the genetic basis of human diseases. Finally, these findings have resulted in the early diagnosis, and in certain cases the treatment of diseases, by actually replacing the faulty gene. The science of eugenics will be in the forefront in the future.

Genetics is the science of heredity. Human genetics deals with the **inherited characteristic**—physical and mental, normal as well as abnormal—in an individual, a family, a race or a population. It is concerned with the ways in which these characteristics are transmitted from generation to generation. It also includes the study of hereditary factors, and the ways in which they express themselves during the development and life of an individual.

Beginnings of the Science of Genetics

The work of an Austrian monk **Gregor Mendel** in the latter half of the nineteenth century laid the foundation of the science of genetics. He selected seven contrasting characters in **garden peas** for his work. For each experiment he crossed varieties of pea differing only in one of these characters. He proposed that each **character or trait** was determined by a pair of factors (now known as genes). From his numerous, painstaking studies, he enunciated the principles of heredity:

1. The first law or law of segregation of alleles: During the formation of gametes, the two members of a single pair of genes (alleles) are never found in the same gamete, but instead, always segregate and pass to different gametes. In an individual, each member of an allelic pair is originally derived from separate parents, one male and the other female. The traits or characteristics determined by such pairs of alleles do not blend in the offspring, since the alleles retain their identity and can pass unchanged from one generation to the next, irrespective of the expression of a trait in any generation.

2. The second law or law of independent assortment: This law states that during gametogenesis, members of different gene-pairs assort randomly or independently of one another.

Mendel's work reported in 1865–1866, remained unnoticed till 1900, when it was independently rediscovered by three biologists: de Vries, professor of botany at the University of Amsterdam, Correns, a botanist at the University of Tubingen, and von Tschermak-Seysenegg, an assistant in the agricultural experimental station of Esslingen near Vienna. Thus, the development of genetics as a science started not from Mendel's own paper, but from the papers that reported the rediscovery of his laws.

The chromosome theory of inheritance: In 1903 Sutton and Boveri independently proposed the chromosome theory of inheritance. The theory suggested that the chromosomes are the carriers of hereditary factors or genes, and the behaviour of the chromosomes at the time of cell division provides the cytological basis for Mendel's laws of inheritance.

The Growth of Human Genetics

In the eighteenth and nineteenth centuries, prior to Mendel's work some simple patterns of inheritance were known and reported. However, there was no understanding of the how and the why of these patterns. The characteristics which were known to be inherited were very obvious ones like, polydactyly (extra fingers), hemophilia, and colour blindness. Maupertuis of France studied the inheritance of albinism and polydactyly in the eighteenth century. Otto described hemophilia in a family from New Hamsphire in 1903.

Galton, in 1875, made a distinction between the effects of environment and heredity. He suggested the study of twins for finding out the difference between the influence of **heredity** and that of **environment**. Galton also studied the inheritance of physical features and of special talents. He found that qualitative analysis was not a satisfactory method for the study of inheritance of such traits. He initiated the study of quantitative genetics (**polygenic inheritance**) for such traits. He introduced the statistical concept of the regression co-efficient to genetics. This marked the beginning of the mathematical aspect of human heredity.

Until the beginning of the twentieth century, human genetics was essentially concerned with tracing of pedigrees and studies on the effects of marriages between cousins (consanguineous marriages). Then came a series of breakthroughs by independent researchers.

In 1902, **Garrod**, who ranks with Galton as a pioneer in human genetics, reported for the first time, alkaptonuria as an example of mendelian inheritance in man. In 1908, Garrod developed his concept of 'the inborn errors of metabolism.' With further understanding of biochemical genetics, this concept was elaborated in 1941 by **Beadle** and **Tatum** who suggested the 'one gene-one enzyme hypothesis.'

Landsteiner in 1900 discovered the ABO blood groups. This discovery initiated the study of the genetics of blood groups.

Hardy, a mathematician at Cambridge University, and **Weinberg**, a physician in Stuttgart, independently propounded a law, the Hardy-Weinberg law, which laid the foundation of **population genetics**.

Galton put forward the idea of hereditary improvement of man and animals by selective breeding, for which he coined the term **eugenics**, an impracticable and hazardous plan for use on human beings because the knowledge of human genetics is as yet elementary.

Most of the diseases known to be genetically transmitted, tended to be fatal in early life. However, with improved medical care, more and more patients with these disorders now survive. The science of genetics has playd an important role in to the study of such diseases. This branch of genetics is known as **medical genetics**.

Some of the other significant events in the development of human genetics are:

1) Ford, Haldane and others suggested the role of infectious disease in influencing the genetic constitution of man. Allison in 1954 gave the first clear evidence of such a role, by his study of the relationship of malaria and the gene for sickle hemoglobin.

2) Haldane studied linkage quantitatively in man for the first time by estimating the distance separating the colour blindness and hemophilia loci on the X chromosome. Mohr discovered an autosomal linkage in man by studying the linkage between the Lutheran blood group and the Secretor factor.

3) Gerty Cori and Carl Cori in 1952 demonstrated the first specific enzyme defect in an inborn error of metabolism — deficiency of glucose-6-phosphatase, in one form of the glycogen-storage disease. Jervis in 1953, detected deficiency of phenylalanine hydroxylase in phenylketonuria (PKU). Garrod's prediction of an enzyme defect in alkaptonuria was confirmed by La Du and his colleagues in 1958.

4) In 1956, Tjio and Levan on the one hand, and Ford and Hamerton on the other, independently showed for the first time that the number of chromosomes in man is 46, and not 48 as was believed till then.

5) Ingram in 1957 detected the role played by a gene in determining the amino acid sequence of a protein. He studied the difference between normal hemoglobin A and sickle hemoglobin in humans.

6) Lejeune and his colleagues, in 1959 discovered for the first time a chromosomal aberration, providing the basis for a congenital malformation in humans: mongoloid idiocy (also called Down's syndrome).

7) Ford and Jacobs and their colleagues in 1959 established the role of the Y chromosome in sex determination in man.

8) Nowell and Hungerford, in 1959 identified the specific chromosomal aberration associated with cancer—in this case, chronic myeloid leukemia (CML).

9) Several researchers simultaneously suggested in 1961 that one X chromosome in the normal female is relatively inactive genetically (the Lyon hypothesis).

Genetics is one of the most recent and rapidly advancing sciences and many a Nobel Prize in Physiology and Medicine has been awarded to geneticists.

1930 Karl Landsteiner for research on blood groups and immunology.

1933 Thomas Hunt Morgan for research on the nature of the gene.

1946 Herman Joseph Muller for the discovery of the induction of mutation by X-rays.

1958 George Wells Beadle and Edward Lawrie Tatum for contributions in biochemical genetics; and Joshua Lederberg, for the discovery of sexual recombination in bacteria.

1959 Arthur Kornberg and Severo Ochoa, for studies of the chemistry of DNA and RNA.

1961 James Watson, Francis Crick and Maurice Wilkins for elucidation of the structure of DNA.

1965 Francois Jacob, Andre Lwoff, and Jacques Monod, for their discoveries concerning genetic control of enzyme and virus synthesis.

1968 Marshall Nirenberg, Har Gobind Khorana, and Robert Holley, for 'cracking the genetic code' and determining the means by which a gene determines the sequence of amino acids in a protein.

1975 Howard Temin and David Baltimore, for challenging the central dogma which had till then denied the possibility of cytoplasmic RNA directing nuclear DNA synthesis.

1977 Hamilton Smith, Daniel Nathans and Werner Arber for work with restriction enzymes used in DNA research.

1983 Barbara McClintock for her discovery that genes can move from one spot to another on chromosomes of plants and change future generations of plants they produce, thereby introducing the concept of 'jumping genes'.

1984 Niels Jerne, Cesar Milstein and Georges Köhler for the concept and the production of 'monoclonal antibodies'.

1986 Stanley Cohen and Rita Levi-Montaloni, for discovering the hitherto unknown growth factors controlling cellular growth.

1987 Susumu Tonegawe, for proving that cells accomplish the task of making antibodies to order by reshuffling parts of genes that govern the production of antibodies.

1989 Bishop John Michael and Varmus Harold Eliot for derivation of oncogenes.

1990 Joseph E. Murray and Thomas E. Donald for organ transplantation.

1991 Neher and Sekmann for ion detection in cell membranes.

1992 Kreba and Fisher for discoveries on reversible protein phosphorylation as a biological regulatory mechanism.

1993 Richard Roberts and Philip Sharp for studies on genes, DNA and introns.

1995 Edward B. Lewis, Christiane Nusselian-Volhard and Eric F. Wieschaus for their research on how genes control early embryonic development in the fruitfly.

It is convenient to divide the subject of human genetics into the following interrelated parts:

A. Principles of Genetics:

1. Cytogenetics: A study of normal chromosomes
2. Molecular genetics: A study of molecular structure of genetic material and its functional significance.
3. Modes of inheritance and genetic basis of variation.
4. Population genetics.

B. Application of Genetics:

1. Immunogenetics, including blood groups.
2. Developmental genetics.
3. Abnormal chromosomes.
4. Biochemical genetics including hemoglobinopathies and other inborn errors of metabolism.
5. Pharmacogenetics.
6. Cancer and behavioural disorders—as models of diseases with a genetic basis.
7. Prenatal diagnosis and treatment.
8. Genetic counselling and eugenics.
9. Laboratory genetics, gene map, linkage, recombinant DNA technology.

SUMMARY

Genetics: The study of inherited traits and their transmission from generation to generation.

Mendel (1866): Through his garden - pea experiments laid the foundation for a scientific study of this discipline. His laws of 'segregation' and 'random or independent assortment' are a byword in genetics.

Sutton and Boveri (1903): Suggested chromosomes as the carriers of hereditary factors or genes.

Galton (1875): Studied identical and fraternal twins to assess the relative influences of heredity and environment.

Garrod (1902): Initiated the concept of 'inborn errors of metabolism'.

Landsteiner (1900): His discovery of ABO blood group system pioneered blood transfusion and study of genetics of blood groups.

Other noteworthy landmarks in the progress of human genetics are:

1. demonstration of chromosomes under the microscope and the study of chromosomal aberrations;
2. Lyon hypothesis of X chromosome inactivation;
3. elucidation of the structure of DNA by Watson and Crick;
4. cracking of the genetic code by Nirenberg, Khorana and others, and consequently
5. detailed direct observations on DNA with the use of 'restriction endonuclease' enzyme systems.

2 THE CELL

The belief that the nucleus controls the cytoplasm has been disproved beyond doubt. It has been indisputably established that the genes govern the metabolic activities of a cell. The nebulous cytoplasm with its various organelles controls the activities of the genes. Before embarking upon a detailed study of chromosomes and genes within the nucleus, and their role in governing the activities of the cell, it is essential to have a panoramic view of the structure and function of other cell organelles.

Introduction

The human body consists of over 60 trillion cells that are organised into various tissues, organs and organ-systems for optimal functioning. The cells within the various systems are interrelated and behave in concordance with the role they ought to perform, aimed at achieving a common goal: survival of the individual and the propagation of the species.

Each cell has the capacity to perform all the essential life functions. Each differentiated cell has specialised morphology and is designed to perform a given job. Every function of any differentiated cell is a mere amplification of one (or more) fundamental cellular function. Differentiation is improving one skill at the cost of another. Differentiation is not a unidirectional entity and cells are known to be *de*-differentiated or become primitive (probably an age-related degenerative step)! The classic example of this retrograde differentiation is a cell undergoing a cancerous change.

There are two reasons for the similarity in size of cells regardless of the size of the organism. (A large majority of human cells also vary in size from 6 to 20 μ). As the cytoplasm increases, the nucleocytoplasmic ratio falls, and the DNA in the nucleus is unable to cope with the metabolic requirements of the cell. The skeletal muscle cell and the megakaryocyte overcome this problem because of multiple nuclei. Secondly, the nutrition of a cell which is by diffusion, from the periphery to the centre. The large ovum with a diameter of over 100 μ and a neuronal cell have their surfaces clothed by numerous satellite cells (follicular and glial cells respectively). These satellites provide auxiliary metabolic support for the central cell.

The protoplasm of the structural unit, the cell, is remarkably similar in all eukaryotes (organisms with nucleated cells). The prokaryotes (bacteria and blue-green algae) have cytoplasm where hereditary and metabolic materials are not segregated from each other. The purpose of this section is to understand the structure-function correlation of a eukaryotic cell.

Before beginning the study, it is important to understand the method of study. The various components of a cell, *the cell wall* or plasma membrane with the glycocalyx coat, *the cytoplasm* including the living organelles and inclusion bodies, and *the nucleus* have been visualised with the electron microscope. The resolving power of the microscope improved 200 times from a limited 200 nm in the light microscope to 1 nm. (Resolving power is the minimum distance between two distinct objects to be perceived as two separate units. It is equal to half the wavelength of electromagnetic radiation used to view the objects.)

Light and electron microscopy have been combined with X-ray diffraction study, histochemistry and immunohistochemistry to heighten the structural and functional understanding of many biological processes.

THE UNIT MEMBRANE

The semipermeable barrier separating the interior of the cell from the exterior is called the plasma membrane or the plasmalemma. This membrane and the membrane of the membrane-bound organelles of the cytoplasm are remarkably similar in structure. This has prompted the usage of the term **unit membrane** to describe this prototypic structure.

The unit membrane consists of phospholipid molecules. Phospholipids are essentially nitrogenous compounds conjugated via a phosphate group to a lipid molecule (Fig.1). Nitrogenous compounds such as choline, serine, or ethanolamine constitute the polar, hydrophilic head of the phospholipid. Two long-chain fatty acids covalently linked to glycerol constitute the hydrophobic tail. Cholesterol molecules are also present in the membrane to stabilise the latter and to regulate its fluidity. The amphipathic nature of the phospholipids causes them to arrange as a bilayered membrane (about 7.5 nm in thickness) in an aqueous medium. The hydrophobic end lies sandwiched between the hydrophilic ends.

A variety of protein molecules are associated with the bilayer. Some are incorporated within the membrane (intrinsic or integral protein) while others are held either to the inner or the outer surface (extrinsic or peripheral protein). Some intrinsic proteins extend throughout the thickness of the unit membrane, in which case they are called transmembrane proteins (Fig 2). These act as pores for hydrophilic molecules to pass through the unit membrane. Lipid soluble substances can directly pass through the phospholipid bilayer.

The proteins in the lipid bilayer are responsible for the functional differences between any other unit membrane and the plasma membrane. The proteins in the bilayer are mobile along the membrane to a certain extent, but they do not cross the junctional complexes. This explains the differences in the functions of the luminal, basal

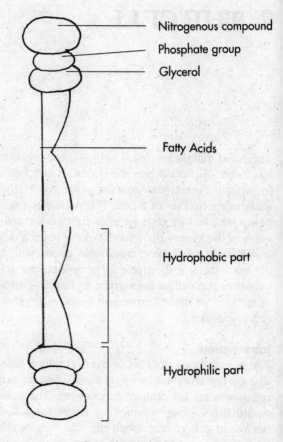

Fig. 1 Phospholipid bilayer

and intercellular surfaces of an epithelial cell. The surface modifications such as of the luminal surface microvilli, stereocilia, cilia and flagella are cytoskeletal modifications of the plasma membrane.

Steroid hormones can pass through the lipid bilayer and act directly on the nucleus. Non-steroid hormones act on receptors which are intrinsic proteins on the plasma membrane and thereby activate a *second messenger* which changes the metabolism and motility of the whole cell. Some intrinsic proteins on the internal surface, act as anchors for the elements of the cytoskeleton.

On the external surface, membrane proteins and lipids are conjugated with short chain polysaccharides, forming glycoproteins and glycolipids, respectively. This layer is analogous to the cell wall of plant cell, bacteria and fungi and is called

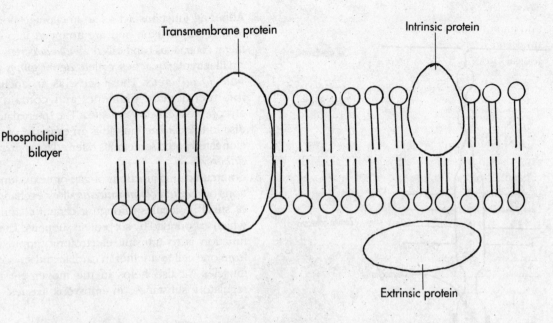

Fig. 2 Unit membrane

as the **glycocalyx coat**. The functions of this coat are cell recognition, intercellular adhesion, and mechanical and chemical protection (such as protecting the intestinal epithelium from the lytic action of digestive enzymes).

Functions
The unit membrane
1) Acts as a boundary for physiologically distinct compartments within the cell: those within the channel systems (vacuoplasm) and those outside it (hyaloplasm or cytosol).
2) Transports electrolytes and other molecules.
3) Generates bioelectric potentials across the membrane.
4) Serves as receptor for hormones and other chemical stimuli.
5) Recognises other cells and their attachments.
6) Provides sites for anchorage of intracellular structures for locomotion and cytoskeletal stability.

Transport across Plasma Membrane
The various means of transport are:
1) **Passive diffusion** of lipids, lipid soluble metabolites, and gases directly through the membrane, and of small molecules like water and urea through the pores.
2) **Facilitated diffusion** with the help of carrier proteins which bind reversibly to glucose and amino acids.
3) **Active transport** requires energy to transport Na^+ out of the cell through the Na-K ATPase pump.
4) **Bulk transport** within the cell is called **endocytosis** and outside the cell is called **exocytosis**. Engulfing small particles is called **pinocytosis** while engulfing larger particles is called **phagocytosis**. The endocytosis may be receptor mediated, in which case the steps are as follows:
   a. The substance to be engulfed is called a *ligand*.
   b. The receptors are present in *coated pits*.
   c. The protein *clathrin* lies on the protoplasmic aspect of a coated pit.
   d. The engulfed particle loses the clathrin which goes back to the surface membrane to form more coated pits.

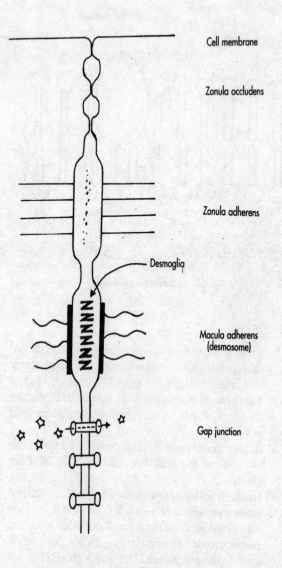

Cell membrane

Zonula occludens

Zonula adherens

Desmoglia

Macula adherens
(desmosome)

Gap junction

Fig 3 Cell junctions

Cell junctions: (Fig 3)

The intercellular surface shows specialised cell junctions of three types:

1) Occluding junctions or tight junctions or *zonula occludens* are a continuous band near the apex of the epithelial cells and separate the luminal surface from the intercellular surface. This is responsible for the polarity of the epithelial cells.

2) Adhering junctions act as an anchorage point to the cytoskeleton and are arranged into either a continuous band called *zonula adherens* or small circular patches called *desmosomes* or *macula adherens*. These serve as an anchor for intermediate filaments and contain a glycoprotein called *desmoglea*. The Intercalated disc in the cardiac muscle is an example of an elongated patch sometimes referred to as *fascia adherens*.

3) Communicating junctions or gap or nexus junctions or *macula communicans* allow exchange of small molecules through a central channel which is bounded by six protein subunits. Their function is to transmit electrotonic impulses from one cell to another in cardiac and smooth muscles. It also helps in the movement of regulatory substances in embryonic tissues.

CYTOPLASMIC ORGANELLES

The cytoplasm consists of cytosol in which dynamic, metabolically active bodies called organelles that are essential to the cell, are suspended. There are, however, other bodies within the cytoplasm such as secretory granules, lipid droplets and glycogen vesicles which are not regarded as being essential to the life processes of the cell and are called inclusion bodies.

Ribosomes (Fig 4)

An electron-dense, basophilic organelle composed of ribosomal RNA and ribosomal proteins, arranged as two subunits of 40S and 60S units, together forming a 80S unit. S is the Svedberg unit of sedimentation rate , not the molecular weight.) The function of ribosomes is the synthesis of proteins. Ribosomes are of two types: free and attached. The free ribosomes are either single (monosome) which are inactive, or multiple (polysome) which are in the active state. The 40S subunit of polysome anchors to the mRNA and the 60S subunit helps in peptide formation with the help of tRNA. The 60S subunit anchor to the endoplasmic reticulum in the attached variety of ribosomes and synthesise proteins within the

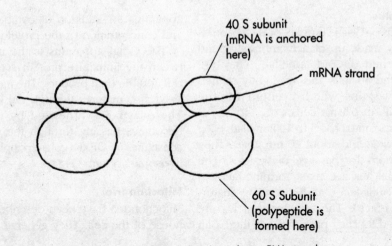

Fig 4 Ribosomes with two sub-units and an mRNA strand

endoplasmic reticulum. The free ribosomes synthesise proteins for use in cytosol (enzymes for cellular function).

Endoplasmic Reticulum

Endoplasmic reticulum (which on centrifugation gives rise to microsomes) is of two varieties, the smooth endoplasmic reticulum (sER) and the rough or granular endoplasmic reticulum (rER or gER).

The sER and the rER are parts of membranous systems continuous with each other. The membrane of the endoplasmic reticulum is similar to that of any unit membrane consisting of a lipoprotein bilayer. This system is present as lamellae, vesicles or tubes.

The rER is studded with electron-dense ribosomes that account for its basophilic granularity. As seen earlier the 60S subunit of the ribosomes anchors to the endoplasmic reticulum, the subunit that is responsible for the peptide formation. The polypeptide is thus formed within the rER (Fig 5).

The function of the sER is the metabolism of small molecules as in detoxification of many drugs and poisons, and therefore it is abundantly found in the hepatocytes. Smooth endoplasmic reticulum also helps synthesis of in cholesterol, bile acid and steroid.

The rER synthesises proteins for plasma membrane formation and repair production of hormones, enzymes and mucus to be secreted outside the cell, and lysosomal enzymes for digestion of phagocytosed particles.

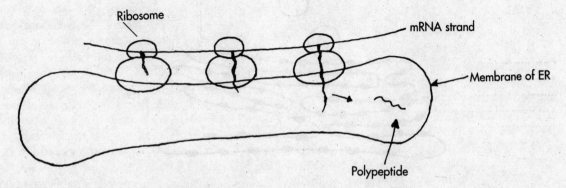

Fig 5 Polypeptide formation within an rER

Golgi Apparatus

Golgi apparatus or Golgi complex or dictyosomes are structurally made up of a membrane-bound array of flattened discoid lamellae. They are present near the nucleus and are lightly stained with ordinary stains which account for the perinuclear halo in plasma cells.

The Golgi apparatus has 5 to 10 lamellae, each about 25 nm wide and about 20 nm apart. They have fenestrations for passage of vesicles. The Golgi apparatus has a convex forming-face towards the rER (cis-face), and a concave maturing-face (trans-face). The transfer vesicles are formed in the rER. They pass through the Golgi apparatus for addition of complex polypeptides and concentration of the proteins.

The Golgi apparatus is the intermediary between the immature protein synthesised by the rER and the final product. The membrane synthesised also matures through the Golgi apparatus. The enzymes synthesised by the rER for the lysosomes passing through the Golgi apparatus constitute the GERL (golgi-endoplasmic reticulum-lysosome) system (Fig 6).

Mitochondria

Mitochondria have been described as the powerhouse of the cell. They generate a large amount

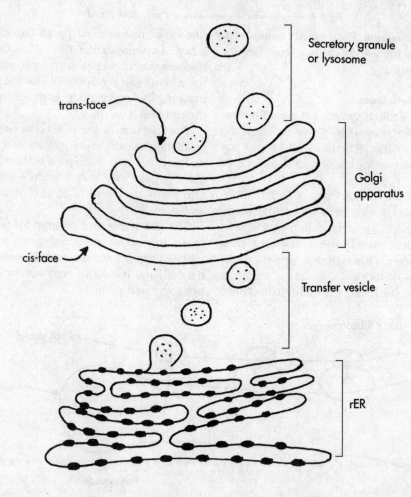

Fig. 6 Scheme of protein secretion

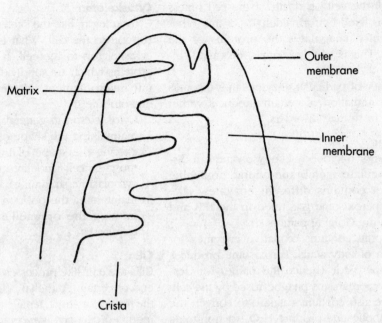

Fig. 7 Part of mitochondrion

of ATP through aerobic metabolism. In the absence of oxygen, glycolysis in the cytosol generates much less ATP.

Mitochondria are discrete particulate organelles 2–5 microns long. They are situated at sites where substantial amount of ATPs are required, such as near cilia, flagella, microvilli, between myofibrils for muscle contraction, and near rER for protein synthesis.

Mitochondria have two covering unit membranes. The outer covering is similar to the plasma membrane. The inner one has numerous folds called cristae which project into the inner amorphous matrix. The outer membrane, inner membrane and the matrix have different enzymes for different metabolism.

The mitochondria have enzymes for the Krebs cycle, for the electron transport chain, for ATP synthesis. The mitochondria also help the sER in steroid synthesis, fatty acid oxidation and nucleic acid synthesis.

The mitochondria are different from other cell organelles. They contain DNA which is different from the nuclear DNA (exclusively maternal in origin) but similar to prokaryotic nucleic acids.

Mitochondria are self replicative and synthesise some of their own enzymes. Other enzymes are created through nuclear DNA activity. Mitochondria are thought to be endosymbiotic bacteria. The host cell provides the nutrition and looks after other functions lost by the guest who in turn efficiently produces ATP for the host.

Lysosome

The lysosome is a discrete particulate membrane-bound organelle. Lysosomes contain various digestive enzymes like esterases, glycosidases, peptidases and other hydrolytic enzymes. The lysosome is formed in the rER and matures in the Golgi apparatus. The lysosome emerging from the Golgi apparatus is called primary lysosome. These lysosomes have not yet taken part in any metabolic event.

Primary lysosome combines with a phagosome (phagocytosed organic material) to form a secondary lysosome (Fig 8). The end-product of degradation of the material could be stored as residual bodies or may get extruded by exocytosis. Lysosome degrades old and worn out cytoplasmic organelles (autophagy). Lysosome also causes autolysis of the cell on death of the cell unless the tissue is fixed by formaldehyde or any other fixative which coagulates the proteins of the lysosomes. This is why lysosomes are called suicidal bags of the cell.

Deficiency of particular enzymes in lysosomes causes accumulation of certain products within the cell as in storage disorders.

Peroxisome

Peroxisome or microbody-like lysosome is a discrete particulate membrane-bound organelle. However it contains different enzymes. Like lysosome, peroxisome is formed in the rER and matures in the Golgi apparatus.

Peroxisome contains oxidative enzymes for ß-oxidation of fatty acids. Peroxisome produces hydrogen peroxide (hence the name) for destroying microorganisms phagocytosed by the cell. Peroxisome also contains catalase to convert the toxic metabolic end-product H_2O_2 to non-toxic water and oxygen.

Cytoskeleton

Cytoskeleton, like the skeleton of the body, gives support to the cell. What is bone to the body is cytoskeleton to the cell. It comprises of fibrous proteins which are subdivided based on their size into microfilament, intermediate filament and microtubule.

Cytoskeleton in general helps in:
1) maintaining the shape of the cell.
2) altering the shape of the cell (contraction in muscle, cell motility in flagellated cells and cytoplasmic streaming)
3) maintaining the position of the organelles.
4) moving the organelles within the cell as required.

Cilia

Cilia are hair-like processes present at the luminal end of certain epithelial cells. Cilia are located in the respiratory tract, female reproductive tract, and modified cilia act as receptors of olfactory, auditory and visual epithelia. Cilia are extensions of

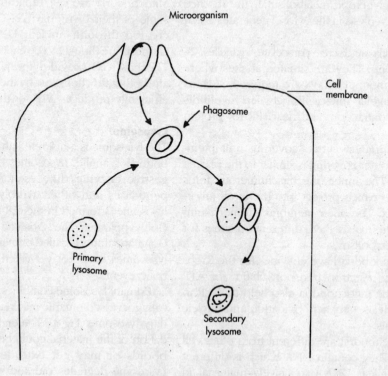

Fig 8 Action of the Lysosome

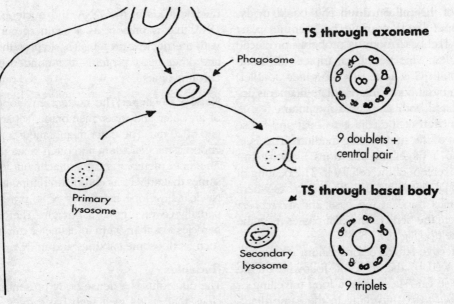

TS through axoneme

Phagosome

9 doublets +
central pair

TS through basal body

Primary
lysosome

Secondary
lysosome

9 triplets

Fig 9 Cilium

the plasma membrane, 5–10 μ long.

The extension is called the axoneme. The axoneme is made up of nine outer pairs of doublets of microtubules and one central pair. The central pair is surrounded by a central sheath. The outer doublet is made up of a complete

subunit A and an incomplete subunit B. Subunit A contains an outer arm, an inner arm, with ATPase protein dynein. It also has a radial spoke with the spoke-head towards the central sheath.

The central pair ends at the axosome that is present at the root of the axoneme. The anchor

Table 1. A comparison of the three subgroups of the cytoskeleton

Microfilament	Intermediate filament	Microtubule
Solid filament	Solid or hollow filament	Hollow tube
5–6 nm in diameter	10–12 nm in diameter	25 nm in diameter
Consists of G (globular) — actin subunits which join to form F (filamentous) — actin	Consists of 4 to 5 protofilaments (Desmin, Keratin, Vimentin, etc.	Consists of 13 protofilaments made up of globular protein — α and ß tubulin
Function: 1. Muscle contraction 2. Change in cell shape 3. Cytokinesis 4. Cytoplasmic streaming	Function: 1. Desmin helps in integration of contractile unit in muscle tissue 2. Tonofilaments form desmosomes in epithelial tissue 3. Vimentin in fibroblasts, Neurofilament in neurons and Glial filaments in neurolgia help in cytoskeletal integration	Function: 1. Cell motility 2. Chromosomal movement 3. Beating of cilia 4. Maintenance of cell shape

point of a cilium is called the basal body, kinetosome, basal granule or blepharoplast centriole. The basal body is probably produced by centrioles. Nine peripheral triplets (an additional subunit C is added to the outer doublet) end in the basal body. Intermediate filaments anchor the basal body to plasma membrane.

The function of the cilia is to beat and cause movement of the surrounding medium. This is in contrast to a flagellum that does likewise but causes movement of the cell itself. The beating of an individual cilium has an *effective stroke* where the rigid cilia bend at the base and a *recovery stroke* where the bend of the cilia passes from the base to the tip (Fig 10).

The effective stroke of one cilium is immediately followed by the adjacent, followed by the third, and so on. These form a long travelling or *metachronal wave*, travelling in the same direction as the effective stroke.

Centrosome: The centrosome or cell centre is a non-membrane-bound organelle. It is present near the nucleus. It contains a pair of centrioles often called diplosome. Centrioles separate and migrate to the poles of the cell and form mitotic spindles. Centrioles have nine peripheral microtubule triplets without the central pair. Centrioles in ciliated epithelia form the basal bodies of the cilia.

NUCLEUS

The nucleus (derived from *nux*, meaning a nut) is a membrane-bound organelle, 4–10 microns in diameter. It stains with basic dyes because of nucleic acids in the DNA and nucleoli. It is the DNA that is present as a chain of genes along with the nuclear proteins (basic proteins *histones* and other acidic proteins) that condenses to form chromosomes.

Nuclear envelope: The nuclear envelope consists of an outer and inner membrane, separated by a gap of 20 nm. The outer membrane is a part of the endoplasmic reticulum and often bears ribosomes. The inner membrane is for attachment to chromosomes that adhere as chromatin during interphase. Nuclear envelope has pores of 80 nm across but partially covered by a diaphragm. Therefore, only particles less than 9 nm in diameter can traverse it, such as ribosome subunits and mRNA.

Nucleolus

The nucleolus is a dense body present in the nucleus that stains well with basic dyes. Centrally within the nucleolus lie the nucleolar organising genes of acrocentric chromosomes (that is numbers. 13, 14, 15, 21, 22) called *pars chromosoma*. The newly synthesised rRNA are extremely long and form the *pars filamentosa* of the nucleolus. The long rRNA is broken down and combines with ribosomal proteins to form the *pars granulosa* of the nucleolus. All these 3 units of nucleoli are embedded within the *pars amorpha* of the nucleolus, which is a structureless matrix.

Nucleoli are large and numerous in cells with high rate of protein synthesis such as large neurons, active embryonic cells and malignant neoplastic cells.

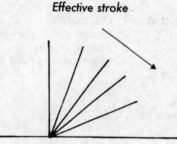
Effective stroke

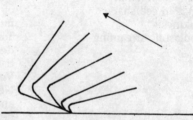
Recovery stroke

Fig 10 Beating of a Cilium

In neurons of female mammals, the inactivated X chromosome is tagged on to the nucleolus as the nucleolar satellite (Barr body).

Chromatin

Nuclear matrix contains fibrous material consisting of DNA interspersed with nuclear protein either highly coiled as heterochromatin or relatively less coiled as euchromatin.

Nuclear Matrix

Nuclear matrix contains proteins that control DNA replication, transcription, RNA metabolism and transport.

SUMMARY

Structure	Function
Plasma membrane	1) Acts boundarias a for physiologically distinct compartments within the cells: those within the channel systems (vacuoplasm) from those outside it (hyaloplasm or cytosol). 2) Transports electrolytes and other molecules. 3) Generates bioelectric potentials across the membrane. 4) Serves as receptor for hormones and other chemical stimuli. 5) Recognises other cells and their attachments. 6) Provides sites for anchorage of intracellular structures for locomotion and cytoskeletal stability.
Ribosome	Helps in protein synthesis.
Smooth endoplasmic reticulum	Metabolism of small molecules as in detoxification of many drugs and poisons. Smooth endoplasmic reticulum also helps in cholesterol, bile acid and steroid synthesis.
Rough endoplasmic reticulum	Plasma membrane formation and repair; production of hormones, enzymes, mucus to be secreted outside the cell; and, lysosomal enzymes for digestion of phagocytosed particles.
Golgi apparatus	Packaging of secretory granules, lysosome by addition of complex polypeptides and concentration of the proteins.
Mitochondria	Generator of energy (powerhouse of the cell). The mitochondria have enzymes for the Krebs cycle, for the electron transport chain, for ATP synthesis; the mitochondria also help the sER in steroid synthesis, fatty acid oxidation and nucleic acid synthesis.
Lysosome	Autophagy of old, worn-out organelles, digestion of phagocytosed particles.
Peroxisome	Contains oxidative enzymes for ß-oxidation of fatty acids; produces hydrogen peroxide for destroying microorganism phagocytosed by the cell; contains catalase to convert the toxic metabolic endproduct H_2O_2 to nontoxic water and oxygen.
Cytoskeleton	Maintains the shape of the cell; alters the shape of the cell (contraction in muscle, cell motility in flagellated cells and cytoplasmic streaming); maintains the position of the organelles; moves the organelles within the cell as per its needs.
Cilia, flagella	Cilia: to beat and cause movement of the surrounding medium. Flagella: to beat and cause movement of the cell itself.
Centrosome	Forms the basal body of cilia; forms mitotic spindles.
Nucleus	Carrier of hereditary information.

3 CYTOGENETICS: THE CHROMOSOMAL BASIS OF INHERITANCE

Introduction

Chromosomes are the vehicles of heredity. They are passed on to subsequent generations by the process of fertilisation, that is, the union of mature gametes, the sperm and the ovum.

Chromosomes reside in the nucleus of a cell in eukaryotes, except during cell division **mitosis** and **meiosis** (reduction division), at which time the nuclear membrane disappears. Their number in each cell is species-specific and they are definite structural entities in their own right.

The human sperm and the ovum contain half the species-specific number of chromosomes. This is called the **haploid** or 1N number and is 23. After fertilisation, the zygote comes to possess the **diploid** or 2N number. Except the sex-determining chromosomes designated X and Y, the others exist as matching or homologous pairs and are called **autosomes**.

Each chromosome, is essentially, a DNA-protein package, capable of self-replication, and retains its structural and functional integrity through all successive divisions of any cell type.

The units of heredity or genes are said to occupy specific or fixed positions along the length of a chromosome. These positions are called **geneloci**.

The chromosomal constitution of an organism is called its **karyotype**. The human karyotype for the male is 44+XY and that for the female is, 44+XX. Chromosomes are classified on the basis of their length and the position of their **centromere**, **primary constriction** or **kinetochore**. This is the site which provides attachment at the cellular microtubular apparatus during mitosis and meiosis.

It is now relatively simple to obtain chromosomes for direct study from a wide variety of cells. These 'karyotyping' procedures include an array of staining techniques which bring out the intrinsic cross-banded organisation of each chromosome. The stains employed are either the derivatives of quinacrine, a fluorescent dye or the Giemsa dye. Gross chromosomal abnormalities of number and structure can be detected thereby.

All chromosomes play an important role in maintaining an individual and the species. The Y chromosome determines maleness. The presence of at least one X chromosome is essential for survival, as it carries genes concerned with a variety of vital functions. Since, the female has two X chromosomes, she ought to be 'doubly' viable, but that is not so. It was postulated by Mary Lyon, that one of the two X chromosomes in the mammalian female is somehow rendered inactive in each cell of the body. The presence of an inactive clump of chromatin in female nuclei was shown by Barr and Bertram in 1949. The Lyon hypothesis seeks to explain this difference between the male and female nuclei.

OVUM AND SPERM

Parents transmit hereditary material to the offspring through the two cells, the ovum and the sperm. The human ovum, about 140 μ in diameter and weighing 0.0015 mg, has a large vesicular nucleus (the germinal centre) with a prominent nucleolus (the germinal spot). Its cytoplasm contains yolk granules and is enveloped by a cell membrane known as the vitelline membrane. The ovum is surrounded by a thick, refractile capsule called the zona pellucida. The mature human sperm is an actively motile, freely swimming, elongated cell 60 μ–75 μ in length. It consists of a head largely occupied by the nucleus, and a tail which is highly specialised for motility and for orientation of the sperm, preparatory to penetration of the various coverings of the ovum, before fertilisation could occur.

FERTILISATION

Fertilisation is the union of a mature ovum and a single, mature sperm to form the zygote, from which an entire individual is produced. Though the ovum and the sperm differ greatly in size, the hereditary influences of the mother and father are nearly equal. The cytoplasm of the ovum is not held responsible for hereditary transmission, but the nuclei which are similar in the ovum and the sperm are regarded as the material carriers of the hereditary contributions of the parents. The nucleus of a zygote, like that of any other cell, appears like an undifferentiated vesicle. It shows the presence of well-defined structures known as chromosomes when the cell divides. Between cell divisions, the chromosomes are usually highly extended filaments that form a diffuse network collectively referred to as **chromatin**. The chromatin may be seen as dispersed and poorly staining **euchromatin** or as clumped and densely staining **heterochromatin**. In most somatic cells there is a mixture of the two states of chromatin, the heterochromatin lying close against the inside of the nuclear membrane and the euchromatin in the central region of the nucleus. Heterochromatin is distinguished into constitutive heterochromatin and facultative heterochromatin. Constitutive heterochromatin is a normal feature of several chromosomes. Inactive X chromosome in female somatic cells represents facultative heterochromatin.

THE HUMAN CHROMOSOMES

Chromosomes are rod-shaped, V-shaped, or J-shaped organelles, present in the nucleus. They are distinctly visible only during cell division. Each chromosome is endowed with individuality, special organisation and function. Each is capable of self-reproduction and of maintaining its morpho-

logic and physiologic properties through successive cell divisions. Chromosomes are made up of deoxyribonucleic acid (DNA) and proteins. DNA segments are the genes or the units of heredity.

Each species has a characteristic chromosome configuration, i.e., karyotype, with respect to chromosome number, length, shape, and the nature and sequence of the genes carried by each chromosome.

Till 1956, the human chromosome number was believed to be 48, when it was demonstrated beyond doubt that the human chromosome number is 46. These 46 chromosomes constitute 23 homologous pairs. Each parent contributes to an offspring 23 chromosomes, one member of each pair. Homologous chromosomes look alike and have at identical positions the same gene-loci, determining the same characteristic. However, the genes forming a pair, though determining the same characteristic or trait, are not necessarily identical.

The term haploid refers to a single set of all the chromosomes found in normal gametes, sperm or ovum (symbol: 1N). In man, N = 23. The zygote, formed by the fertilisation of an ovum by a sperm, has therefore 23 pairs of chromosomes. This constitutes, in the zygote and all the normal somatic cells derived therefrom, the diploid state (symbol: 2N). A chromosome number which differs by one or more from an exact multiple of the haploid number; e.g., 2N - 1 or 2N+1, where N is the haploid number of chromosomes, is referred to as aneuploid. **Polyploid** means any multiple of the basic haploid chromosome number, other than the diploid; thus 3N, 4N and so on.

There are two types of chromosomes, autosomes and sex chromosomes. **Sex chromosomes** are a pair of chromosomes which are responsible for sex determination. They differ in males and females. The two sex chromosomes in a female are similar and are designated as XX. The two sex chromosomes in a male are different from one another and are designated as XY. The X of the male is similar to the X of the female, while the Y is much smaller in size than the X. The remaining 22 pairs are alike in the male and in the female and hence are called autosomes.

Since females are XX, all ova carry an X chromosome whereas males are XY and hence produce X-bearing and Y-bearing sperms in approximately equal numbers. Because of this, the human female is referred to as the **homogametic sex** (producing only the single type of X-bearing ova) and the human male is referred to as the **heterogametic sex** (producing equal number of X-bearing and Y-bearing sperms). In birds, and many insects this order is reversed—the female is heterogametic and the male is homogametic.

CHROMOSOME STRUCTURE

Each pair of homologous chromosomes shows a common basic structure during cell division. Each chromosome consists of two parallel and identical filaments, **chromatids**, held together at a narrowed region, the **primary constriction**, within which is a pale-staining region, the centromere or kinetochore (Fig. 11). A chromosome becomes attached to the spindle during cell division by means of the kinetochore. Each chromatid shows two arms, one on either side of the centromere.

Chromosomes are classified into four types depending on the position of the centromere (Fig 12). (1) **Telocentric** chromosomes, wherein

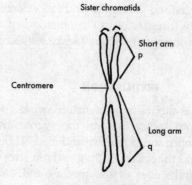

Fig. 11   Components of a chromosome as seen in metaphase. Note that a chromosome is made up of two sister chromatids, which separate during anaphase by splitting of the centromere. After that each sister chromatid is known as a chromosome made up of one short arm, one long arm and a centromere. As a chromosome is best visible during metaphase, it is always drawn showing two sister chromatids stuck together at the centromere. In the remaining phases of the cell cycle a chromosome extends outwards and hence it cannot be seen distinctly as a chromosome.

the centromere is situated at the end, have only one arm (not present in human beings). (2) **Acrocentric** chromosomes, wherein the centromere is situated near the end, have a very short and a very long arm. (3) **Submetacentric** chromosomes wherein the centromere is situated

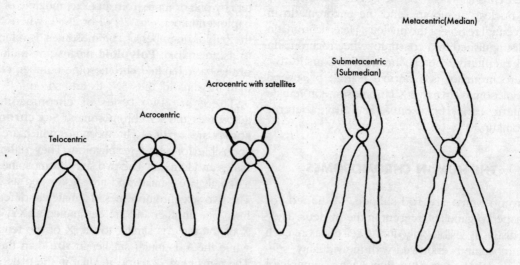

Fig 12   Types of chromosomes as seen in metaphase. Telocentric chromosomes are not found in human beings.

somewhere between the midpoint and the end of the chromosome, making one arm of the chromosome short and the other arm long. (4) **Metacentric** chromosomes wherein the centromere is situated near the centre of the chromosome, making both arms almost equal.

Secondary constrictions, found along the length of a chromosome may be short or long, and are distinguishable from the primary constriction, by the absence of any marked angular deviation of the chromosomal segments. Secondary constrictions are constant in their position and extent. They provide a useful criterion in identifying a particular chromosome in a set.

Telomere: Each extremity of a chromosome is referred to as telomere. It has been observed that the telomere has a polarity that prevents other segments of chromosomes from joining with it.

Satellite: Some chromosomes show a satellite which is a round, elongated body connected to the rest of the chromosome by a delicate chromatin filament, which may be long or short. Chromosomes having a satellite are referred to as SAT-chromosomes. The satellite and the filament are constant in shape and size for a particular chromosome.

Nucleolar zone: Some secondary constrictions are related to the formation of the nucleoli. These specialised regions of the chromosomes are the nucleolar zones or the nucleolar organisers. There are five chromosomes (numbers 13, 14, 15, 21, 22) in each nucleus, which have this special characteristic, and are called nucleolar chromosomes. The DNA sequence here codes for rRNA.

Fragile sites: Non-staining gaps seen on several chromosomes are called fragile sites. They are inherited chromosomal variants and form one of the chromosomal heteromorphism. The clinically significant fragile site is situated near the end of the long arm of the X chromosome, and is the most common cause of mental retardation in males. Fragile sites are demonstrable in specific culture of cells, for example, thymidine deprivation culture for the demonstration of fragile X chromosome.

Karyotype

Karyotype is the chromosome set of a somatic cell. By extension, it also refers to a photomicrograph of an individual's chromosomes arranged in a standard manner. The karyotype is characteristic of an individual, species, genus or a larger group.

Classification of Chromosomes

Chromosomes are identified by their length, the position of the centromere, the presence of satellite bodies, and other morphological characteristics. Now it is a standard practice to number the autosomal pairs in decreasing order of size from 1 to 22 for their classification (the Denver-London system). The sex chromosomes retain their distinctive labels (X and Y). An alternative system is the Denver classification where all the chromosomes, including the sex chromosomes, are assigned the groups from A to G, in order of decreasing length.

Group A	Chromosomes 1, 2, and 3
Group B	Chromosomes 4 and 5
Group C	Chromosomes 6 to 12 and the X chromosome
Group D	Chromosomes 13 to 15 (the larger acrocentrics, with satellite short arms)
Group E	Chromosomes 16 to 18
Group F	Chromosomes 19 and 20
Group G	Chromosomes 21 and 22 (the smaller acrocentrics, with satellite short arms) and the Y chromosome

The **Paris nomenclature** of 1971 and 1975, have added greater accuracy to the identification of portions of the individual numbered chromosomes. The scheme allows the unequivocal identification of each chromosome by its **banding pattern**, and gives number to the bands of each chromosome. The short arm (p) and the long arms (q) are thus considered to be made up of regions numbered 1, 2, etc. starting at the centromere. Each region is then subdivided into numbered bands, e.g. 2-q, 2, 1 would mean band number 1 in the second region of the long arm of chromosome 2.

Symbols for chromosomal nomenclature:

The internationally accepted symbols to denote certain normal and abnormal chromosomal features are as follows:

46 XX   normal female karyotype

46 XY   normal male karyotype

A–G   the chromosome groups

1–22   the autosome numbers

X, Y   the sex chromosomes

Diagonal lines indicate **mosaicism**, e.g., 46/47 designates a mosaic with 46 chromosome and 47 chromosome cell lines.

Key to abbreviations:

del   Deletion

der   Derivative of chromosome

dup   Duplication

i   Isochromosome

ins   Insertion

inv   Inversion

p   Short arm of chromosome

q   Long arm of chromosome

r   Ring chromosome

s   Satellite

t   Translocation
    rep: Reciprocal translocation
    rob: Robertsonian translocation
    tan: Tandem translocation

ter   Terminal (may be specified as pter or qter)

→   From → to

+ or –   Placed before the chromosome number, these symbols indicate addition (+) or loss (–) of a whole chromosome: e.g., +21 indicates an extra chromosome 21, as in Down's syndrome. Placed after the chromosome number, these symbols indicate increase or decrease in the length of a chromosome part; e.g., 5p – indicates loss of part of the short arm of chromosome 5, as in *cri du chat* syndrome.

Preparation of Chromosomes for Study

For chromosome analysis, cells which grow and divide rapidly in culture are chosen. The most commonly used tissues are skin fibroblasts, bone marrow and peripheral blood cells, and amniotic

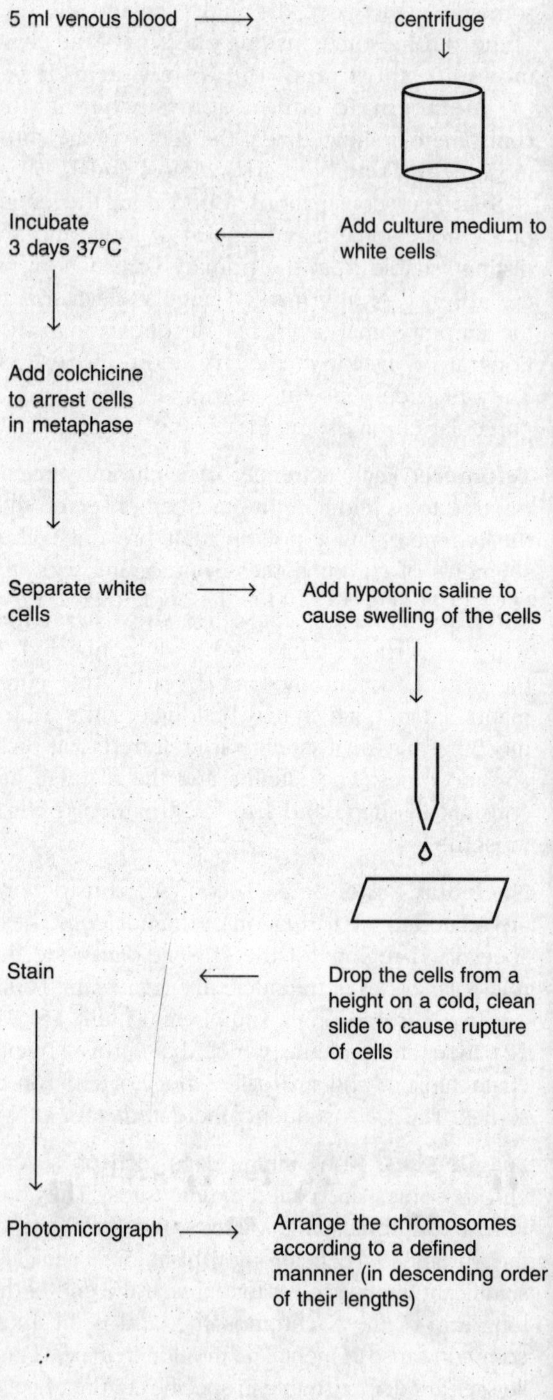

5 ml venous blood ⟶ centrifuge

Incubate 3 days 37°C ⟵ Add culture medium to white cells

Add colchicine to arrest cells in metaphase

Separate white cells ⟶ Add hypotonic saline to cause swelling of the cells

Stain ⟵ Drop the cells from a height on a cold, clean slide to cause rupture of cells

Photomicrograph ⟶ Arrange the chromosomes according to a defined mannner (in descending order of their lengths)

Fig. 13 Karyotyping

fluid cells from pregnant women. Viable cells can also be obtained within a few hours after the death of an individual or following spontaneous abortion of an embryo.

From peripheral blood, the leukocytes are separated and added to a small volume of nutrient medium containing **phytohemagglutinin**, which stimulates the leukocytes to divide. The cells are cultured under sterile conditions at 37°C for about three days. During this period the cells divide and then a small amount of **colchicine** is added to each culture. Colchicine prevents the formation of the spindle and stops mitosis at the stage of **metaphase** (explained later). After an hour or so a hypotonic saline solution is added. This makes the cells swell and the chromosomes spread out, which otherwise would remain clumped together. This is followed by taking a high power photomicrograph (Fig 14). Later the individual chromosomes are cut out from the photograph, arranged in pairs and in decreasing order of size and numbered 1 to 22 with the two sex chromosomes indicated separately (Fig 15). The resulting arrangement is the karyotype. The process is called **karyotyping** and it reveals the number and gross structure of chromosomes. However, it

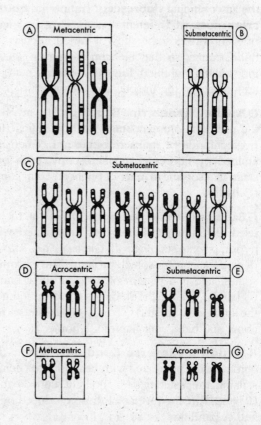

Fig. 15   Human chromosomes, one member of each homologous pair, shown in groups A to G, and in numerical order of the Denver-London classification. Banding pattern indicated. The sex chromosomes X and Y are shown in groups C and G respectively.

is difficult to detect small structural abnormalities. The newer techniques for chromosome study mentioned below have improved the identification of individual chromosomes (Figs. 15 16), and of specific chromosomal aberrations.

Methods for Study of Chromosomes

Chromosome Banding: A number of techniques demonstrate the banded appearance of chromosomes. While the general banding techniques show the full range of bands throughout the chromosomal complement, special banding techniques produce a restricted staining of one or the other subset of bands.

Chromosome banding was discovered by Caspersson when he stained chromosomes with

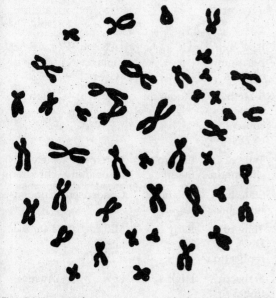

Fig. 14 Human chromosome spread—karyotype—highly magnified.

the DNA-binding **fluorescent** compound **quinacrine mustard**. Different regions along the length of each chromosome show a varied intensity of fluorescence, so that the chromosomes can be individually identified. Identical banding patterns are present in the meiotic chromosomes.

Q Banding (Quinacrine Banding): This involves the use of fluorescent stains such as quinacrine hydrochloride or quinacrine mustard. When examined by fluorescence microscopy, each pair stains in a specific manner of bright and dim bands (Q bands).

G Banding (Giemsa Banding): In this commonly used technique chromosomes are treated with trypsin prior to staining with Giemsa stain. Trypsin denatures chromosomal protein. The chromosomes stain in a pattern of dark and light bands (G bands), with the dark bands corresponding to the fluorescent (bright) Q bands. G banding shows about 400 bands per haploid genome.

R Banding (Reverse Banding): When the chromosome pretreated with heat prior to Giemsa staining, the resulting dark and light stained bands (R bands) are the reverse of those produced by Q and G banding.

Special Banding Techniques: C banding can be done by alkali extraction of DNA from the chromosome. Highly repetitive DNA sequences resist such extraction. C banding can also be done by staining with the AT-specific DNA ligand, Hoechst 33258, which produces intense fluorescence of the highly AT-rich satellite DNAs found in the C band regions. These techniques stain a small region adjacent to the centromere of all chromosomes and in addition they also stain the distal portion of the Y chromosome. The C bands contain highly repetitive, non-transcribed DNA, called heterochromatin.

AgNOR staining or the silver staining of the **nucleolus organising regions** marks the sites of transcriptionally active ribosomal RNA genes. Usually present on six to eight of the D and G group chromosomes, it may be on as few as three, or on all ten of them.

High resolution banding or Prometaphase banding: This technique requires (i) arresting DNA synthesis in a cell culture by methotrexate (folic acid antagonist) so as to synchronise the cells and then (ii) releasing the block by addition of folic acid and (iii) harvesting the culture by colchicine at a time when numerous cells are in early metaphase, before they get maximally condensed.

This reveals 800 or more bands per haploid genome.

Flow cytometry: The cells are ruptured, stained with a fluorescent dye selectively for DNA and projected as a fine jet through a flow chamber across a laser beam that excites the chromosomes to fluoresce. This method of chromosome analysis

Table 2: Characteristic features of chromosomal bands

Characteristic Feature	R-bands	Q- or G-bands	C-bands
Location	Chromosome arms	Chromosome arms	Centromeres distal Y
Type of DNA sequences	Unique	Repetitive	Highly repetitive satellite DNA
Base composition of DNA	GC-rich	AT-rich some GC-rich	AT-rich
5-Methylcytosine content of DNA	Moderate	Low	High
Type of chromatin	Euchromatin	Heterochromatin	Heterochromatin
State in interphase	Extended	Condensed	Condensed
Time of DNA replication	Early S	Mid to late S	Late S
Transcriptional activity	High	Low	Absent

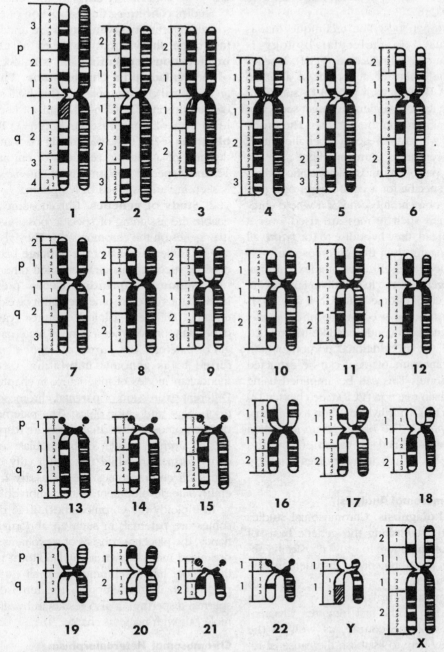

Fig. 16   Human chromosomes showing the banding patterns and numbering as adopted at the Paris conference 1971. Note that black areas represent positive Q and G bands and negative R bands. The white areas represent negative or pale-staining Q and G bands and positive R bands. The shaded areas represent variable bands.

Note that the short and the long arms p and q are made up of regions numbered 1, 2, etc., starting at the centromere. Each region is subdivided into numbered bands, e.g. 13-p, 1, 2 would mean band number 2 in the first region of the short arm of chromosome 13.

is called flow cytometry or fluorescent activated cell sorter (FACS).

Molecular cytogenetics: The technique that is commonly used in molecular biology is fluorescents in situ hybridisation (FISH). It relies on the unique ability of a portion of a single stranded DNA (known as a probe) to anneal or hybridise with its complementary target sequence wherever it is located in the genome. The probe is conjugated with a fluorescent label allowing it to be easily seen under ultraviolet light.

Different types of chromosome-specific probes can be used: specific for a centromere, or a particular region of a chromosome or a whole chromosome. When such probes are used over a metaphase spread, they hybridise to (or *paint*) all material originating from that chromosome.

This technique is useful for complex chromosomal rearrangement, and in identifying the nature of additional chromosome material, if any. FISH technique can also be used in interphase nuclei for rapid diagnosis in conditions like trisomy 21.

As a corollary, an additional portion of unidentified chromosome material can be extracted using a cell sorter. This can be amplified using polymerase chain reaction (PCR) (see chapter 12) and used as a probe for hybridisation to a normal metaphase spread. The origin of un-identified chromosome material is revealed by the chromosome to which it hybridises (reverse painting).

Uses of Chromosomal Analysis:

1. **Clinical diagnosis**. Chromosomal studies are helpful in establishing the genetic basis of mental retardation, failure to grow physically, abnormal sexual development, or disorders involving multiple systems.

Chromosomal abnormalities are a very frequent cause of abortion in the first trimester. Chromosomal studies of the couple, as well as the conceptus, may help to establish the cause of repeated abortions or of infertility.

Karyotyping of the fetus may be carried out in cases of older pregnant women or in cases of familial chromosomal abnormalities to rule out any gross abnormality affecting the fetus.

Studies concerning the association of chromosomal abnormalities with cancer are underway. It has been shown that in cases of **chronic myelogenous leukemia** there is an occurrence of the **Philadelphia chromosome (Ph[1])**. It is an abnormal chromosome 22. The distal segment of chromosome 22 (22q–) is translocated to the long arm of chromosome 9 (9q+). **Retinoblastoma** seems to be commonly associated with deletion of a specific segment of chromosome 13, and a specific abnormality of chromosome 14 is seen in various kinds of lymphoma.

2. **Study of genetics**. Chromosome studies enable the assigning of specific positions to human genes on the chromosomes. They also facilitate an understanding of the **linkage** between a disease, specific (marker) gene and other genes.

3. **Genomic imprinting**. Genes present on homologous chromosomes need not be expressed equally. Different clinical features can result depending on whether a gene is maternal in origin or paternal. This *parent of origin* effect is referred to as genomic imprinting. (see nonmendelian modes of inheritance in chapter 5.)

Different expression of parental chromosomes in trophoblast and embryoblast: The paternally derived chromosomes in an embryo are responsible for the normal growth of trophoblast and placenta formation while the maternally derived genes on chromosomes are necessary for early embryonic development of the embryoblast.

In triploidy (69 chromosomes), if 46 chromosomes are paternal, in such an abnormal pregnancy, the placenta consists of a proliferating disorganised mass known as hydatidiform mole. If the zygote has 46 chromosomes, all exclusively paternal in origin (empty ovum fertilised by 2 sperms: dispermy), it also results in hydatidiform mole but with no fetus chapter 9).

Chromosomal Heteromorphism

Minor heritable differences in banding patterns are seen frequently, especially in the pericentromeric regions of chromosomes 1, 9 and 16, and the long arm of the Y chromosome. With advances in molecular cytogenetics, detection of heteromorphism in other chromosomes (pericentric regions or short arm of acrocentric chromosomes) is possible. These morphologic variations (heteromorphisms) may be useful in tracing individual chromosomes through families. Heteromorphisms may be used as markers in family studies or to help in the determination of the source of the abnormal gamete in chromosomal abnormalities.

THE Y CHROMOSOME

This is a small acrocentric chromosome without any satellite on its short arm. It gives vivid fluorescence with quinacrine stain both in metaphase as well as interphase because of a large block of heterochromatin. The Y-pter is homologous to the X-pter and pair with each other during meiosis, and are therefore called the *pseudoautosomal regions*. Close to this region, is the region called

the testis determining factor (TDF), now said to be located in the sex-determining region of Y chromosome (SRY). Deletion or translocation of SRY gene leads to conditions such as XY females or XX males respectively.

THE X CHROMOSOME

This medium-size submetacentric chromosome has several genes present on it which have special roles in sex determination or X inactivation. The genes present in the X chromosome are called X-linked or sex-linked. Over 400 X-linked traits have been identified so far, in human beings.

The X-pter (which is homologous to the Y-pter, see above) is called the *pseudoautosomal region*. The band Xq13 contains an X inactivation centre. In female somatic cells, it is this locus which determines X inactivation. Although one X is inactivated, several regions of the short arm (in-

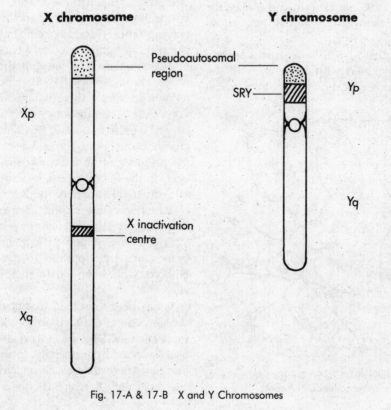

Fig. 17-A & 17-B   X and Y Chromosomes

cluding the pseudoautosomal region) and at least one region of the long arm (apart from the X inactivation centre) escape inactivation and continue to be expressed in both X chromosomes. An example of this is the gene for steroid sulphatase (STS) whose deficiency produces icthyosis, an X-linked disorder. Such genes can account for clinical symptoms of X chromosome aneuploidy (see abnormal chromosomes).

SEX CHROMATIN

Barr and Bertram in 1949 discovered a small chromatin body in the nuclei of neurones of female cats. Similar observations were then extended to neuronal and other tissues of man and animals. The chromatin body is also called the **sex chromatin** or **Barr body**. The frequency with which the sex chromatin can be detected in the females, varies from tissue to tissue. In nervous tissue the frequency may be 85 per cent, whereas in mounts of amniotic or chorionic epithelium, it may be as high as 96 per cent. In oral smears the frequency varies between 20 and 50 per cent in normal females.

Sex chromatin is seen as a small chromocentre heavily stained with basic dyes in the interphase nucleus. As shown in Fig. 18, it can be found attached to the nucleolus, as in nerve cells of certain species; attached to the nuclear membrane, as in cells of the epidermis or of the oral mucosa, and seen as a nuclear expansion, in about 3 per cent of neutrophil leucocytes, forming a small rod called the drumstick. It may be also seen free in the nucleoplasm, as in neurones after electric stimulation.

The tests for nuclear sex determination include the detection of drumstick in leucocytes and the Barr body in the cells of the epidermis, the oral mucosa and amniotic fluid. The study of the sex chromatin is widely used in medicine. It helps to link certain congenital diseases with sex chromosomal anomalies; and also helps in ascertaining the sex in an intersex during fetal and postnatal life.

Sex chromatin is derived from one of the two X chromosomes which is dark-staining (heteropyknotic) at interphase. The other X is euchromatic. The number of sex chromatin bodies at interphase is equal to nX–1. This means that there is one Barr body fewer than the number of X chromosomes. This relationship between sex chromatin and sex chromosomes is particularly evident in those humans who have an abnormal number of sex chromosomes. The Barr body exhibits alteration in size, if there is any structural aberration of the X chromosome, such as deletion, ring or an isochromosome X. The abnormal X chromosome always forms the sex chromatin and the presence of an unusually small or large Barr body in the buccal smear, indicates the presence of a structural variant of the X.

Barr bodies are absent from oocytes and female germ cells, and only appear at about the 12th day of gestation in extraembryonic membranes, and by about the 16 day in cells of the embryo, with some variation from tissue to tissue.

It has been observed that at the time of cell division one of the X chromosomes completes its replication of DNA later than the other, and is usually located peripherally, in the region of the nucleus where the sex chromatin is found. The late replicating X, which is condensed and out of

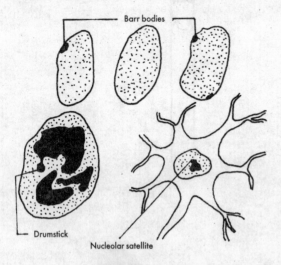

Fig. 18 Sex chromatin (Barr body) as seen in nuclei of epithelial cells, leucocytes and neurones.

phase with the rest of the chromosome set, forms the sex chromatin.

The Principle of X Inactivation or the Lyon Hypothesis

This hypothesis is named after Mary F. Lyon, who stated it first, explicitly and in detail. The hypothesis states that in the somatic cells of female mammals, only one X chromosome is active. The second X chromosome is condensed and inactive, and appears in interphase cells as the sex chromatin. Inactivation of the chromosome occurs in embryonic life and is random, i.e., the inactive X can either be the paternal or the maternal one (X_P or X_M) in different cells of the same individual. However, after the decision has been made regarding which X would be inactivated in a particular cell, all the clonal descendants of that cell will show the same inactive X. Thus, inactivation is random but once it has occurred, it remains fixed. However, they do get reactivated in the female germ cells.

The Lyon hypothesis rests on the following observations.

1) The females have the Barr body and the males do not have it.

2) In mice, genes determining fur colour are of two types: autosomal and sex-linked. Autosomal genes always give uniform colouring to the mouse fur (say dark brown for dominant, white for recessive, the heterozygotes manifesting an uniform light-brown a shade between dark brown and white).

Sex-linked genes are **X-linked genes**. In a male mouse, there would always be only one X chromosome and thereby the X-linked gene manifests itself phenotypically as uniform colouring of the fur, either brown or white, depending on the genotype. If the genes are homozygous, then in a female mouse having two X chromosomes, the result is also a uniform dark brown fur or a uniform white. If the mouse has only one X chromosome with missing X or Y chromosomes, then too the fur presents uniform dark brown or white depending on the genotype.

However, some surprising patterns show up in females who have the heterozygous genotype.

Here one would expect the uniform dark brown or white colour of the homozygous phenotype or the intermediate between homozygous (dominant and recessive) i.e., a uniform light brown colour, but what is found is that the coat is not uniformly coloured. The coat shows dark brown and white patches randomly distributed all over the body. This could be only accounted for by the phenomenon of **random Lyonisation** that renders an X chromosome (derived either from the mother or the father) inactive in all cells of the body differently.

3) The number of sex chromatin bodies in interphase cells is always one less than the number of X chromosomes seen at metaphase.

4) During cell division, one X completes its replication later than the rest of the chromosome complement and the late-replicating X is located in the area where the sex chromatin is found.

These observations indicated that the sex chromatin is a condensed, dark-staining (heteropyknotic) X chromosome, and that only one X is active in cellular metabolism; the other X, chosen randomly, appearing as the sex chromatin body. In the male, the single X is uncoiled and active at all times, and consequently there is no sex chromatin.

Mechanism of X Inactivation: The process of inactivation begins as early as 15 to 16 days of gestation in embryoblasts. The inactivation is initiated at the X-inactivation centre on the Xq13 band and spreads along the chromosome. Many CG dinucleotides in the 5^1 regions of the genes get methylated to render the X inactive.

Evidence for the Lyon Hypothesis:

1) **Dosage compensation**. The amounts of enzyme such as G6PD or antihemophilic globulin, which are produced by genes located on the X chromosome are equal in the two sexes. Inactivation of one of the two chromosomes explains this.

2) **Variability of expression in heterozygous females**. Females with an abnormal X-linked gene present on only one X chromosome, i.e., heterozygous, do express abnormalities when there is a **total Lyonisation**, whereby the abnormal gene is functional in a majority of the cells.

3) **Mosaicism**. Women show mosaicism at cellular level, having two populations of cells, one population with one X active, the other with the alternative X active. In tissue cultures, two different clonal populations can be demonstrated.

Ocular Albinism: An X-linked recessive condition, characterised by lack of melanin production in the retina, is an example in humans. Males show uniform lack of melanin in the retina while female heterozygotes exhibit alternate patches of pigmented and non-pigmented zones.

Skewed X Inactivation: X inactivation is normally random. However, there are exceptions to this rule, where one X chromosome is more often inactivated than another; this is called as skewed X inactivation.

1) In structural abnormalities of X chromosome (i.e. deletion, ring chromosome, iso-Xq, etc.), the abnormal X is inactivated.

2) In a balanced translocation of the X chromosome with an autosome, the normal X is inactivated to avoid inactivation of the autosome.

3) In an unbalanced translocation, the normal X is active while the abnormal X carrying the inactivation centre in inactivated.

4) Mutation at the inactivating centre would necessarily lead to inactivation of the other X chromosome.

5) In extraembryonic tissues, the paternal X is inactivated.

Skewed X inactivation itself is under genetic control and is passed along families where the same X chromosome is seen to be inactivated in several generations.

There are some facts that do not conform to the Lyon hypothesis. The most striking of these is the abnormal phenotype of XO and XXY individuals, who physically differ from normal XX females or XY males, respectively. If one X chromosome is inactivated, XO females should be normal since XX normal females are effectively XO, and XXY males should be normal as they are effectively XY as in normal males. This is because of incomplete X inactivation.

Composition and Functions of Chromosomes

Chromosomes are made up of fine filaments of the nucleic acid, DNA. Each filament of DNA is surrounded by a sheath of basic proteins classified as histones (Figs 19, 20, 21). A small amount of acidic protein is also present. The DNA and the protein together constitute the nucleoprotein (chromatin).

The complete diploid set of chromosomes, present in every normal somatic cell, contains the cell's hereditary instructions. Each cell in the body,

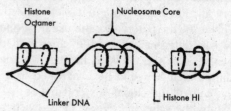

Fig. 19 A schematic representation of nucleosomes. 140–160 base pairs of DNA wound around a histone core, an octamer of H2A, H2B, H3 and H4. Linker DNA of 20–60 base pairs connects the adjacent nucleosomes. H1 histone is associated with linker DNA. This arrangement of chromatin material converts the DNA helix of 2 nm into a 10 nm nucleosome filament.

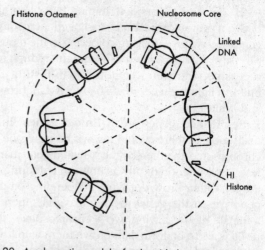
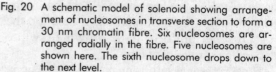

Fig. 20 A schematic model of solenoid showing arrangement of nucleosomes in transverse section to form a 30 nm chromatin fibre. Six nucleosomes are arranged radially in the fibre. Five nucleosomes are shown here. The sixth nucleosome drops down to the next level.

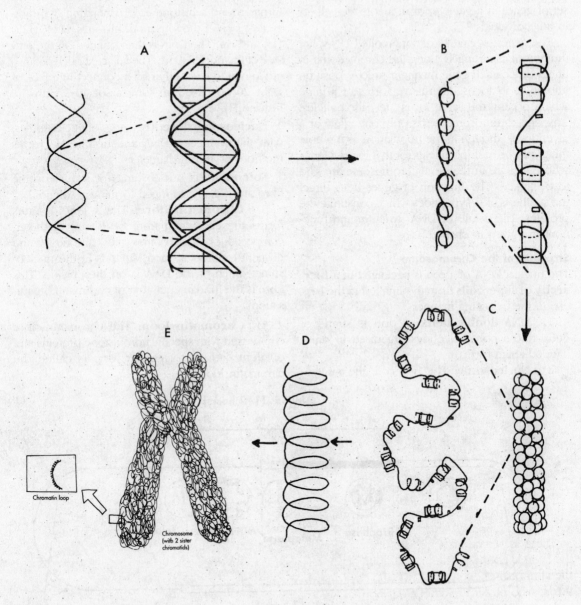

Fig. 21 Levels of packing of chromatin material to form a chromosome.
A.   DNA (2 nm) – the double strand organised in right-handed spiral form.
B.   10 nm nucleosome filament.
C.   25 nm chromatin fibre.
D.   Folded loops (0.5 m). Each 25 nm fibre forms a series of loops, each about 0.5 m in length. All the loops are formed
       along a single axis.
E.   A chromosome with two sister chromatids.

except the germ cells, has an identical genetic complement. The term genome indicates the full set of genes in a gamete, or in a somatic cell, or in an individual.

The genes, segments of supercoiled DNA, are thought of as arranged along the chromosome in linear order, each gene having a precise position known as its locus. Alternative forms of a gene which occupy the same locus are called alleles. Any one chromosome bears only one allele at a given locus, though in the population as a whole there may be multiple alleles for that locus. Genes whose loci are in the same chromosome are said to be linked. The function of genes is to direct the synthesis of polypeptides which constitute the proteins. The details of DNA structure and functions are given in chapter 4.

Structure of the Chromosome

The nuclear DNA of a cell is packaged in a **hierarchy of supercoils** from the smallest to the largest, in the following manner:

1) **DNA double helix:** A double strand of deoxyribose polynucleotides organised in right-handed spiral form.

2) **Nucleosome:** The first coil, the nucleosome is a cylinder about 8–11 nm in size. In it, some 146 base pairs of DNA are wound in two turns around a histone core containing two molecules each of the four inner histones, H2A, H2B, H3, and H4. The DNA is thus situated on the outside of the nucleosome. The adjacent nucleosomes are joined to each other by a connecting piece of DNA 20–60 base pair long associated with the histone H_1.

Nucleosome fibre: This series of nucleosomes, with the connector DNA and histone H_1, forms the fibre of 10 nm diameter.

Solenoid: Six nucleosomes of a nucleosome fibre are radially arranged forming a solenoid.

3) **Chromatin fibre:** The solenoid series forms the chromatin fibre of 30 nm diameter, composed of nucleosomes plus histone H_1 and divalent cations Ca^{++} and Mg^{++}. As in the nucleosome, much of the DNA is on the outside. This fibre is the fundamental unit of chromatin organisations.

4) **Chromatin loop:** The chromatin fibre complexed with specific non-histone proteins and divalent cations forming a loop is called the chromatin loop.

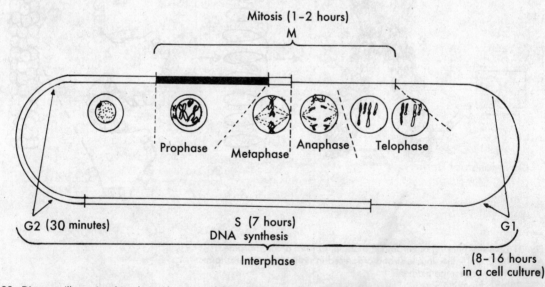

Fig. 22 Diagram illustrating the relative durations of the subdivisions of the mitotic cell cycle. Double lines indicate a double chromatid structure. The relative lengths of the lines would vary from tissue to tissue and from organism to organism. Mitosis and intermitotic phases, G1 (Gap 1), S (Synthesis) and G2 (Gap 2) indicated.

Chromomere: A chromomere or a chromosome band is a segment of a chromosome in condensation variable from more than that of a chromatin loop up to as much as that of a chromosome in metaphase.

5)   **Chromosome:** Highly condensed form of long series of chromatin loops constitutes a chromosome.

About half the DNA is available to interact with external molecules, and only localised uncoiling or decondensation is necessary for transcription or replication. The other half of the DNA remains packed with the large amounts of histone and non-histone proteins found in the chromosomes.

In the metaphase chromosome, which represents the highest level of packaging, some RNA is present and some of the histone proteins are phosphorylated. These changes produce the thickest and shortest possible chromosome forms, in which the genes are no longer capable of being transcribed. At the same time, such chromosomes become capable of freely moving about during cell division, without harm to themselves.

Mitochondrial Chromosome

Mitochondria are thought of as symbiotic microorganisms residing in the host cell (see cell biology). Mitochondrial have their own chromosomes and genes. The mitochondrial chromosome is a small circular molecule. The DNA molecule is 16 kb long and encodes 13 structural genes and numerous RNA genes. Mutations in the mitochondrial genes are responsible for several neuromuscular disorders which show maternal inheritance (i.e. mothers transmit to all children, fathers to none).

Chromosomal Behaviour in Cell Division

Cell division involves (1) the division of the nucleus and (2) the division of the cytoplasm. Nuclear division, the more prominent of the two and characterised by complex chromosomal maneuvers, is accomplished by mitosis and meiosis.

Cells that undergo division regularly, continue to pass consecutively through interphase, mitosis, interphase, mitosis and so on. One complete passage through the interphase and mitosis is termed a cell cycle. As shown in Fig. 22, there are three stages through which a cell passes during its interphase. After completing mitosis, the cell enters the **G1 (Gap 1)** or preduplication stage. The preduplication stage is the state in which most cells of the body exist and function. A cell which is going to divide, enters the DNA duplication stage, also called the S (Synthesis) stage, from the preduplication stage. It takes about seven hours for all the DNA of a cell to be duplicated. After finishing DNA duplication, a cell passes into the postduplication or G2 (Gap 2) phase, which lasts for about half an hour, before the cell begins mitosis.

In the **S phase**, the single doublestranded DNA molecule (without a sister chromatid) replicates and becomes a two-chromatid chromosome. The chromatids are, however, joined at the centromere. DNA synthesis begins at many sites within a single chromosome. Homologous pairs replicate together. However, the inactivated X chromosome in female somatic cells undergoes late replication.

In the G_2 **phase**, the DNA material has doubled (even though the chromosome number is diploid). RNA and proteins are still produced; the cell enlarges and doubles its mass.

In a typical cell culture G_1, S and G_2 phases take 16 to 24 hours, while mitosis takes 1 to 2 hours.

Cells which never divide or are facultative dividers (that is, they usually do not divide, but have the capacity to divide) are said to be in the G_0 (Gap zero) phase. Facultative dividers can revert back to G_1 phase and complete the cell cycle.

Mitosis (Fig 23)

This type of division occurs in somatic cells and results in the distribution of identical copies of the parent cell's genome to the two daughter cells.

A cell which is not actively dividing is said to be in interphase. As seen earlier, new DNA is synthesised during the S phase of interphase, so that in normal diploid cells the amount of DNA has doubled by the onset of mitosis to the tetraploid DNA value, although the chromosome number is still diploid. During mitosis, this amount

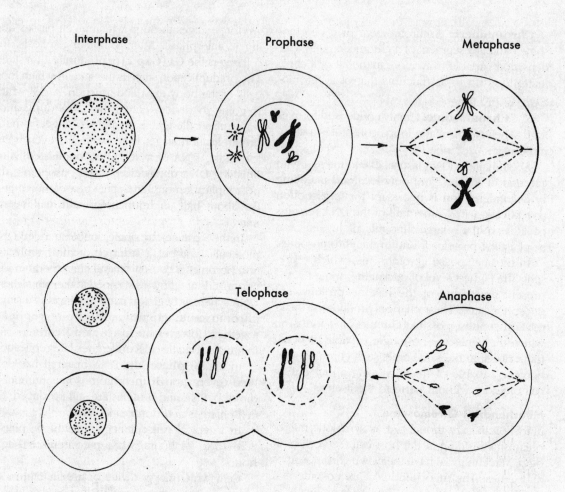

Fig. 23 Schematic representation of various phases of mitosis. I and II. The four gametes formed are indicated.

is distributed equally between the two daughter cells, so that DNA quantity and chromosome number become diploid in both the cells. Mitosis is usually described in four stages: prophase, metaphase, anaphase and telophase.

Prophase: (Prophase: beginning, before) 1) The strands of chromatin get shorter, thicker and become recognisable as chromosomes, each made up of two chromatids joined at the centromere.

2) The centrioles in the cytoplasm separate and move, one to each pole of the cell.

3) Parallel microtubules are synthesised between the two centrioles to create the central spindle. Other microtubules are synthesised to

radiate out from the centrioles to form the astral rays, collectively termed asters.

4) The nucleoli disintegrate and disappear.

5) The nuclear membrane disappears.

Metaphase:

(Metaphase: beyond after,) 1) The spindle microtubules invade the central region of the cell.

2) The chromosomes move towards the equator of the spindle.

3) The chromosomes become attached by their centromeres to the spindle microtubules.

4) The chromosomes appear as a star-like ring when viewed from either pole of the cell.

5) Mitochondria and other organelles get

distributed equally around the cell periphery.

Anaphase: (Anaphase: again, upward, backward) 1) The centromere in metaphase is a double structure. It now separates into its two components, each carrying an attached chromatid, so that each of the original chromosomes has, in effect, split into two new chromosomes.

2) The two new chromosomes move apart, one towards each pole of the cell.

3) The chromosomes become grouped at each end of the cell, both groups being diploid in number.

4) Cytoplasmic division begins, by infolding of the cell at the equator.

Telophase: (Telophase: end) 1) The chromosomes re-extend.

2) The nuclear membrane reappears.

3) The nucleoli reappear.

4) The cytoplasmic constriction deepens and eventually the furrow divides the cell into two, each with its derived nucleus.

5) The spindle remnants disintegrate and disappear.

Non-disjunction and lagging of chromatids may occur, so that two sister chromatids pass to the same pole. Of the two new cells, one will have more, and the other less chromosomes than the diploid number. Ionising radiation increases such events and may, because of chromosomal damage, inhibit mitosis altogether. Chemical agents like colchicine, its derivatives colcemide, podophyllotoxin, and vinblastine arrest mitosis in metaphase by inhibiting spindle microtubule formation. This phenomenon is of great help in chromosomal studies, since chromosomes are most easily examined in the metaphase condition.

Meiosis

Meiosis (Fig 24) involves two sequential divisions: meiosis I and meiosis II. During the S phase of interphase prior to the first division, DNA is replicated in the usual manner, resulting in the tetraploid amount of DNA, the number of chromosomes being diploid. During meiosis I, the DNA is reduced to the diploid amount in each chromosome, and the chromosome number is halved to the haploid. In meiosis II, the DNA in each new daughter cell is reduced to the haploid amount, the chromosome number remaining haploid.

Meiosis I and II each, like mitosis, can be divided into prophase, metaphase, anaphase and telophase.

Meiosis I:

Prophase I. This is a long and complex phase which differs markedly from mitotic prophase. It is divided into leptotene stage, zygotene stage, pachytene stage, diplotene stage and diakinesis.

Leptotene stage: (Leptos: slender; tainia: ribbon) 1) The chromosomes become visible as individual threads. 2) One end of the threads is seen to be attached to the nuclear membrane. 3) Chromosomal threads show characteristic beads (chromomeres) throughout their length.

Zygotene stage: (Zygon: yoke; synaptic: joined) 1) Chromosomes come together side by side in homologous pairs. 2) The homologous chromosomes pair, point for point, so that corresponding regions lie in contact. This process is synapsis or conjugation. In the case of the unequal X and Y sex chromosomes, only limited segments (the pairing segments) may be homologous; the remaining segments are differential segments.

Pachytene: (Pachys: thick) 1) Each chromosome becomes shorter and thicker and is now seen to be formed of two chromatids joined at the centromere. Each bivalent pair thus consists of four chromatids and is called a tetrad. 2) Two chromatids, one from each bivalent chromosome, become partially coiled around each other. With electron microscopy, an elongated striated fibrillar organelle, the synaptinemal complex is seen to unite them throughout their length. 3) During coiling around of two chromatids the genetic material is exchanged between the two. This phenomenon is known as cross over, **crossing over** or recombination. However, the precise timing or nature of the DNA exchange is uncertain, and it could occur as early as in the S phase of the previous interphase.

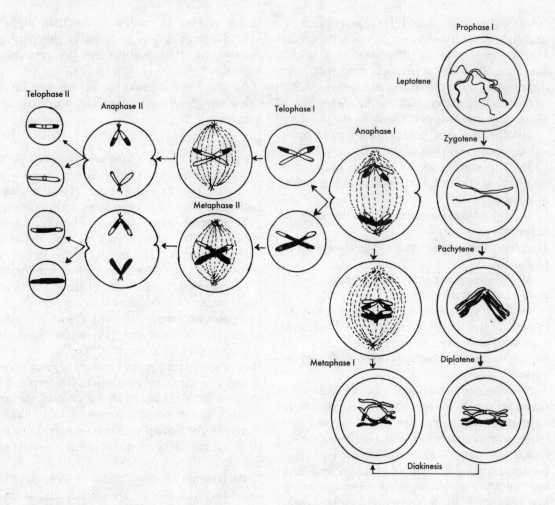

Fig. 24 Schematic representation of various phases of meiosis I and II. The four gametes formed are indicated.

Diplotene stage: (Diplous: double) 1) The homologous pairs move slightly apart except at the points seen as chiasmata, where crossing over has occurred. Sometimes the chiasmata move towards the end of the chromatids. Normally at least one chiasma forms between each pair of homologous chromosomes, and up to five have been observed. 2) The chiasmata break.

In human meiosis, primary oocytes become diplotene by the fifth month in utero, and remain in this state till the period prior to ovulation.

Diakinesis: (Dia: across; kinesis: movement, motion) 1) The remaining chiasmata finally break. 2) The chromosomes, still bivalents, become shorter and thicker. 3) The bivalents move away from each other and spread out against the nuclear membrane. 4) Nucleoli disappear. 5) Spindle and asters form as in mitosis.

The end of prophase is marked by dissolution of the nuclear membrane and movement of the bivalent chromosomes towards the equatorial plate.

Dictyotene: (Dictyos: network.) Prophase I is completed before the individual's birth in primary oocytes. Instead of entering metaphase I, they go into a resting state, characterised by reticular arrangement of chromatin — dictyotene. The metaphase I is entered shortly before ovulation. Metaphase I: This resembles the metaphase of mitosis except that the bodies attaching to the spindle microtubules are bivalents (tetrads) and not single chromosomes. The chromosomes arrange in such a manner that the homologous pairs lie parallel to the equatorial plate, with one member on either side.

Anaphase I and Telophase I: These are similar to those of mitosis except that in anaphase, the centromeres do not split. Thus, instead of the paired chromatids separating to move towards the poles, whole homologous chromosomes made up of two joined chromatids depart to opposite poles. Due to random positioning of maternal and paternal chromosomes in bivalent pairs, there is a random assortment of maternal and paternal chromosomes in each telophase nucleus.

Cytoplasmic division occurs as in mitosis to produce two new daughter cells.

Meiosis II:

This takes place after meiosis I following a brief interval during which *no DNA synthesis occurs*. The second meiotic division is similar to mitosis with the exception that the separating chromatids in the anaphase are genetically dissimilar. Cytoplasmic division follows and thus a total of four cells results from meiosis I and II. In an ovum meiosis II is completed only on fertilisation.

If cytoplasmic division fails to occur during meiosis I, gametes with the diploid number of chromosomes result, and thus following fertilisation a triploid zygote results. Other abnormalities are produced by **non-disjunction** of chromosomes (Fig. 25), or by the lagging of individual chromosomes, during anaphase. There is some indication that with increasing maternal age, there is increased frequency of such abnormalities.

HUMAN SPERMATOGENESIS

Male gonad. The testis or the male gonad, lies in the scrotum covered by a serous sac, the **tunica vaginalis**. Its dense fibrous capsule called the **tunica albuginea** is thickened posteriorly to form the **mediastinum testis** which sends in fibrous

partitions to divide the testis into about 250 lobes or lobules. Each lobe contains 1–4 highly convoluted **seminiferous tubules,** varying in length from 30 to 70 cm and 150 to 250 μ in diameter, as also the interstitial endocrine tissue (Fig. 26). The stratified epithelium of the tubules produces the male gametes, the **spermatozoa**, and the **interstitial cells of Leydig** produce the male hormone **testosterone**. The sperms are conducted to the prostatic part of the urethra via a tortuous course from the convoluted portion of the seminiferous tubule to its straight part, and then through the rete testis, efferent ductules, canal of the epididymis, ductus deferens and finally the ejaculatory duct.

A functionally active, postpubertal seminiferous tubule is lined along its length and around its circumference, by two distinct cell types.

1)   Single layered and scattered sustentacular **cells of Sertoli** resting on the basement membrane of the tubule and

2)   Multiple rows of spermatogenic or germ cells at varying stages of maturation. The basal row of these cells also rests on the basement membrane.

Each Sertoli cell is an elongated pyramidal cell with its base attached to the basement membrane. Its irregular apical surface faces the lumen, and its deeply recessed sides are moulded by the maturing spermatids of varying shapes. The developing germ cells get protection, mechanical support and some nutrition from the Sertoli cells. The Sertoli cells play an active role in the liberation of mature sperms, as is suggested by their irregular sides and apices, their notably large surface area and their everchanging shapes. Sertoli cells have not been seen to divide in a mature testis and unlike the germ cells they are highly resistant to a number of cytotoxic agents, ionising radiation and heat.

The spermatogenic cells from the periphery of the tubule to its centre include spermatogonia, primary spermatocytes, secondary spermatocytes, spermatids and spermatozoa. These structurally distinct cell types are successive stages in the differentiation of germ cells (Fig. 27)

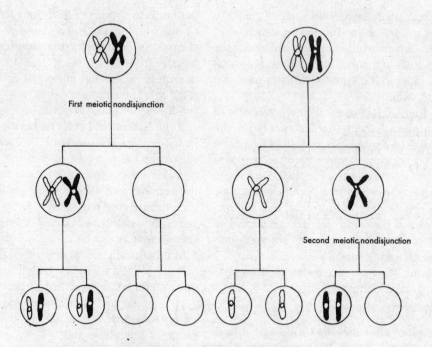

Fig. 25 Scheme to show non-disjunction in meiosis I and II and the resulting abnormal gametes.

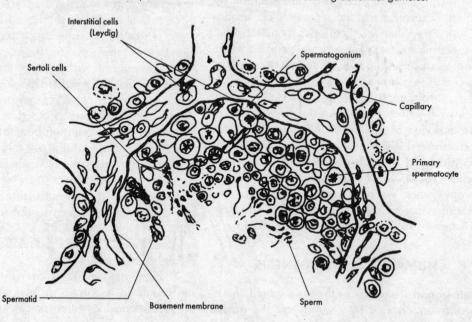

Fig. 26   Transverse section of the seminiferous tubule and its surroundings, showing the spermatogenic and Sertoli cells and the endocrine interstitial cells.

Spermatogenesis

The continuous series of events by which spermatogonia are changed to sperms is called spermatogenesis. occurs in three phases:

1. Spermatocytogenesis
2. Meiosis
3. Spermiogenesis

1) **Spermatocytogenesis**

- Spermatogonia multiply by mitotic division, thus assuring a continuous supply of spermatogonia.
- Some spermatogonia modify themselves, increase in size and push themselves towards the lumen of the tubule to become primary spermatocytes.
- Primary spermatocytes contain enough nutrient material to provide for succeeding stages of maturation.
- All but the earliest spermatogonia remain interconnected by cytoplasmic bridges with the result that one spermatogonium gives rise to a large cluster of interconnected spermatids (Fig. 28).

2) **Meiosis** takes place in two stages.

Stage I

- Primary spermatocytes undergo duplication of

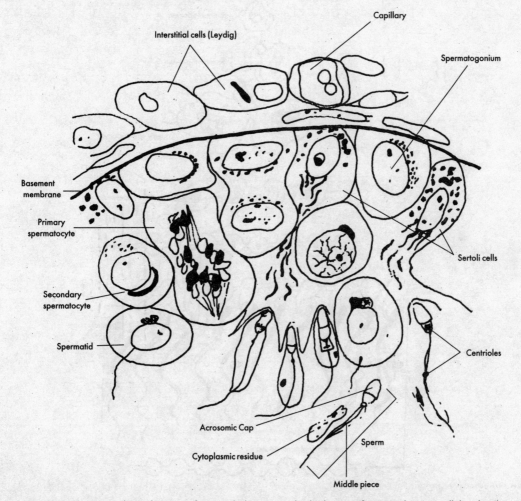

Fig. 27 Transverse section of a seminiferous tubule seen under high magnification, showing cellular detail.

their chromosomal material.

- Primary spermatocytes enter a long prophase lasting for 22 days.
- During the prophase the homologous chromosomes form pairs and exchange parts of their segments this is known as crossing over.
- During anaphase, the centromeres do not split and thereby each member of a homologous pair of chromosomes made up of two joint chromatids, departs to opposite poles.
- The end result is a secondary spermatocyte, slightly smaller than the primary, having only

half the number of chromosomes, some of which are paternal and some maternal in origin.

Stage II

- After a brief prophase II, the secondary spermatocytes—haploid cells—enter metaphase II followed by anaphase II.
- During anaphase II, the centromeres holding the chromatids together in each chromosome, divide to separate these chromatids.
- One set of chromatids passes to each new daughter cell, which is now called a spermatid.
- A spermatid contains half the species number

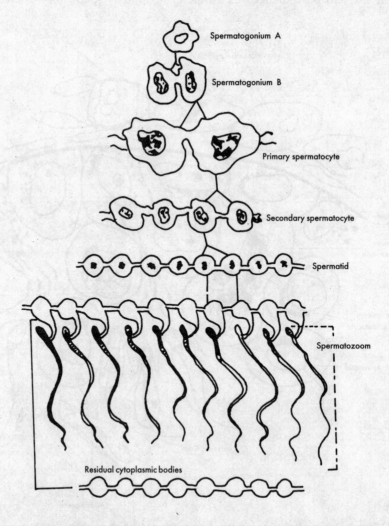

Spermatogonium A

Spermatogonium B

Primary spermatocyte

Secondary spermatocyte

Spermatid

Spermatozoom

Residual cytoplasmic bodies

Fig. 28 Stages in spermatogenesis. Male germ cells arise as a clone of cytoplasmically interconnected cells.

of chromosomes and half the genetic material of a secondary spermatocyte.

To summarise, one spermatogonium gives rise to two interconnected primary spermatocytes, which in turn divide to give four interconnected secondary spermatocytes which again divide to form eight interconnected spermatids.

3) Spermiogenesis

This is a process by which cytological changes transform inert spermatids into actively motile sperms.

The changes are:

- progressive condensation of the nucleus
- transformation of Golgi material into the acrosome
- origin of the axoneme from the distal centriole
- formation of mitochondrial and fibrous sheaths
- elimination of the redundant cytoplasm of the spermatid as the residual body of Regnaud.

THE FEMALE GENITAL SYSTEM

The female genital system, essentially, consists of the two ovaries, the two uterine tubes, the uterus and the vagina. It shows cyclical changes repeating about every four weeks, starting at puberty and ceasing at menopause.

THE FEMALE GONAD

The ovary or the female gonad (Fig. 29) is a situated in the pelvic cavity along its side wall. It has a peripheral **cortex** and a central **medulla**. During the childbearing period, i.e. from puberty to menopause, the cortex occupies most of the ovary. It consists of:

1) A highly cellular, embryonic connective tissue stroma and

2) The germ cells or oogonia and their enclosing follicular cells, together constituting the ovarian follicles, embedded in the stroma.

A thin fibrous sheath, the **tunica albuginea**, covers the cortex. The tunica is lined on its exterior by cubical cells of the **germinal epithelium**. The medulla consists of vascular connective tissue, lymphatics and some vestiges of the 'testicular,' mesonephric tubular and duct systems.

The cells derived from **the ovarian stroma** and **the ovarian follicles** are endocrine in function.

The Ovarian Stroma

The stromal cells surrounding the follicles constitute a covering, the theca folliculi. The cells of the theca proliferate and differentiate into two zones, an internal, highly vascular **theca (tunica) interna** and an external fibrous **theca (tunica) externa**. Even in the pre-adolescent ovary, when no follicles become fully mature, they continue to grow and later undergo atresia, and the cells of the theca interna proliferate and differentiate to form a thick region of lipid-laden cells, the interstitial gland. The role of these cells is uncertain. They may produce a little estrogen. After puberty however, these cells constitute the well-defined thecal gland which is known to be the chief source of estrogens, mainly estradiol.

During the maturation of ovarian follicles, the follicular cells multiply and differentiate into granulosa cells of the stratum granulosum (membrana granulosa). These also produce estrogens. Following ovulation, these granulosa cells and the theca interna cells differentiate to form the granulosa lutein cells and the theca lutein cells respectively, of the **corpus luteum**, which produce progesterone. Some androgens or male hormones are also produced by the ovarian stromal cells. Another hormone called **relaxin**, which facilitates parturition, by helping to dilate the cervix, is also produced from some unspecified stromal cells.

The Ovarian Follicles

The ovarian follicles are concerned with oogenesis, the process by which mature ova or female gametes are produced. Initially, each follicle consists of an oogonium — or germ cell — the precursor of an ovum, and its surrounding flattened follicular cells. This is known as a **primordial follicle**. The oogonia are derived from the primordial germ cells which appear by the end of the third week of gestation, at the caudal end of the yolk sac. Probably entodermal in origin, these cells migrate to reach the mesoderm of the gonadal ridge via the hindgut wall and its suspending mesentery (Fig. 29). They initiate and induce the gonadal ridge mesoderm to form the gonad. The gonadal mesoderm, in turn, is essential for the survival and multiplication of the germ cells. In the male, the same cells, by their proliferation and differentiation, are believed to give rise to spermatogonia.

Oogenesis: Oogenesis occurs in three phases:

1) Multiplication of oogonia by repeated mitotic divisions.
2) Enlargement of some oogonia to form primary oocytes.
3) Maturation of some of these oocytes into

ova, through the **two meiotic divisions — reductional** (first) and **equational** (second).

1) Oogonia continue to multiply by mitosis throughout embryonic and foetal life, but cease to proliferate after birth.
2) Some oogonia continue to enlarge and differentiate into primary oocytes, which are later surrounded by a layer of flat stromal (follicular) cells to form primordial ovarian follicles. At birth, each ovary contains about two million of these. The primary oocytes show nuclear changes preparatory to meiosis-1. Most of these remain in this state till puberty, and continue to degener-

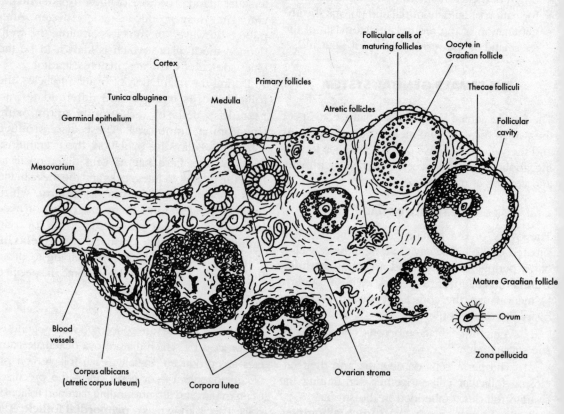

Fig. 29   Schematic panoramic section of the ovary, showing ovarian follicles in various stages of maturation. A ruptured follicle and two corpora lutea also shown.

ate, so that at puberty they number about 40,000. 3) The primordial follicles, and the primary oocytes they contain, continue to grow during foetal life, and can come to full maturation only after puberty (Fig. 30). During maturation they pass through the following stages:

i.   **Primary follicles:** The follicular cells become columnar. The oocytes grow and secrete a thick, pale, structureless covering, the zona pellucida.

ii.   **Secondary follicles:** The follicular epithelium proliferates to become stratified and is called the membrana granulosa. The zona pellucida is fully formed. It is, in fact, a product of the oocyte and the covering follicular cells. In the region of the zona, the microvilli of the oocyte plasma membrane mingle with the inward projecting cytoplasmic processes of the innermost layer of follicular cells. Thus, the follicular cells can convey nutrition to a large surface area of the oocyte. By six months IUL, many primary and secondary follicles are present. At birth, most of the primary oocytes have reached a stage of dictyotene (resting state, at the end of meiosis I), and remain in this stage till they mature fully prior to ovulation.

iii.   **Vesicular or Graafian follicles:** While most of the follicles degenerate to become atretic follicles, some of the secondary follicles enlarge and develop a crescentic follicular cavity containing fluid — the liquor folliculi, within the mass of granulosa cells. These are then called vesicular or Graafian follicles. At ovulation, one of these follicles matures and ruptures to release the contained ovum.

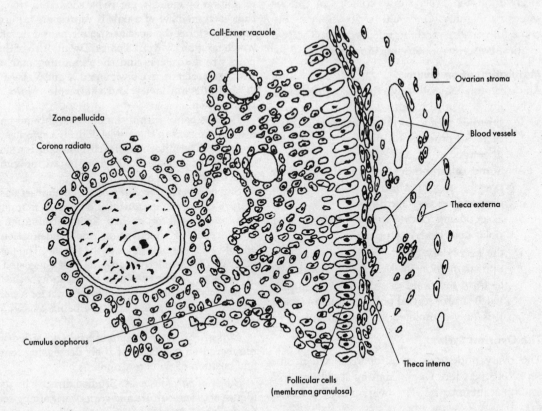

Fig. 30 A section through a Graafian follicle.

Mature Vesicular Follicle

The mature follicle is a fibrocellular sac, which has an eccentric cavity, the antrum folliculi, filled with fluid, the liquor folliculi. The wall of the follicle shows from the centre to the periphery:

   i. the cells of the stratum granulosum
   ii. the cells of the vascular theca interna and
   iii. the fibrous theca externa.

On one aspect of the follicular wall, there is a hillock of granulosa cells, the **cumulus oophorus**, in which the ovum is embedded. The granulosa cells immediately surrounding the ovum are called the **corona radiata** cells. The contained ovum (still a primary oocyte), has increased its diameter by four times from the original 35 µ and is filled with yolk granules.

Some follicles begin maturing only after puberty and continue doing so till menopause. So, at any time, the ovary shows follicles in various stages of maturity. Only 400 to 500 oocytes become fully mature and are released from the two ovaries, between puberty and menopause.

Maturation of an Ovum

An oogonium passes through the following stages to become a mature ovum:

1) It proliferates to form more oogonia. Most of these proceed no further and just degenerate.
2) Some differentiate to form the primary oocytes each of which forms by reduction division (meiosis stage I).
3) a secondary oocyte and a much smaller polar cell (body) or polocyte.
4) the secondary oocyte undergoes the second maturation division (meiosis stage II) to form the ootid or mature ovum and a much smaller second polar cell. Meiosis stage II is only completed at fertilisation.

The Ovarian Cycle

The ovary undergoes cyclic changes which are repeated every four weeks, starting at puberty and ending at menopause. The ovarian cycle consists of:

1) Proliferation and maturation of oocytes.
2) Discharge of an ovum at ovulation.

3) Repeated formation of corpus luteum following each ovulation and the accompanying changes occurring in the ovarian stroma in general, and the thecal gland in particular.

Several ovarian follicles begin maturing at each cycle. Except the fully mature ovum to be discharged at ovulation and another mature ovum kept ready for the ovulation, all other maturing ova with their follicles undergo degeneration and are called **atretic follicles**. Follicular atresia is widespread and is repeated through all successive ovarian cycles.

SUMMARY

Organelles found in pairs in the eukaryotic nuclei, have a species-specific number and during gamete formation by meiosis, get redistributed in them so that each member of a pair is represented. Fertilisation restores the species-specific paired number, which for man is 46 or 23 pairs. Twenty-two of these pairs are autosomes and the remaining pair, the sex chromosomes, are designated X and Y, because of their dissimilarity and their role in sex determination.

Besides being within the nucleus, chromosomes are also present in the mitochondria, a cytoplasmic organelle. The mitochondrial chromosome is a small circular chromosome, inherited by an individual from the maternal ovum.

Sex chromatin or Barr body: A characteristic feature of interphase nuclei of all female mammals and can be used for 'nuclear sex determination'. It is the result of 'inactivation' and condensation of one of two X chromosomes of the female. The possibility of 'one X-inactivation' was first suggested by Mary Lyon — now known as the Lyon hypothesis.

Karyotype: The chromosome formula for a cell or an individual, female karyotype being 44+XX and male 44+XY.

Classification of chromosomes: Classified and numbered on the basis of their decreasing length and position of their centromeres.

Study of chromosomes: Studied directly by techniques of tissue-culture and variety of staining-techniques, chief of which are quinacrine fluorescent and Giemsa methods. With these, each chromosome shows a characteristic 'banding pattern'. Elaborate nomenclature has been established to describe chromosomal fractions and subfractions.

Recently, high resolution banding patterns have been used for a more detailed study of chromosomes. The banding is done before the chromosomes are maximally condensed, that is before metaphase, and is therefore called prophase or prometaphase banding.

For a rapid screening of chromosomes, fluorescent activated cell sorter (FACS), also called flow cytometry may be used.

Chromosomal fragments can be studied because of the advances in the field of molecular cytogenetics. Fluorescent in situ hybridisation (FISH) technique is one such method.

Each chromosome is a supercoiled package of DNA and several proteins. The levels of packaging are as follows:

1) DNA double helix
2) Nucleosome and nucleosome fibre
3) Solenoid and chromatin fibre
4) Chromomere
5) Chromosome

Chromosomes are best seen when they are maximally coiled. This takes place during metaphase of mitosis and meiosis. Metaphase chromosomes are best suited for detailed karyotyping.

Mitosis: All cells except maturing gametes increase in number by means of mitosis. Following doubling or replication of DNA, a replicating cell passes through the following continuous, overlapping phases:

1) Prophase   2) Metaphase
3) Anaphase and 4) Telophase

Meiosis: Occurs only in gonads during gametogenesis, in two steps, meiosis I and meiosis II. The two steps follow in quick succession without an intervening DNA replication phase. Stages in meiosis I and II are the same as in mitosis, except that the prophase of meiosis I is long-drawn and complex. It is characterised by the following stages:

1) Leptotene   2) Zygotene   3) Pachytene
4) Diplotene   5) Diakinesis

At the end of meiosis I, each of the two daughter cells carries 23 bivalent (two sister chromatids) chromosomes.

Meiosis II is an equating division, wherein 23 bivalents give rise to 46 chromosomes due to the longitudinal splitting of each centromere, and each sister chromatid becoming an independent chromosome and these 46 get shared as 23 each in the resulting daughter cells or gametes.

In spermatogenesis, all resulting gametes are functional. In oogenesis, only one out of four daughter cells is functional, the other three being polar bodies or cells.

4 MOLECULAR GENETICS: THE GENETIC BASIS OF INHERITANCE

Introduction

Chromosomes contain DNA, the genetic material which is transmitted not only from parent cells to daughter cells during mitosis, but also from one generation to another following meiosis and fusion of male and female gametes. The chromosomes also contain proteins, which constitute the 'non-genetic' but functionally essential material, and small amounts of RNA.

The conceptual unit of heredity is called a gene and, depending upon the aspect from which it is considered, it may be defined in several ways.

Genes are segments of DNA, long or short. They are directly concerned with the formation of all RNAs, including the different tRNAs, the ribosomal subunits, the precursor and the final mRNA and the nucleolar RNA. Through the agency of these RNA molecules, the genes regulate all protein synthesis, structural as well as enzymatic. The proteins, in turn, of course promote or inhibit the activity of the genes.

Genes replicate themselves prior to cell division. They regulate the activity of other genes, which may be in their vicinity or are placed more remotely. They can undergo a structural change or mutation and can recombine during the exchange of genetic material in meiosis.

Genes also regulate mitotic activity, cell-growth and cell-differentiation as in embryogenesis, and are suspected to play an important role during the cancerous change of a cell or tissue.

It is evident from what has been said that DNA plays a pivotal role in the **growth**, **differentiation, metabolism** and **multiplication of cells**.

Small amounts of DNA are also found in the mitochondria and constitute the mitochondrial genes. These are capable of replication and play a role in cellular metabolism.

During embryonic development, it appears that the sequence of events is the result of the **switching on** or **switching off** of particular gene-loci. The precise mechanism of gene regulation is still unclear. Apparently, some gene products such as proteins function as **messenger molecules** to suppress or activate the genes, as required by the overall economy of the cell. Since all gene-loci are never active at the same time, and the cytoplasmic constituents play a crucial role in regulating gene activity, the cytoplasm is now believed to play a primary role in cell differentiation, which is merely a reflection of differential gene activity.

Chromosomes are composed of deoxyribonucleic acid (DNA) and protein. Variable lengths of DNA constitute the genes, the units of heredity, of which there are about 100,000 in each human cell.

The genotype of an individual is his genetic constitution. The genome is the full set of genes, haploid in the gametes and diploid in the somatic cells of an individual. The phenotype is the expression of any of these genes as a physical, biochemical or physiological trait.

In this chapter genes will be discussed from various aspects which relate to molecular genetics.

Molecular Basis of Genes

Molecular genetics deals with the study of genetic material, deoxyribonucleic acid (DNA), the replication of DNA to produce more DNA, the transcription of DNA into ribonucleic acid (RNA), and the translation of RNA into protein in the form of polypeptide chains. The unidirectional DNA-RNA-protein relationship is called the

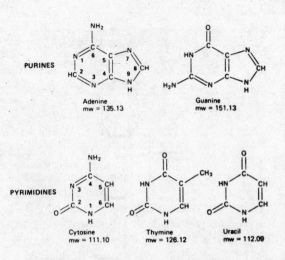

Fig. 31   Purines and pyrimidines, the nitrogen containing bases are the basic components of DNA and RNA

central dogma of molecular genetics.

The criteria required to be met by genetic material are:

1)   Genetic material must contain biologically useful information that is maintained in a stable form.

2)   Genetic information must be reproduced and transmitted faithfully from cell to cell or from one generation to the next.

3)   Genetic material must be able to express itself, so that other biological molecules and ultimately cells and organisms will be produced and maintained. Hence some mechanism must be available for decoding or translating the information contained in the genetic material into its 'productive' form. Thus there would be a molecule, which could not only generate its own kind, but also generate other and new kinds of molecules. In this respect it would differ from 'non-living' matter.

4)   Genetic material must be capable of variation. Two sources of change have been recognised in present day genetic systems — mutation and recombination.

Molecular Structure of Nucleic Acids

DNA and RNA are composed of two different classes of nitrogen containing bases, the **purines**

and the **pyrimidines** (Fig. 31). The purines in DNA are **adenine** and **guanine** and pyrimidines are **cytosine** and **thymine**. RNA contain **uracil** in place of thymine (thymine is, in fact, methyluracil). Purines and pyrimidines can form chemical linkages with **pentose (5-carbon) sugars** (Fig. 32). The carbon atoms on the sugars are designated 1^1, 2^1, 3^1, 4^1 and 5^1. It is the 1^1 carbon of the pentose that forms the bond to the nitrogen atom in position 1 of a pyrimidine or to the nitrogen atom in position 9 of a purine. The resulting molecules called **nucleosides** can serve as elementary precursors for DNA or RNA synthesis. DNA precursors contain the pentose deoxyribose and the RNA precursors contain ribose instead. Ribose contains an additional oxygen atom at position 2^1, which is absent in deoxyribose.

A nucleoside must become complexed with a phosphate group to form a **nucleotide** before it is capable of becoming a part of a DNA or RNA molecule.

Nucleosides may have one, two, or three phosphate groups, e.g., in the molecules respectively called Adenosine Mono-Phosphate (AMP), Di-Phosphate (ADP) and Tri-Phosphate (ATP). It is the nucleotide triphosphates that serve directly as precursors for DNA and RNA synthesis (Fig. 33).

DNA and RNA are polymers of nucleotides. Two nucleotides joined together constitute a

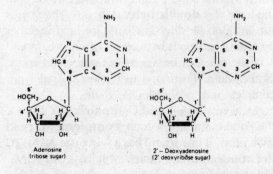

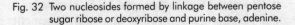

Fig. 32 Two nucleosides formed by linkage between pentose sugar ribose or deoxyribose and purine base, adenine.

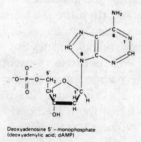

Fig. 33 Nucleotide formed by linkage between a nucleoside and a phosphate group

dinucleo tide; three form a **trinucleotide**; several form an **oligonucleotide** and many together form a **polynucleotide**. Only one phosphate group of each precursor triphosphate is included in the polymer. This phosphate group, is bound to the 5^{l} carbon of the pentose sugar on one nucleotide, and bound to the 3^{l} carbon of the sugar of the next nucleotide, so that a series of 5^{l}–3^{l} phosphate linkages, holds the nucleotides together along the length of the polymer (Fig. 34). The phosphate bonds also called phosphodiester bonds are covalent bonds and so are extremely strong. Polynucleotides are structurally polarised, meaning that a 3^{l}-hydroxyl (3^{l}-OH) end and a 5^{l}-phosphate (5^{l}-P) end can be identified for any chain (Fig. 35).

DNA

DNA molecule is composed of two long, parallel, polynucleotide chains, which are twisted in the form of a **double helix** (Fig. 36). The chains run in opposite directions and are held together by hydrogen bonds between A of one chain and T of the other, or between G of one chain and C of the other. There are 10 nucleotide pairs per complete turn of the double chain.

As normally A–T and G–C **pairing** is a must, the parallel strands become **complementary** to each other. If one strand has a sequence AAAGTC the complementary strand will have TTTCAG. This facilitates quick and fidel replication of DNA and formation of messenger RNA. Almost infinite variations are possible in the arrangement

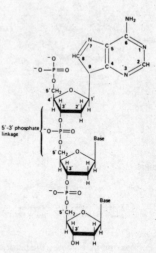

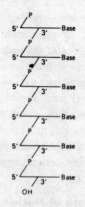

Fig. 34 DNA and RNA are polymers of nucleotides. Here a trinucleotide of DNA is shown, which results from the joining of three nucleotides. Note that the phosphate group, which is bound to the 5^{l}-carbon of the pentose sugar on one nucleotide, also becomes chemically bound to the 3^{l}-carbon of the sugar of a second nucleotide, so that series of 5^{l}—3^{l} phosphate linkages hold the nucleotides together along the length of the polymer. The phosphate residues along the chain are acidic, whereby the term nucleic acid is also used for the nucleotide chain.

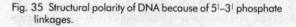

Fig. 35 Structural polarity of DNA because of 5^{l}–3^{l} phosphate linkages.

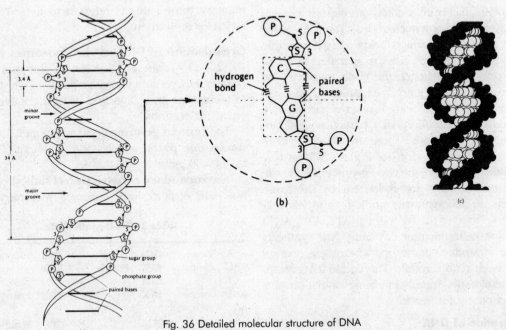

Fig. 36 Detailed molecular structure of DNA

of the bases along the length of a polynucleotide chain.

As the distance between bases in the polynucleotide chain is 3.4Å, it follows that in the double helix, a strand makes one complete turn every 34Å. The specific hydrogen bonding between base pairs requires that the two polynucleotide strands are oriented in opposite directions. One strand is oriented in 3'-OH→5'-P end and the other is in a 5'-P→3'-OH fashion.

Mitochondrial DNA: In a cell, the DNA occurs at two sites: in the nucleus where it forms the largest bulk as part of the chromosomes, and in the cytoplasm, in a very small amount, as part of the mitochondria. Mitochondrial DNA differs from chromosomal DNA in certain details.

In mitochondria, the DNA thread is joined at each end to form a ring (55 S). It has a proportion of nitrogenous bases different from that of chromosomal DNA. Since in a zygote the mitochondria are wholly derived from the ovum, it follows that the few mitochondrial genes in the mitochondrial DNA show strictly **maternal inheritance**.

The Genetic Code

DNA directs the synthesis of proteins which are molecules made up of amino acids arranged in a specific linear sequence. As there are 20 different amino acids, it is necessary for DNA to provide a code for each one of these. DNA has only 4 nitrogenous bases, which, taken one at a time, could code for only four amino acids. If two sequential bases would code for one amino acid there would be 4 × 4 or 16 possible combinations which are inadequate for 20 amino acids. If three successive bases would specify one amino acid, then the possible number of combinations would be 4 × 4 × 4 or 64. These 64 possible triplet combinations of bases, which constitute a code for amino acids are known as **codons**. The sequence in which amino acids are incorporated into a polypeptide chain is determined by the order of the corresponding triplets of bases in one of the chains in DNA. A gene is considered as a segment of DNA — a polynucleotide chain — which codes for one polypeptide chain.

The genetic code for all the amino acids found in proteins has been worked out experimentally, using synthetic polynucleotides (Table 3). Since there are only 20 amino acids and 64 possible codons, most amino acids are specified by more than one codon; hence the code is said to be degenerate. There is no overlapping of bases in the code, one base being forever a part of only one codon. The codons of a particular gene are arranged in sequence. There are no spaces between successive codons of a gene. With a few possible exceptions, the code is universal, i.e, the same amino acids are coded for by the same codons, in all organisms studied, from bacteria to man. Three of the 64 codons (ATT, ATC, ACT) code for the termination of a gene. The synthesis of a polypeptide chain stops when these codons have been read through. The codon TAC codes for methionine, and also indicates initiation of a transcription of a gene.

Replication of DNA

Watson and Crick made an epochal suggestion that the two chains unwind and separate. Each chain serves as a template for the synthesis of its complementary chain. The enzyme DNA polymerase mediates the union of nucleotides during DNA synthesis. Since the two chains are complementary, each synthesises a second chain identical to the one from which it had been separated, and the end result is two complete molecules, each identical to the original. DNA replication occurs in both directions along a chromosome (Fig 37).

Meselson and Stahl confirmed the Watson-Crick hypothesis of DNA replication in 1958. They used heavy nitrogen, an isotope of nitrogen. Bacteria were reproduced in a medium in which the only source of nitrogen was N^{15}, so that the DNA of the bacteria became labelled with heavy nitrogen. They were then grown in a medium containing ordinary N^{14} and allowed to reproduce for two more generations. The proportion of N^{15} and N^{14}

in the bacterial DNA was measured after each generation. The results are shown in Fig 38. As the old DNA strands are preserved, and each old strand induces the formation of a new complementary strand, this is referred to as semiconservative replication.

Organisation of DNA in chromosomes (Figs. 19, 20, 21, Table 4): As seen in the previous chapter, DNA combines with a protein — histone. In a chromosome, DNA and histone combine in equal proportions.

The **human genome** contains about 2.7×10^9 **nucleotide pairs**, which code for about 50,000 to 100,000 genes.

The **secondary constrictions (stalks)** of the five pairs of acrocentric chromosomes carry the

Table 3: The Genetic Code

AAA	Phenyl-	GGA		TTA	Asparagine
AAG	alanine	GGG	Proline	TTG	
		GGT			
AAT	Leucine	GGC		TTC	Lysine
AAC					
		TGA		CTA	Aspartic
GAA		TGG	Threonine	CTG	Acid
GAG	Leucine	TGT			
GAT		TGC		CTT	Glutamic
GAC				CTC	Acid
		CGA		ACA	Cysteine
TAA		CGG	Alanine	ACG	
TAG	Isoleucine	CGT			
TAT		CGC		ACT	Stop
TAC	Methionine	ATA	Tyrosine	ACC	Tryptophan
		ATG			
CAA		ATT	Stop	GCA	
CAG	Valine	ATC		GCG	Arginine
CAT				GCT	
CAC				GCC	
		GTA	Histidine		
		GTG		TCA	Serine
AGA		GTT	Glutamine	TCG	
AGG	Serine	GTC		TCT	Arginine
AGT				TCC	
AGC				CCA	
				CCG	Glycine
				CCT	
				CCC	

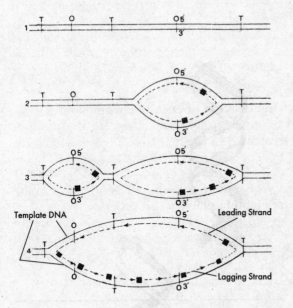

Fig. 37   Schematic representation of DNA replication occurring in both directions along a chromosome. O = point of origin of DNA replication. T = point of termination of DNA replication.

genes for synthesis of ribosomal RNA. The stalks of the acrocentric chromosomes are the nucleolus organiser regions of the genome. Numerical aberrations of the acrocentric chromosomes are frequently the causes of abnormality in live newborns or in first-trimester abortions, yet the mechanism by which the risk of non-disjunction is increased in these chromosomes is not known.

<u>Classification of DNA</u>: Two classes of DNA have been recognised:

1) **Unique** sequence — **nonrepetitive** — DNA constituting 75 per cent of the genome.
2) **Repetitive** DNA constituting the remaining 25 per cent of the genome.

There are two major subgroups of the repetitive DNA:

1) *dispersed repetitive* DNA (15 per cent), and
2) *satellite* DNA (10 per cent).

Dispersed repetitive DNA are of two major types:

1) Short Interspersed Elements (SINE) 100–500 base-pairs long, and

2) Long Interspersed Elements (LINE) 7 kilobases long.

Table 4: Levels of Organisation of the Genetic Material

Component	Thickness	Length
DNA	2 nm or 20Å	2 m per cell
Nucleosome	8 × 11 nm	—

Component	Thickness	Length
Chromatin Fibre	25 nm	8 cm per cell
Chromosome Band or Chrommomere Metaphase	0.4—0.8 μm	—
Chromosome	0.8–1.2 μm	200–300 μm per cell or 2–12 μm per chromosome

One of the varieties of SINE is *Alu* Family 300 base-pair sequence repeated 300,000–500,000 times.

Satellite repeats occur in tandem (repeat occurs immediately at the end of the earlier one). On centrifugation, the DNA appears like a *satellite*, separate from other DNA (hence the name). Depending on the size of the satellite repeats and the number of repeats, satellite DNA is further classified as μ -satellite (171 base-pair sequence extending over several million base pairs), minisatellite (20–70 base-pair sequence extending over few thousand base-pairs) and microsatellites (2–4 base-pair sequence extending over a few hundred base-pairs). Mini and micro satellites vary in length among individuals and are therefore useful for gene mapping.

Satellite DNA is found in regions of constitutive heterochromatin, such as the C bands.

RNA

RNA — ribonucleic acid — is composed of a single polynucleotide chain. It is synthesised on a DNA template by a process known as **transcription** which takes place in the presence of the enzyme **RNA polymerase**.

Messenger RNA (Fig 39), **transfer RNA** (Fig 40)

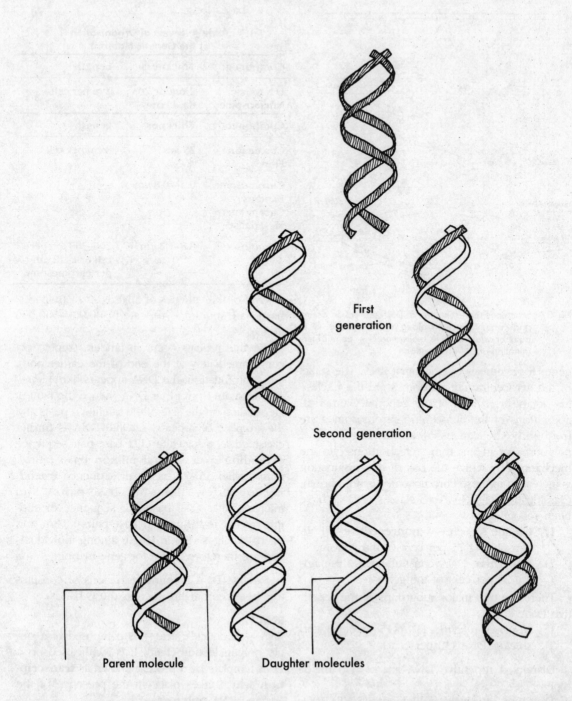

First
generation

Second generation

Parent molecule   Daughter molecules

Fig. 38 Scheme showing semiconservative replication of DNA. New complementary strands shown in outlines; old strands shaded dark.

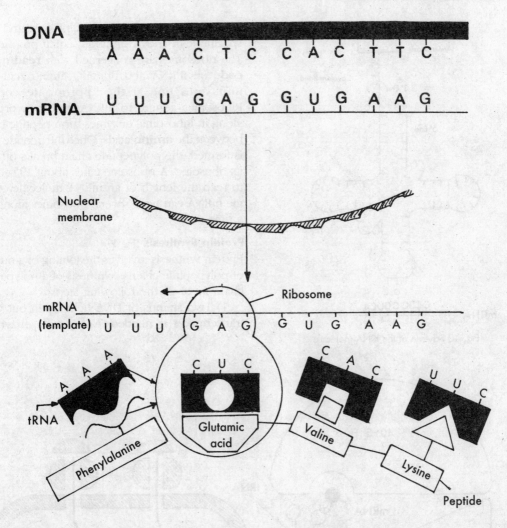

Fig. 39 Transcription and translation. An mRNA molecule is being transcribed along a DNA master strand which acts as a template. In the cytoplasm, the mRNA molecule is being translated by means of ribosomes into specific amino acid linkages. The intermediaries for this are the tRNA molecules, which are specific for each amino acid.

and **ribosomal RNA** (Fig 41) are three types of RNA concerned with protein synthesis. Messenger RNA (mRNA) is produced in the nucleus. It represents a strand complementary to the DNA template, with the difference that uracil replaces thymine. It passes out from the nucleus to the cytoplasm and it dictates the sequence in which amino acids are incorporated into a polypeptide. Transfer RNA (tRNA), [also known as soluble RNA (sRNA) because it remains in suspension following centrifugation or as adaptor RNA because of its structure], is concerned with bringing amino acids from the cytoplasm to their required places along the mRNA template. Each amino acid needs an amino acid activating enzyme, whereby special sites on the amino acid molecule and on the tRNA molecule are recognised. The tRNA molecule has an **anticodon** which is complementary to and reads a specific codon on the mRNA chain. The amino acid-tRNA complex is placed in the correct position on the linear mRNA molecule by the matching of codon and anticodon.

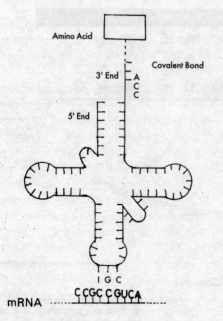

Fig. 40 Scheme of the tRNA molecule.

Ribosomes are made up of protein and non-specific RNA (rRNA) in about equal proportions. The ribosomes are concerned with **reading the code** on mRNA and bringing amino acid-tRNA units into line at the appropriate codons. Ribosomes adhere to mRNA and then proceed along it. Ribosomal enzymes form peptide bonds between the **amino** acids. Once the peptide bond is formed, the polypeptide chain breaks off from its ribosome. A ribosome takes about 10 seconds to read the length of an mRNA molecule. A single mRNA can have several ribosomes along it at a time.

Protein Synthesis (Fig 39)

Protein synthesis involves the joining of a number of polypeptide chains. Synthesis of a polypeptide chain involves the following steps:

1) Two strands of DNA helix open out when transcription is needed. No specific enzyme is

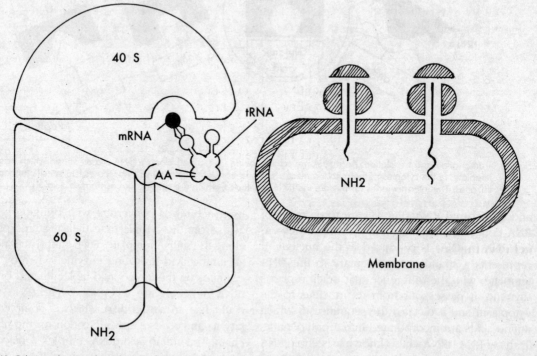

Fig. 41 Scheme showing the subunits of ribosomes and their relation with protein synthesis. The figure on the right shows a growing polypeptide chain collecting inside the endoplasmic reticulum.

known to facilitate this. Only one of the two DNA strands acts as a template for RNA synthesis.

2) In the presence of **RNA polymerase**, a molecule of mRNA is formed on the **DNA template** in the nucleus.

3) The mRNA molecule reaches the cytoplasm.

4) In the cytoplasm, amino acids are activated and brought in association with tRNA to form amino acid-tRNA complexes by specific enzymes. Each amino acid has a specific enzyme for activation and for attaching itself to a corresponding tRNA. The tRNA has an anticodon complementary to the appropriate codon of the mRNA.

5) Ribosomes adhere to sticky points on the mRNA molecule and move along the molecule. Under the influence of ribosomes, amino acid-tRNA complexes are brought into a desired order along the mRNA chain, commencing at an AUG mRNA codon.

6) The ribosomal enzyme brings about formation of peptide bonds between the amino acids of successive amino acid-tRNA complexes.

7) With the formation of the peptide bond, the amino acid-tRNA complex breaks up and the tRNA is set free to unite with another activated amino acid.

8) As the polypeptide molecule is being formed, it begins to separate from the mRNA strand. It takes about 10 seconds for a ribosome to reach a **terminator codon** at the end of one gene. It detaches itself from the mRNA and becomes available to induce the formation of another polypeptide.

Genetic control of protein synthesis (Fig 42): Our present knowledge regarding protein synthesis is based on studies conducted on bacteria. **Protein synthesis** is controlled partly by genes and partly by factors in the external environment.

Jacob and Monod postulated the now widely accepted **operon concept** in 1961. A group of closely related **structural gene (cistrons)** is activated by an **operator gene** located close to them. Together, the **operator gene** and the cistrons under its control constitute on **operon**. Operon is controlled (i.e., activated or inactivated) by two segments of DNA that act as regulatory elements, namely, the **regulatory gene, and the promoter gene**, which may or may not be in the vicinity of the operon.

Normally, only a few genes of the total genome are active. A regulator gene is a DNA segment independent of an operon. It synthesises a **repressor protein** — a first order messenger — by means of a complementary mRNA strand. Specific second order messengers — **effectors** — presumably similar to the first order messengers, determine the state of activity of the repressor protein. Only when the repressor protein is active can it combine with, and inactivate the operator gene. Some repressors are active and are able to block the operator gene only when assisted by **corepressor molecules**. Some second order messengers combine with the repressor so that it is unable to combine with and repress the operator gene thus allowing the related structural genes to become active.

The promoter gene is the DNA segment to which the RNA polymerase first becomes attached to initiate the transcription of the structural genes. The promoter is a key regulatory element, since it controls the rate of mRNA synthesis of a given operon. Both the structural genes and regulator genes have their own promoters.

Only one known operon called the *lac* operon has been studied in *E. coli*. In the *lac* operon, there are three structural genes one each for the enzymes ß-galactosidase, permease, and transacetylase, that are regulated by the same operator; and all of them are involved in the utilisation of lactose. The RNA polymerase initiates transcription of the structural genes by binding with the promoter, which is located to the left side of the operator, which in turn is located to the left of the structural genes of the *lac* operon. Therefore, the RNA polymerase is required to negotiate the operator before transcription can occur. Regulation of the *lac* operon is by way of repressor which binds to the operator, thereby interfering with the transcription by RNA polymerase. In this condition, the *lac* operon remains inactive and no enzymes are produced. In the presence of an **inducer** (suitable metabolite

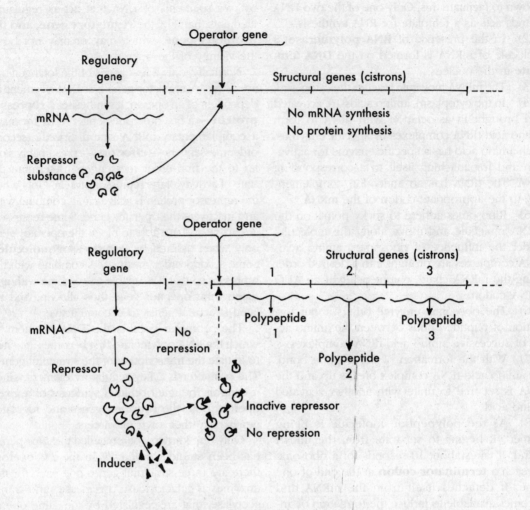

Fig. 42 The Jacob and Monod concept of regulation of protein synthesis.

in case of *lac* operon), the repressor is inactivated and the operator becomes free. Under such circumstances, the entire operon can be transcribed by the RNA polymerase. The *lac* repressor is a protein of 160,000 daltons with four subunits of 40,000 daltons, each of which has a binding site for the inducer.

The *lac* **operon** has a positive control mechanism operated by cyclic AMP, which interacts with a receptor protein. The cyclic AMP-receptor-protein-complex gets bound to the promoter, allowing the RNA polymerase to recognise the promoter. When cells are grown in glucose, cyclic AMP levels go down and by a phenomenon known as catabolic repression, ß-galactosidase levels are also brought down.

Gene structure in detail: The earlier ideas of the **eukaryotic gene structure** stand considerably revised following the use of the techniques of **restriction endonuclease analysis, recombinant DNA cloning** and **DNA sequencing**. Perhaps the most unexpected discovery has been that the eukaryotic genes exist in pieces thus the **DNA sequences** coding for a particular protein, the **exons**, are interrupted by one or more sequences of DNA, the **introns**, which do not code for protein. All genes do not contain the same number of introns, and introns as well as exons can vary greatly in length. Each intron or intervening DNA sequence is different but all introns studied so far show the same base sequences, that is, GT at their 5^1 end, and AG at their 3^1 end.

The other similarities in the DNA sequence of eukaryotic genes are: (1) the presence of the sequence TATA, 30 or more nucleotides from the 5^1 (**upstream**) of the first exon and (2) the sequence AATAAA, several hundred nucleotides from the 3^1 end (**downstream**) of the last exon. These structural features have an important bearing on the process of **transcription**, i.e., the formation of mRNA transcripts.

Transcription: The sequence TATA, present at the 5^1 end of eukaryotic genes, appears to be essential for the initiation of transcription (Fig 43). Sometimes known as the **Hogness box**, it represents a **promoter site** for RNA polymerase II. Mutations or deletions in this sequence reduce remarkably the initiation of transcription of the gene. However, other regions of DNA, often hundreds of bases to the 5^1 side of the TATA box, can also affect the initiation of transcription. It is suggested that these distinct regulatory sequences may influence the spacing or phase of nucleosome structure in relation to the DNA sequence, which might in turn then determine whether or not a gene is transcribed.

Synthesis of the primary RNA transcript proceeds in a 5^1 to 3^1 direction, while the strand of the gene that is being transcribed is actually read in a 3^1 to 5^1 direction. Because the RNA synthesised is corresponding to the 5^1 to 3^1 strand of DNA (not the one from which transcription took

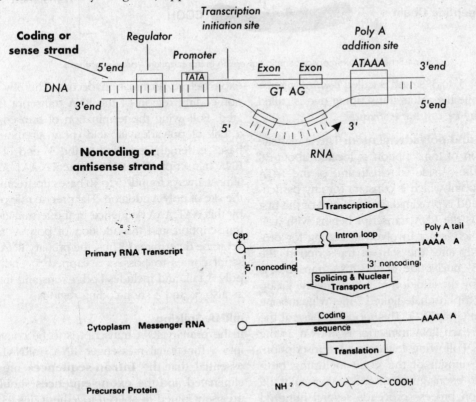

Fig. 43 Eukaryotic gene structure and the steps involved in eukaryotic gene transcription.

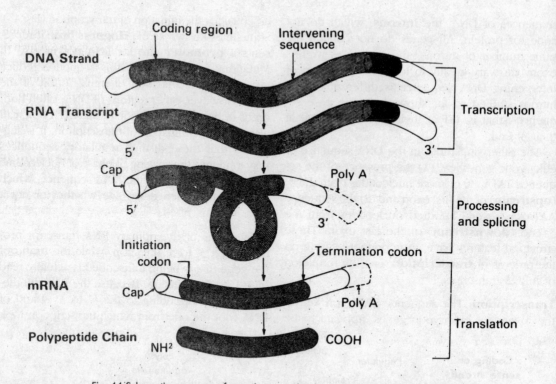

Fig. 44 Schematic summary of genetic expression in transcription – protein synthesis.

place); this 5' to 3' strand is called *coding* or *sense strand* while the actual transcribing one is called *non-coding* or *antisense strand*.

Capping and polyadenylation: The actual site of initiation of transcription is located about 30 bases to the 3' side (downstream) of the TATA box, at a point which is constant for any particular gene, and is proximal to the 5' end of the first exon. Thus the RNA transcript begins with a 5' region which is not involved in coding for protein. Shortly after the start of transcription, the terminal 5' nucleotide of the RNA transcript is modified by the addition of a 2'–0 methyl group and a 5'5' triphosphate-linked 7-methylguanosine residue (m^7GpppX^{m-}). This modified base at the 5' end of each RNA transcript is known as the **RNA cap**. Following initiation of transcription, the entire length of the gene including both introns and exons gets transcribed. Normally the transcription process proceeds several hundred nucleotides beyond the end of the final or last

exon before termination occurs. Thereby, a 3' non-coding region of the RNA transcript is created. Following the termination of transcription, a 'tail' of polyadenylic acid (poly A) about 100 bases in length, is added to the 3' end of each RNA transcript. The DNA sequence AAT AAA is almost always found 15 to 30 bases upstream from the site of poly A addition. The precise role played by this AAT AAA sequence in the termination of transcription and the addition of poly A 'tail' is yet to be determined. Thus, the primary RNA transcript comes to possess a capped 5' end, a 3' poly A tail, and includes both exons and introns, as also 5' and 3' non-coding regions.

mRNA Splicing

If the primary RNA transcript is to be converted into a functional messenger, RNA (mRNA), it is essential that the **intron-sequences** must be eliminated and the **exon-sequences** should be precisely joined or spliced together (Figs 43, 44). The **splicing mechanism** has been conserved during the course of evolution. This is suggested by the fact that any eukaryotic cell is able to splice correctly the primary RNA transcripts derived from other species. Also, it has been shown that intron splicing is crucial for the nuclear transport and production of a stable mRNA. The dinucleotides, GT and AG at the 5^1 and 3^1 ends of the introns, respectively, are critical for proper splicing.

A small RNA molecule called U1 RNA, is found in the form of **ribonucleoprotein particles** in the nucleus. It is remarkable in that its base sequence is highly conserved in different species. It may play a role in **RNA splicing**. Since the ends of the introns are complementary to U1 RNA, it is believed that they may be brought together by base pairing with this RNA, thus looping out the intron and creating a duplex structure which might serve as a substrate for a splicing enzyme (Fig 43). These conjectures are supported by the observation that antibodies against U1 RNA-nucleoprotein complexes dramatically inhibit RNA splicing. However, as yet, no splicing enzyme has been recognised.

Translation: The **mature messenger RNA** (mRNA), following the splicing out of the intron sequences from the **primary RNA transcript**, is transported from the nucleus to the cytoplasm where it gets translated into a **polypeptide chain**. In the cytoplasm, the various transfer RNA molecules (tRNA) provide an interface between mRNA and the free amino acids. One site on each tRNA molecule contains a specific sequence of three bases (the anticodon) which permits that tRNA to base pair with the complementary sequence of three bases in the mRNA (the mRNA codon). Another site on the tRNA molecule is recognised by one of the twenty different enzymes (aminoacyl synthetases) which specifically attaches one of twenty amino acids to the tRNA. Thus each tRNA molecule serves as an **adaptor**. It links a specific amino acid to a specific codon in the mRNA. The relationship between the DNA codons and amino acids is determined by the genetic code, as given in Table 3.

All amino acids except methionine and tryptophan, are represented by more than one codon. Some of these codons are used more frequently and preferentially than others for specifying a given amino acid. Since a special tRNA which recognises the AUG mRNA codon is required for polypeptide chain initiation, all polypeptides contain methionine as the N^- terminal amino acid which is often dropped subsequently in a final polypeptide chain. Three of the codons are not recognised by any of the tRNA molecules and so these codons serve as **polypeptide chain terminators**.

Translation of mature mRNA into a polypeptide occurs on cytoplasmic ribonucleoprotein particles, the ribosomes. Each ribosome is made up of two subunits. The smaller subunit (40S) consists of 18S ribosomal RNA and about 20 proteins; while the larger subunit (60S) is made up of 28S ribosomal RNA, 5S ribosomal RNA and about 30 proteins. Translation begins with the formation of an **initiation complex**. It is formed by the binding of aminoacylated initiator Met-tRNA^{met}, GTP and mRNA to the 40S ribosomal subunit. This process is facilitated by a specific soluble protein, designated elf-2, and a second larger protein, designated elf-3. The 5' cap structure of eukaryotic mRNA also plays a significant role in the initial binding of mRNA to the 40S subunits. Base pairing between the 5' non-coding region of the mRNA and the 3' region of 18S ribosomal RNA present in the smaller ribosomal subunit, is known to occur but its functional significance, if any in protein synthesis, is still in doubt. The poly A tail of mRNA is not involved in **mRNA translation**; but it may play a role in **mRNA stability**. Although mRNA binds to the 40S subunit at or near the 5' cap, it gets reposited on the ribosome prior to translation so that the 5' non-coding region is not translated. The anticodon of the initiator Met-tRNA^{met} may be involved in the correct positioning of the 5' proximal AUG, the initiator codons of the mRNA on the ribosome. Soon after the binding of mRNA, a 60S subunit is joined to the 40S initiation complex with the help of several accessory proteins, and elongation of the polypeptide chain proceeds. Two soluble protein factors. Ef-1 and Ef-2, and an enzyme, peptidyl transferase, play key roles in the process of polypeptide elongation. The final step in translation is **chain termination**. This involves the release of a completed polypeptide chain from the mRNA-ribosomal complex. When this complex contains an **mRNA termination codon** (UGA, UAG, or UAA), a **specific protein factor** (RF) binds to the complex and activates **peptidyl transferase**, releasing the peptide chain from the tRNA.

Most nascent eukaryotic polypeptides have similar rates of elongation and termination. However, eukaryotic mRNA molecules do differ in the rates at which they form initiation complexes with the 40S ribosomal subunit. At present, no evidence has been produced in support of the idea that there are mRNA-specific protein factors, which selectively regulate the translation of eukaryotic mRNA molecules.

Post-translational processing: Many polypeptides, after translation, undergo modifications before they become functional proteins. These modifications are called post-translational processing. The polypeptide could get folded into a specific three-dimensional structure. Two μ-globin and two ß-globin chains combine to form a tetrameric hemoglobin molecule. A polypeptide, proinsulin, is broken down into two smaller polypeptides to become a functional insulin molecule.

Promoters and enhancers: Promoters are sites, upstream of the first exon, where RNA polymerase-II enzyme initially binds for initiation of transcription. Some of the known promoters are TATA box or CCAAT box. Mutation of the promoter site decreases the transcription and therefore results in reduced protein synthesis.

Enhancers increase transcriptional activity by interacting with promoters. Enhancers could be present near the promoters or far away from them.

Protein Structure

Signal sequences: Many proteins synthesised on ribosomes are directed to their appropriate sites in a cell by means of information contained in their amino acid sequences. These directing sequences are called signal sequences. There is considerable variation in the exact compositions of the various sequences. However, all those which have to pass into the endoplasmic reticulum (ER) appear to contain hydrophilic amino acids on the ends and a stretch of hydrophobic amino acids in the middle, out of the 15 to 30 amino acid residues at the amino ends. With the elongation of a protein on the ribosomes, the signal sequence is exposed and binds to a receptor on the ER. The signal sequence promotes the transfer of the growing polypeptide chain across the ER membrane and during this passage the signal sequence itself is cleaved from the peptide chain that follows it. Likewise, the addition of a particular carbohydrate core to polypeptides directs them to the Golgi complex, while mannose-6-phosphate is the signal which directs certain enzyme proteins to lysosomes. Many proteins, e.g., proinsulin, also contain terminal sequences which are required for attaining a three dimensional structure. Such sequences are removed after folding of the polypeptide chain and bond formation of the disulphide bonds.

Structural-functional domains: Apart from its directing ability as stated above, the primary amino acid sequence of a protein contains information which determines the secondary, tertiary and quarternary structure of the protein molecule, enabling that molecule to carry out a specific cellular function. In many protein molecules, discrete structural domains or territories exist. These domains may represent a different functional part of the molecule. An example is the heavy chain polypeptide of the immunoglobulin molecule. It consists of four distinct structural domains, each of which corresponds to a different functional part of the immunoglobulin molecule.

It now appears that each exon of a eukaryotic gene codes for one structural-functional domain of a protein. For example, the heavy chain polypeptide gene for immunoglobulin contains four exons, each of which codes for a different structural domain of that polypeptide.

Existence of eukaryotic genes in pieces would allow for a more rapid evolution that would not have been possible if the genes had no intervening sequences (introns). Since two pieces of DNA are more likely to recombine as the distance between them increases, genes with intervening sequences separating their exons could recombine more frequently to form new functional combinations than genes in a single piece. However, the presence of introns is not a necessity for gene expression in eukaryotic organisms, as shown by the absence of introns in the histone and the interferon genes.

Eukaryotic genes exist in pieces as a result of evolutionary changes which have made it possible to build functionally and structurally complex molecules from the earlier simpler ones.

Regulation of eukaryotic gene expression: Recombinant DNA technology has shown that regulation of gene expression can occur at several of the points between DNA replication and protein synthesis.

DNA rearrangement: One form of genetic regulation, which controls cellular differentiation, involves alternatives in the structure of the main genes themselves, as for example in immunoglobulin synthesis. Early in development each antibody forming cell begins to produce only one type of light chain and one type of heavy chain out of a possible several thousands. The regulation of the production of both types of polypeptide chains involves structural rearrangement of the DNA coding for these polypeptides.

Chromatin structure: Many factors other than DNA rearrangements also have an influence on whether a given gene will be expressed or not. Chromatin containing actively transcribed DNA is much more sensitive to endonuclease digestion than chromatin which is not actively engaged in transcription. This may be due to variation in the types and amounts of non-histone chromosomal proteins bound to nucleosome cores and DNA linkers.

Histone and DNA modification: Certain non-histone chromosomal proteins are preferentially associated with actively transcribed genes. There is also an association between selective histone regulation and gene expression.

A gene has also been shown to contain a lower proportion of methylated cytosine residues when it is actively transcribed, than when it is not expressed. Conversely, maintenance of X-inactivation may require methylation of certain sites on the X chromosome. However, factors playing a primary role in the regulation of gene expression are yet to be determined.

In addition to genes coding for proteins, there are also DNA sequences which code for structural RNAs, viz., ribosomal RNA and transfer RNA, which are actively involved in protein synthesis. Some small DNA sequences, in addition, code for other small RNAs, which may function in the nucleus as control elements. These RNA-coding genes also make up as much as one per cent of the total DNA despite the fact that such genes are very small in size and are only of a few types. The reason for this is that they usually occur in many copies each.

For any one type of cell or tissue, up to one per cent of the DNA is transcribed to messenger RNA coding for protein, and up to 10 per cent is transcribed to nuclear RNA. In different cells or tissues, many of the sequences are transcribed in all cells, perhaps owing to their universal importance, e.g., for some enzymes and cell membrane proteins; but other sequences appear to be unique to a particular cell or tissue. If embryonic tissues are also taken into account, it becomes obvious that a large proportion of the DNA is transcribed in the nuclei of some tissue cells or the other. For example, as much as 40 per cent of the total gene sequence in the nuclear DNA, in the embryonic rat brain, is transcribed into nuclear RNA.

Jumping genes: One of the dogmas of genetics was that the position or 'locus' of gene on a chromosome was fixed or static, and could only change either through mutation or through crossing over (recombination). It has been shown in bacteria and in **Drosophila** that genes and segments of DNA do move between and on chromosomes with frequencies as great as 10^2. These have been called 'jumping genes.' The heretical concept of jumping genes was first propagated in the early 1930s by Barbara McClintock, the recipient of the 1983 Nobel Prize for Medicine and Physiology. McClintock, a botanist and plant geneticist, has worked life long on the Indian corn or maize plant. As far back as 1951, she claimed that genes are not fixed on the chromosomes but can move around in a rather random manner. Her claim was entirely disbelieved and disregarded, much in the same way as was Mendel's claim based on his work on the pea plant. But for the results of the research of molecular biologists of the 1960s, which demonstrated that indeed genes are not fixed entities, her work would not have seen the light of day.

McClintock found that colour changes in the successive generations of corn did not follow predictable hereditary patterns. She concluded that genes which control the colour of a kernel and other similar characteristics could be activated or shut off by other genes acting as switches and that these switches could move from one part of a chromosome to another under the influence of yet another type of genetic element, which she called an activator.

Today, it is recognised that when bacteria develop resistance to an antibiotic, they can pass this trait to other bacteria by means of these jumping genes or transportable elements as McClintock has called them. Such genes may possibly play a part in the change of normal cells into cancer cells and even in speeding up the evolutionary process.

Overlapping genes: The discovery that genes overlapped came by way of sequencing of proteins and nucleic acids, and was pioneered by Frederick Sanger in the 1950s. It was then realised for the first time that the sequence and the number of amino acids in a protein were orderly and fixed. However, till then, no simple technique for knowing the base sequence of DNA was available. The development of the *plus* and *minus* method by Sanger and Coulson (1976) and lately of the chain terminator method by Sanger, Nickolson and Coulson (1977) provides an ingenious way of determining the base sequence of DNA, and is indeed a major landmark in molecular biology.

With these techniques, the entire genome of the phase Ø X 174 (phi Ten 174) and phage G_4, have been sequenced. The virus Ø X 174, a bacteriophage, is a **tailless icosahedron** (a solid figure having 20 faces or sides). Its diameter is 250Å, and it has spikes at its apices. Its **capsid** (or coat) is made up of an assortment of proteins. Its single-stranded and **circular genome** (DNA) is made up of approximately 5386 nucleotides.

Genetic mapping shows nine sequential genes A,B,C,D,E,J,F,G and H with the following functions: A — for DNA replication; B and D — for the assembly of phage particle; C — function not known; F,G,H — make structural proteins of the viral capsid (coat); J — for a small basic protein involved in the condensation and packaging of DNA; E — makes a substance for the lysis of the host *E. coli*.

A number of genetic tests indicated that gene E is completely included within gene D, i.e., the genes D and E utilise the *same* DNA sequence for protein synthesis but use different coding frames. Thus, gene D **overlaps** gene E. It was shown that gene E coincides with 60 per cent of gene D and lies towards its ends. So, gene J becomes adjacent to gene D. The end part of gene D was found to overlap the start of gene J. Also, gene B was found to be contained within gene A, so that they are both transcribed from the same DNA sequence. *Hence, each gene need not be a separate entity.*

A genome of around 5480 bases should have a maximum **coding capacity** equivalent of 1800 amino acid residues (5400 + 3, a triplet for each amino acid). These amino acids would have a combined molecular weight of 200,000 daltons. In estimation, however, the combined weight of these proteins turned out to be much more, i.e., around 250,000 daltons. The new technique enabled Sanger *et al* to arrange amino acid sequences of some proteins of the phage alongside the base sequence of the corresponding genes and to their surprise they observed three facts:

1) The *same* gene was found coding for *two* different proteins.

2) One protein was coded for, in part, by one gene and *in part* by another, and

3) The **termination codon** for one gene was the **initiation codon** for the next contiguous gene. For example, the 360 nucleotide-long B gene is completely contained within the region of the 1536 nucleotide-long A gene, but is read in a different reading frame. Similarly, gene E of 273 nucleotides is contained entirely within a gene D of 456 nucleotides. Also, the terminator codon for gene D overlaps the initiator codon of the next contiguous gene J by one nucleotide. Similar overlapping genes have also been discovered in the virus G_4, also a single-stranded DNA virus that infects *E. coli.*

Overlapping of genes obviously appears to be a compacting or space-saving device in minute organisms, where the quantity of DNA is small in relation to the number of proteins needed. But, unaccountably, overlapping is seen to occur even in larger organisms such as *E. coli:* In the tryptophan operon of *E. coli*, the terminator codon of the cistron A serves as the initiator codon for the next cistron B. Overlapping genes are thought to have evolved in viruses because they are under selective pressure to conserve a genome small in size.

Split genes: The epoch making discovery of **overlapping** and **jumping genes** had not challenged the concept that the DNA sequence (cistron) needed for the synthesis of a particular polypeptide (or protein) was a continuous polynucleotide chain, so that a complementary, continuous, linear and functional sequence of mRNA could be transcribed. It would now appear that this DNA sequence *is not* present at one place, but in fact lies scattered in pieces in the chromosome. This means that bits of protein coding DNA are separated by sequences that do not code for the protein. Among the initial reports of this stunning find was one that came from Breathnack, Mandel and Chambon of the CNRS Laboratory for Eukaryotic Molecular Genetics at Strasbourg, France. In an attempt to isolate the chicken gene which codes for ovalbumin (protein of egg-white), the easily extractable mRNA carrying information for the structure of ovalbumin, was isolated. This mRNA was then subjected to the action of the enzyme *reverse transcriptase*, in the presence of radioactive tracers. The enzyme synthesised back the radioactive RNA sequence for ovalbumin, thus giving a copy of the radioactive gene ovalbumin mRNA. The radioactive DNA copy was incubated with the fragments of the original non-radioactive chromosomal DNA, which had the ovalbumin gene in one complete fragment. The two DNA fragments were expected to hybridise together. But the team was "shocked" to find radioactive DNA hybridising with *three* quite different pieces of chromosomal DNA, instead of with one complete gene of ovalbumin. They knew that their enzyme could not have cut the ovalbumin gene and so "they were forced to the conclusion that the gene is split into three on the chromosome." So the "genes in mammals lie broken into pieces — and so do some of the basic assumptions of molecular biology."

Quite in contrast with gene-overlap as a device for gene compacting found in the **prokaryotes**, is the occurrence of split genes. **Split genes** appear to provide a method for accommodating more DNA than is necessary for the functioning of a gene. Whereas, prokaryotes require maximum coding capacity with minimum amount of DNA, the higher organisms or **eukaryotes** provide for a large amount of redundant DNA. A cell in a eukaryote contains about 1000 times more DNA than a prokaryote cell.

In eukaryotes, a gene is not made up of functionally contiguous units. Instead, in a single gene, there are five or more silent regions, the effects of which never appear in the final gene product. That is to say, the genes are split. The **silent regions** or **intervening sequences** are called **inserts**. They have now been termed '**introns**' to contrast with the functioning inter-intronic regions which are called exons. Exons could probably, and in rhyme with introns, be called 'extrons.' The introns seen so far range from 10 to 10,000 bases in length.

The **exon-intron concept** may serve to solve many a genetic riddle concerning mutation, recombination, and so on. Introns have been described as "frozen remnants of history" and "the sites of future evolution."

The concept of the **colinearity of genes** and their products was shaken during a study of the animal virus, adenovirus 2, at the Cold Spring Harbor Laboratory, New York. When the virus infects a nucleated cell, it is capable of making its own mRNA and other components by making use of the enzymes of the nucleated cell in which it multiplies. Therefore, the mRNA of these viruses has the characteristics typical of the eukaryotic mRNA, i.e., addition of 7-methyl guanosine at the 5^1 end also called 'capping,' and polyadenylation which means addition of poly A tails to the 3^1 end.

In eukaryotes, the primary gene transcript is *a non-functional* precursor RNA and is called hetrogeneous nuclear RNA, or hnRNA. It can mature into the functional mRNA, only by a process of 'tailoring' at its 5^1 end and 3^1 end, as described above. The DNA of the adenovirus is a double-stranded linear molecule coding for about 20 proteins. Late in the life of the virus, eight of its genes are transcribed in large amounts (the 'late' genes). The transcript or transcribed product is a single large RNA fragment which gets cleaved into eight mRNAs. Peculiarly enough, the total length of these eight mRNAs which actually get translated into the various proteins is *shorter* than the original single transcript. When one of these 'late' genes, the hexon gene, was paired with its mRNA and the resulting duplex was examined with an electron microscope, it was noticed that while most of the duplex was paired, there were also unpaired regions which stood out as loops, this was the first ever *visual* indication that looping out could be a mechanism for excluding the extra DNA. Apparently the hexon mRNA was made by joining together *four different segments*. The insert sequences or introns are cleverly removed before the transcript goes into action as mRNA, and is ready to combine with the ribosomes. Split genes have also been encountered in several other

viruses like the Rous sarcoma and murine leukemia viruses. Apart from viruses, such genes have now been confirmed in the ribosomal genes of *Drosophila*, ovalbumin gene and ovomucoid gene of chickens, ß-globin gene of mice and rabbits, tRNA genes of yeast, and the immunoglobulin gene of mice.

The precursor mRNA (hnRNA) of all the genes studied so far contains **insert sequences**. This indicates that hnRNA is a faithful unaltered complementary transcript of the entire gene (including the inserts). In the production of active mRNA from this precursor, the inserts or introns get eliminated by the action of specific enzymes. The precise role of introns is under debate. Several possibilities have been projected, such as:

1) Introns regulate the **turning on, or off of genes**. This theory is being discarded.

2) Introns serve as **structural genes** or cistronic sites.

3) Looping out of introns is a simple device for discarding the **redundant DNA** which the cell had helplessly acquired during the course of its evolution.

4) According to Flavell, Glover and Jeffreys, inserts are a means of introducing diversity in gene sequences which gives a **selective advantage** to the organism.

DNA polymorphisms: Analytical techniques, such as **restriction endonuclease analysis** and **Southern hybridisation**, have revealed that not all restriction sites are identical on the DNA of all individuals. For instance, digestion of DNA from some individuals with the enzyme HpaI results in a 7.6 kb fragment containing the human ß-globin gene (1000 bases = 1 kilobase = kb). However, a similar digestion in other individuals who lack one of the HpaI restriction sites flanking the ß-globin gene, produces a 13 kb ß-globin gene-containing fragment instead. Such **DNA polymorphisms** appear to be quite common in humans, and it seems likely that they will play an important role in human genetics in the future. The tight linkage of certain polymorphic DNA restriction sites with the μ- and ß-globin genes in man has already provided a new approach to the prenatal diagnosis of disorders such as thalassemia and sickle-cell anemia.

RNA-directed DNA synthesis: Contrary to the central dogma of unidirectional DNA-directed RNA synthesis. Temin and Baltimore suggested from viral studies that genetic information could also flow in a reverse direction, i.e., from RNA to DNA to effect RNA-directed DNA synthesis. Parts of DNA in a normal cell serve as templates for the synthesis of RNA which in turn acts at a template for the DNA synthesis. The DNA gets incorporated with the cellular DNA and enlarges it. Temin has postulated that the resultant enlargement of some part of DNA may be an important factor in embryonic differentiation and possibly in cancerogenesis.

DNA repair (Fig 45): DNA aberrations arise by exposure to ultraviolet rays or radiations or from internal cellular events whose origins are as yet not known. There are mechanisms prevalent in all forms of life to repair the **damaged DNA**. Evidence for the presence of **DNA repair mechanisms** is obtained from serious consequences caused by malfunctioning of the same. The rare human autosomal recessive disease **xeroderma pigmentosum** is accompanied by extreme sensitivity of the skin to ultraviolet light and increased incidence of skin cancer. It has been shown that the cells of such affected individuals are unable to repair DNA damage induced by ultraviolet light. The defect in this case appears to lie in the inability of an endonuclease enzyme to make the original cut that initiates the **excision-repair process**. In patients suffering from premature aging — progeria — the ligase enzyme which is necessary to rejoin broken DNA strands is defective.

When DNA is exposed to ultraviolet light or irradiation, the DNA molecule is damaged. There now appear thymine, thymine-cytosine, or cytosine dimers (pyrimidine dimers) in the DNA molecule. The repair begins with a **special endonuclease** enzyme producing a cut in the phosphate-sugar backbone at a nucleotide position adjacent to the thymine dimer. The 3^1 phosphate group at this point is then removed by another enzyme phosphatase or 3^1 exonuclease leaving a nucleotide end bearing a 3 hydroxyl group. A 5^1 exonuclease then removes a 6 or 7 nucleotide-long-section including the thymine dimer. The deleted portion of the excised strand is then refilled by the DNA polymerase enzyme in the 3^1–5^1 direction, using the complementary strand as a template. The 3^1–5^1 gap that remains between adjacent nucleotides after polymerase activity is closed by a joining enzyme called polynucleotide ligase.

DNA damage brought about by ultraviolet rays is undone by **photoreactivation mechanism**. In this repair mechanism, the ultraviolet ray induced damage is reversed by exposing the cells to light containing visible wavelengths in the blue spectrum. The photoreactivation mechanism indicates that the damage caused by ultraviolet light can be reversed before the genetic material is permanently affected. In photoreactivation, the photoreactivation enzyme locates itself on the DNA molecule at the point where pyrimidine dimers are formed. Absorption of visible light radiation in the blue end of the spectrum provides the energy, which enables the enzyme to split the dimer. The DNA molecule then resumes its normal shape and the enzyme is released.

The examples of diseases resulting from deficient DNA repair are xeroderma pigmentosum, Bloom syndrome, ataxia telangiectasia and Fanconi's anemia.

Molecular biology in relation to medical genetics: It is now possible to analyse heredity directly by means of a detailed study of gene structure and function, through a knowledge of the DNA of which genes are made up. A diploid human cell is shown to contain a staggering quantity of DNA, viz., a total of 6×10^9 base pairs, or a molecular weight of 3.6×10^{12} daltons (2.8 picograms). Hypothetically, this amount of DNA would be enough to specify the sequence of about 5 million different polypeptides, if all proteins were the size of a globin, and if every gene were to code as globin genes do.

Various techniques place the current estimates

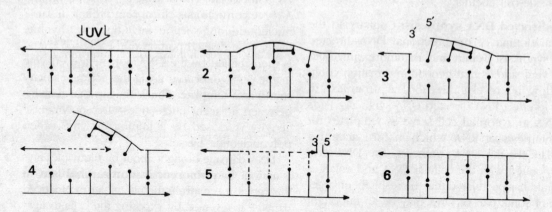

Fig. 45 A schematic representation of DNA repair, following its damage by ultraviolet radiation.
1. Damage of DNA strand by ultraviolet light.
2. Formation of thymine/cytosine/thymine-cytosine dimer.
3. A special endonuclease enzyme cleaves the DNA strand adjacent to the dimer.
4. Synthesis of a new DNA strand begins, using the intact strand as a template by DNA polymerase in 3^{1}-5^{1} direction.
5. Complete excision of the damaged strand by an exonuclease.
6. The 3^{1}-5^{1} gap that remains between adjacent nucleotides after polymerase activity is closed by polynucleotide ligase, the joining enzyme.

of the number of coding genes at about 20,000 or one per cent of the total nuclear DNA. These estimates are based on the finding that 20,000 different cell proteins can be identified and on the assumption that one gene codes for one protein. The methods used to arrive at these estimates are:

1) Use of two-dimensional gels for direct protein identification

2) A calculation of the mRNAs by biophysical annealing to radioactive complementary DNA (cDNA) and

3) The extrapolation from organisms such as *Drosophila*, where the number of polytene banks is assumed to be closer to the number of proteins synthesised.

Gene Libraries

A gene library is a collection, complete or partial, of the cloned gene sequences from the DNA of an individual or a species. A genomic library contains sequences of nuclear DNA. A cDNA library,

on the other hand, contains copies of the expressed messenger RNA.

Partial libraries can be obtained by cloning various fractions of DNA, e.g., by size, by base composition or by rate of reannealing. Libraries of mitochondrial DNA, comprise of DNA specifying one type of RNA or of DNA which appears to be actively transcribing RNA.

A genomic library would have enough recombinant clones, so that every DNA sequence in the nuclear genome is represented at least once. Therefore, every coding gene, regulatory element or repeated sequence, would be present. This is the basic source for specific gene isolation, since each DNA sequence is permanently available in pure form in unlimited amount, once cloned.

Another crucial role of gene libraries, in human genetics, is that such a library containing the total genome of a given individual in recombinant form, would enable a comparison of any given gene from this individual with a similar gene from any other individual.

SUMMARY

Molecular genetics: Deals with DNA and RNA, replication of DNA, its transcription and translation into polypeptide chains — the basis of proteins.

DNA: Structure: A helically coiled, double-stranded molecule consisting of linearly arranged nucleotides. A nucleotide is made up of a nitrogenous base — either a purine (adenine or guanine) or pyrimidine (thymine or cytosine) —, a deoxyribose pentose sugar and a phosphate radical.

DNA

Types of DNA:

1) Unique sequence DNA — 75 %.

2) Dispersed repetitive DNA (15 %) constituted mainly by long and short interspersed elements SINE and LINE.

3) Satellite DNA (10 %) — Highly repetitive and is unique for a given individual and therefore useful in gene mapping, DNA fingerprinting.

RNA: Structure: A product of DNA, single-stranded, made of nucleotides: a nitrogenous base — either a purine (adenine or guanine) or pyrimidine (uracil or cytosine) — , a ribose pentose sugar and a phosphate radical.

Types of RNA: 1. Messenger or mRNA. 2. Ribosomal or rRNA and 3. Soluble or transfer or tRNA.

Gene: Made up of varying lengths of DNA.

Genetic code: Codon: A sequence of three successive base pairs (triplets) along DNA strand coding for one amino acid. Sixty-four possible codon arrangements specify the 20 different amino acids found in proteins. This, so-called genetic code, is said to be universal, 'non-overlapping' and 'degenerate.' One specific codon initiates protein synthesis. Three of the codons do not code for any amino acid.

Use of techniques such as restriction endonuclease analysis, recombinant DNA cloning and DNA sequencing has resulted in revision of the earlier ideas of eukaryotic gene structure. Gene is now shown to exist in pieces such that the DNA sequences which code for a particular polypeptide — the exons' are interrupted by one or more sequences of DNA — the 'introns' which do not code for a polypeptide.

Existence of eukaryotic genes in pieces presumably allow a more rapid evolution than would have been possible if the genes had no intervening 'noncoding' sequences — the introns.

Protein synthesis: DNA directs the synthesis of protein through the agency of messenger RNA and ribosomes. DNA is transcribed into a primary RNA transcript (heterogeneous RNA or hnRNA). The post-transcriptional modification includes splicing up of exons, capping the RNA and addition of a poly A tail to form a mRNA. The rate of transcription is modified by promoter, enhancer and regulator genes.

The mRNA reaches the cytoplasm. Translation of the mRNA to polypeptides is done in the ribosomes (free or attached) with the help of tRNA. The post-transcriptional processing converts the polypeptide into a functional protein molecule.

5 MODES OF INHERITANCE

Introduction

Modes of inheritance describe the different ways in which genes handed down from parents to their offspring through several generations, may express themselves. Genes exist in pairs on **homologous chromosomes**, except on the X and Y chromosomes. Even on the X and the Y chromosomes, there is a possibility of a few loci carrying **homologous** or **allelomorphic genes**.

An inherited trait, e.g., a physical feature, a blood group, or an enzyme system may depend on a single gene pair or on the cumulative effect of a large number of genes. The former is called **Mendelian** or **unit factor inheritance** and the latter, **polygenic inheritance**. Mendelian inheritance may be either **autosomal** or **sex-linked**. In autosomal traits, the genes are located on any of the 22 pairs of autosomes and in sex-linked traits, the genes belong to the X or Y chromosome.

An inheritance is called **autosomal dominant**, when one member of an allelic pair is able to express itself in total disregard to the presence of the other member. On the other hand, **autosomal recessive inheritance** depends on the expression of both partners of an **allelic pair**. When the two members of an allelic pair are identical, they are said to be **homozygous** and when they are unlike each other, the combination is said to be **heterozygous**. Thus a **dominant gene** expresses itself, both in its homozygous state and in its heterozygous state, while a recessive gene expresses itself only in its homozygous state.

A trait is said to constitute the **phenotype** of an individual, while the allelic pair of genes determining the trait constitute the **genotype** for that trait.

When both members of an allelic pair are able to express themselves fully in the phenotype, the inheritance is called **codominant**, e.g., the ABO blood group. Sometimes, a trait is the result of a sharing of, or a partial expression of both alleles. It is then called **intermediate inheritance**, e.g., sickle-cell trait.

The Y-linked Mendelian traits can only find expression in the male line and hence are often called holandric. The incidence of X-linked traits on the other hand, differs markedly in the females and the males, since the female karyotype is XX and the male, XY. Thus, X-linked recessive disorders find a ready expression in the male, since the so-called recessive allele is not matched by any counterpart on the Y chromosome. On the other hand the X-linked recessive gene is not ordinarily expressed in the female, since the accompanying dominant allele prevents its expression.

Mendelising genes produce a readily recognisable qualitatively varying trait, whereas by contrast, in polygenic inheritance, the effects are quantitatively varying and require large scale measurements and plotting of curves to assess their effects. However, even in traits depending on single gene pairs, the expression may be highly variable in view of several environmental factors.

The primary effect of a gene pair may be far removed from its phenotypic effect, which may consist of several apparently unrelated signs and symptoms. This phenomenon is referred to as **pleiotropism** or **pleiotropy**. In sharp contrast is the phenomenon called genetic heterogeneity, wherein, the same phenotypic effect in different members of a population, may result from independent activity of several genes.

Genes carried on chromosomes are responsible for the development of inherited characters or traits. When a single gene pair determines a trait, the trait is known as a single-gene trait and its mode of inheritance from one generation to the next generation follows Mendel's law of unit inheritance and segregation. When many genes determine a trait, the trait is known as polygenic and it follows the pattern of polygenic inheritance for transmission from generation to generation.

The terms defined below are used in genetics to convey special meanings with reference to inheritance.

Allele or allelomorph. One or more alternative forms of a gene found at the same (corresponding) locus on homologous chromosomes in an individual and/or in a population.

Homologous genes. Identical alleles occupying the same locus on homologous chromosomes.

Homozygous. An individual (homozygote) who possesses two identical alleles at one particular locus on homologous chromosomes.

Heterozygous. An individual (heterozygote) who possesses two different alleles at one particular locus on homologous chromosomes.

Compound. A heterozygous individual who possess two different mutant (not 'wild or normal') alleles at one particular locus on homologous chromosomes.

The three terms, homozygous, heterozygous and compound are used for an individual as well as for his/her genotype.

Dominant. An allele which is always expressed, both in homozygous and heterozygous combinations. A trait which is expressed in individuals who are homozygous or heterozygous for a particular gene, is also said to be dominant.

Recessive. An allele which is expressed only when it is homozygous. It also refers to a trait which is only expressed in homozygotes for a particular gene, and not in those who are heterozygous for that gene.

Genotype. The total genetic constitution (genome) of an individual, or more specifically the alleles present at one locus, for a particular trait.

Phenotype. The appearance (physical, biochemical, and physiological) of an individual produced by expression of the genotype under the influence of environment.

The study of a particular trait in a family usually begins with the person first found to exhibit the trait and through whom the family draws the attention of the investigator. Such a person is referred to as the **propositus** when a male and **proposita** when a female (also called **proband** or **index case**). The data collected from a family over a number of generations can be represented, in a chart using international conventional symbols (Fig 46). Such charts are known as **pedigree charts**.

SINGLE-GENE TRAIT INHERITANCE

Many genetic traits are determined by genes at a single locus; such traits may be dominant or recessive. Nearly 3000 such conditions, most of which are abnormalities rather than variants of the normal, are known to be single-gene traits. The vast majority are serious, none are curable and relatively few are treatable or manageable.

There are 1364 disorders, where the mode of inheritance has been firmly established. These include 736 **autosomal dominant**, 521 **autosomal recessive** and 107 **X-linked disorders**. There are another 1447 disorders where **unifactorial inheritance** is suspected, but not proven yet.

The patterns followed by single-gene traits within families over a number of generations are determined by the following factors:

1) Whether the trait is dominant or recessive.
2) Whether the gene determining the trait is autosomal or X-linked.
3) Chance distribution of genes from parents to children through the gametes and
4) Factors affecting the expression of a gene, i.e.,
   a. heterogeneity
   b. pleiotropy
   c. reduced penetrance
   d. variable expressivity
   e. variability of age of onset

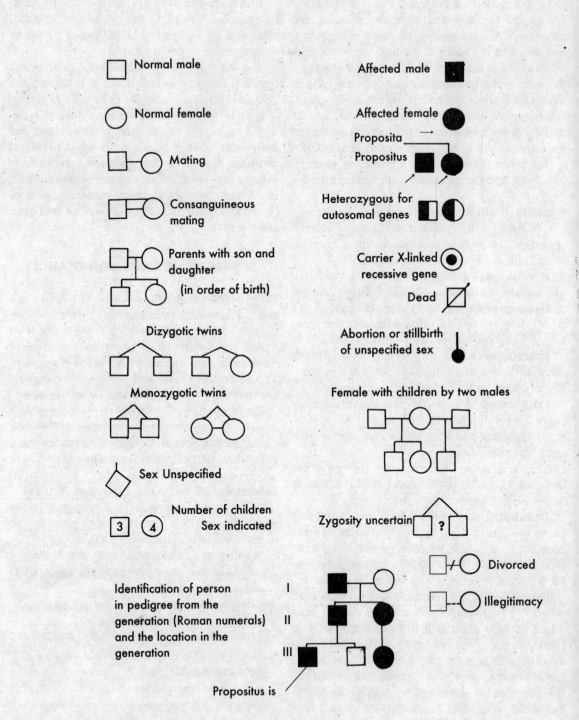

Fig. 46 Chart showing the commonly used genetic symbols

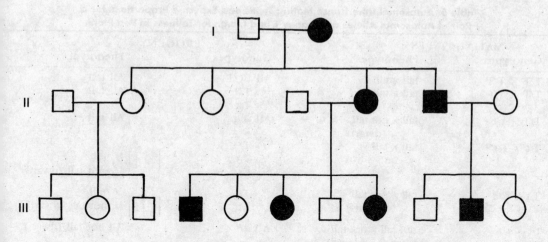

Fig. 47 Typical pedigree chart of autosomal dominant inheritance.

f.   sex limitation, complete or partial
g.   interaction of two or more gene pairs
h.   environmental effects.

Autosomal Inheritance

Autosomal Dominant Inheritance: Examples of autosomal dominant traits (Fig. 47) are rare conditions like dentinogenesis imperfecta, osteogenesis imperfecta, achondroplasia, porphyria variegata, and common conditions like brachydactyly (short fingers). The overall prevalence of autosomal dominant traits is about 7 per 1000.

Usually, in rare conditions, the affected persons are heterozygous, and in common conditions, they may be either homozygous or heterozygous. Usually, the affected person has one affected parent. Very rarely when neither parent is affected, spontaneous mutation in the gametes is the likely cause. The mode of inheritance is as follows:

The father will have genotype T/T, T/t, or t/t depending on whether he is **homozygous affected, heterozygous affected** or **nonaffected**. The same holds good for the genotype of the mother. In each case the gametes produced will be

T/T: all T gametes
T/t: 50 per cent T, 50 per cent t gametes
t/t: all t gametes.

So the possibility of mating types would be as shown in Table 5.

Thus half the children having a heterozygous genotype would be affected, irrespective of the sex of the child.

Autosomal dominant traits show variable expression from minimum involvement to the grossest abnormality. Rarely, the gene may not express itself at all, i.e., it is non-penetrant resulting in apparently skipped generations in pedigree charts.

Summary:

1) Among children, whose parents both have a dominant inherited trait, i.e., both are heterozygous for the gene responsible for the trait, the genotypic expectations follow Mendel's ratio 1:2:1. One-fourth of the children are homozygous affected and one-fourth homozygous normal.

2) The trait appears in every generation. Normally, there is no skipping of generation.

3) The trait is transmitted by an affected person (heterozygous) to half his children on an average.

4) Unaffected persons do not transmit the trait to their children.

5) The occurrence and transmission of the trait are not influenced by sex. Males and females have equal chances of having the trait and transmitting it.

Table 5: Autosomal Inheritance Mating Types and Expected Proportions for a Pair of Autosomal Alleles of Progeny T and t, e.g., for Tallness in Pea Plant

| MATING TYPES | | PROGENY | |
Genotypes	Phenotypes	Genotypes	Phenotypes
T/T × T/T	tall × tall	All T/T	All tall
T/T × T/t	tall × tall	$\frac{1}{2}$ T/T $\frac{1}{2}$ T/t	All tall
T/T × t/t	tall × not tall (dwarf)	All T/t	All tall
T/t × T/t*	tall × tall	$\frac{1}{4}$ T/T $\frac{1}{2}$ T/t $\frac{1}{4}$ t/t	$\frac{3}{4}$ tall $\frac{1}{4}$ not tall (dwarf)
T/t × t/t**	tall × not tall (dwarf)	$\frac{1}{2}$ T/t $\frac{1}{2}$ t/t	$\frac{1}{2}$ tall $\frac{1}{2}$ not tall (dwarf)
t/t × t/t	not tall × not tall (dwarf) (dwarf)	All t/t	All not tall (dwarf)

* This is the usual pattern of inheritance for a rare autosomal recessive trait.
** This is the usual pattern of inheritance for a rare autosomal dominant trait.

Table 6: Traits of Homozygous and Heterozygous Individuals

TRAIT	HOMOZYGOUS FOR ONE ALLELE	HETEROZYGOUS	HOMOZYGOUS FOR THE OTHER ALLELE	ALLELIC RELATION
1. Blood groups O, A (dominance involving 2 frequent alleles)	$I^A I^A$ trait	$I^O I^A$ trait as in $I^A I^A$	$I^O A^O$ another normal trait	I^A dominant I^O recessive
2. Alkaptonuria, Albinism, Phenylketonuria (recessivity of a rare allele)	A A normal	A a normal	aa abnormal	A dominant a recessive
3. Blood groups M, N (codominance)	$I^M I^M$ a normal trait	$I^M I^N$ a normal trait showing properties of both homozygotes	$I^N I^N$ another normal trait	I^M codominant I^N codominant
4. Catalase in blood (intermediateness)	$A^1 A^1$ normal	$A^1 A^2$ intermediate between two homozygotes	$A^2 A^2$ abnormal	A^1 intermediate A^2 intermediate
5. Polydactyly (dominance of a rare allele)	$A^1 A^1$ normal	$A^1 A^2$ abnormal	$A^2 A^2$ unknown, possibly more abnormal than $A^1 A^2$	A^1 recessive A^2 dominant

Autosomal Recessive Inheritance: Examples of autosomal recessive traits (Fig 48) are cystic fibrosis, albinism, galactosemia, Gaucher's disease, hemoglobinopathies, mucopolysaccharidoses, phenylketonuria, porphyria, Wilson's disease (hepatolenticular degeneration), etc. Most of these conditions are rare. The overall prevalence is about 2.5 per thousand.

An autosomal recessive trait is expressed only in the homozygous state, i.e., in an individual who receives the recessive gene from both parents and so is homozygous for it. Males and females have an equal chance of being affected and of transmitting the trait. As related individuals are more likely to have the same rare gene than unrelated individuals, consanguineous marriages have a higher probability of producing children affected by a recessive trait. Hence the rarer the recessive trait, the higher the proportion of consanguineous marriages.

Usually the affected individual has **heterozygous parents** who are **phenotypically normal**. All the children of the affected person are normal, unless the affected person marries a heterozygote, which (because of the rarity of most recessive traits) is very uncommon. There can be more than one affected person among siblings.

The mode of inheritance is as follows:

1) If two affected persons homozygous for the same gene marry, then all their children would be affected; such an event is very rare.
2) If two heterozygotes for the same gene marry, then a fourth of the children are likely to be affected, half would be unaffected heterozygotes, and a fourth normal.
3) If an affected individual marries a heterozygous carrier, half the children will be affected and the other half will be carriers — unaffected heterozygotes.

Summary:

1) An autosomal recessive trait characteristically is seen only in siblings. It is not seen in the parents, offsprings or other relatives.
2) On an average the ratio of affected, carrier and nonaffected is 1:2:1 in siblings; the recurrence risk in such a family is 1 in 4 for each birth.
3) The parents of the affected child may be closely related.
4) Males and females are affected equally and transmit the trait equally.

Codominance and Intermediate Inheritance: When both the alleles of a pair are fully expressed in the heterozygote, the genes and the trait are said to be codominant. If a heterozygote is neither like a homozygote with both the dominant genes, nor like a homozygote with both the recessive genes, the genes concerned and the traits are said to show intermediate inheritance.

Examples of codominance are the various blood groups. A person of blood group AB has both A and B antigens in his red cells, showing

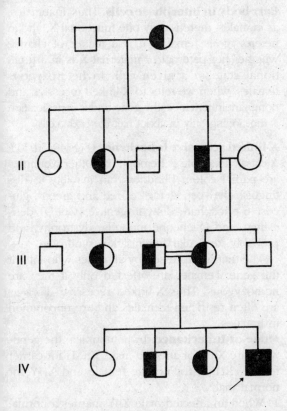

Fig. 48 Typical pedigree chart of autosomal recessive inheritance. Marriage between cousins in the third generation, and its result in the fourth, is shown. The recessive gene was inherited from a common female ancestor (first generation).

that allelic genes A and B are fully expressed and therefore codominant.

Sickle-cell anemia is an example of intermediate inheritance. The homozygote for the abnormal allele has severe sickle-cell anemia. The heterozygote for the abnormal allele does not have severe sickle-cell anemia nor is he completely normal. A proportion of his red cells show the sickling phenomenon. Such a heterozygote is intermediate between normal homozygotes and sickle-cell homozygotes; and is said to have the sickle-cell trait. (The usage of the term trait to indicate the clinical features of a heterozygote is not to be confused with usage of the same term in genetics where it means phenotype, i.e., obviously visible or detectable expression of a gene.) Table 6 indicates the traits of homozygotes and heterozygotes in the various patterns of inheritance discussed above.

Sex-Linked Inheritance: Genes (dominant or recessive) carried on sex chromosomes X and Y, because of the different distribution of sex chromosomes in males and females, produce patterns of inheritance different from genes carried on autosomes. The inheritance of genes on sex chromosomes is known as sex-linked inheritance. For practical purposes sex-linked means X-linked since the only definite Y-linked Mendelising genes are for hairy pinna and the H-Y antigen. The overall prevalence of X-linked disorders is about 0.5 per thousand.

Genes carried on the X chromosomes are referred to as X-linked and genes carried on the Y chromosomes are referred to as Y-linked. Partially sex-linked genes are those genes which are carried on the homologous portions of the X and Y chromosomes.

X-linked inheritance. A male has only one representative of any X-linked gene (always derived from the mother) and hence he is said to be **hemizygous** rather than **homozygous** or **heterozygous**. Whether recessive or dominant, an X-linked gene is always expressed in the male. A female can be homozygous or heterozygous.

Since the X chromosome cannot be transmitted from father to son, a male cannot transmit X-linked traits to his male offspring, i.e., father to son. As a father has only one X chromosome which is always transmitted to his daughters he will always transmit the trait to his daughters in the case of dominant genes or render them carriers in the case of recessive genes.

It may be noted here that though a female has two X chromosomes, only one member of the pair is active; the second one remains condensed and relatively non-functional, and is seen as the **Barr body in interphase cells**. Thus, in females, as in males, there is only one functional X, and in heterozygous females, it is a matter of chance whether her paternal or maternal X is in a functional state in a given cell. In heterozygous females, when we refer to X-linked recessive and dominant inheritance, the gene under consideration is functioning only in about half the body cells.

X-linked recessive inheritance (Figs 49, 50, 51): A classic example is hemophilia. Other examples are partial colour blindness (an inability to distinguish between shades of red and green), glucose-6-phosphate dehydrogenase (G6PD) deficiency, and Duchenne muscular dystrophy, and probably, testicular feminisation syndrome.

The trait is expressed by all males who inherit the gene. Females are affected only if they are homozygous. Thus X-linked recessive diseases are often restricted to males and are uncommon in females.

Mode of Inheritance. In hemophilia, the genotypes are XhY for affected male, XhXH for carrier female, XHXH for normal female and XHY for normal male.

1) When an affected male XhY marries a normal female XHXH, all his daughters would be carriers XhXH and all his sons would be normal. The carrier daughters will transmit the hemophilia trait to half their sons.

2) When an affected male XhY marries a carrier female XhXH, half the sons would be affected, half the daughters would be carriers and the other half would be affected. However, this type of combination is rare, since hemophilia in females is severe and may be lethal. Female hemophilic offspring have a good chance of survival with modern therapy.

3) When a carrier female XhXH marries a normal male XHY, half the offspring would be normal, half the sons would be affected, and half the daughters would be carriers.

Summary:

1) An X-linked trait is generally seen in males. It is uncommon in females.

2) The trait is transmitted from an affected man through all his daughters to half of his grandsons.

3) The trait is never transmitted from male to male, i.e., father to son.

4) The trait can be transmitted through a series of carrier females. The affected males in a family are related to one another through the females.

X-linked Dominant Inheritance: Examples of X-linked dominant traits are Vitamin D-resistant rickets and Xg blood group.

An X-linked dominant trait (Fig 52) is seen in homozygous as well as in heterozygous females, and in the male having the gene under consideration on his single X chromosome. As a result, X-linked dominant conditions are twice as common in females as in males. The affected male transmits the trait to all his daughters, but to none of his sons.

Mode of inheritance

1) When an affected male marries a normal female, he will transmit the trait to all his daughters but to none of his sons.

2) When an affected male marries an affected homozygous female, all the children would be affected, the daughters being homozygous.

3) When an affected male marries an affected heterozygous female, all the daughters and half of the sons would be affected.

4) When a normal male marries an affected homozygous female, all the children would be affected, the daughters becoming heterozygous.

5) When a normal male marries an affected heterozygous female, half the children — sons and daughters — would be heterozygous and affected.

Summary:

1) In rare X-linked dominant disorders, affected females are twice as common as affected males.

2) Affected males pass on the trait to all their daughters, but to none of their sons. Thus, X-linked dominant inheritance can be distinguished from autosomal dominant inheritance only by the progeny of affected males.

3) Transmission by affected females follows the same patterns as autosomal dominant. Affected heterozygous females transmit the condition to half their children of both sexes. Affected homozygous females transmit the trait to all their children.

Y-linked Inheritance: This is also known as holandric inheritance. An example is hairy ears. As the Y chromosome is only found in males the nonhomologous Y-linked genes are only found in males. Males alone are affected and an affected male transmits the trait to all his sons but to none of his daughters. As the Y chromosome is single, genes on the Y chromosome are always expressed phenotypically.

Factors Influencing Hereditary Patterns

1) New Mutation: When a genetic disease appears in an individual with no previous family history of the disorder, the most common cause is a new mutation. The recurrence risk for the individual's siblings is very low, but it will follow the specific pattern of inheritance for a given disease in the subsequent generations of the individual.

2) Germline Mosaicism: When genetic disease appears in two or more offspring with an autosomal dominant disease and there is no family history of the disorder, it is unlikely that multiple muta-

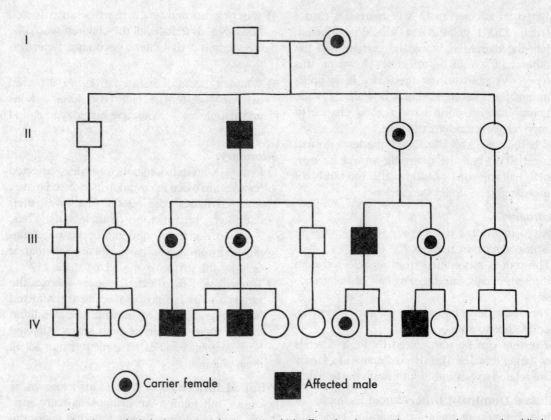

Fig. 49 Typical pedigree of X-linked recessive inheritance in which affected males reproduce, e.g., red-green colour blindness.

tion would take place in the same family. The most likely mechanism in such cases would be germline mosaicism, i.e., the presence of more than one genetically distinct cell line in either of the parents' gonads. Usually this takes place during the embryonic development of one of the parents whereby a mutation affects all or part of germline but not somatic cells. Therefore, the parent carries the mutation but does not express it. This kind of mosaicism increases the risk for the future offspring of the affected parent. It has been observed in conditions like perinatal forms of osteogenesis imperfecta, achondroplasia, Duchenne muscular dystrophy, hemophilia A, etc.

3) Age of Onset: This varies from early embryonic life to late age depending on the genetic trait. For example, some lethal chromosomal aberrations are responsible for early abortions. Some conditions are seen as congenital abnormalities (polydactyly). Some genetic diseases are manifested as the child grows — Tay Sachs disease at four to six months, Duchenne muscular dystrophy when the child begins to walk, and acute intermittent porphyria in the young adult. A condition like Huntington's chorea manifests much later in life.

The distinction between a **congenital anomaly** and a **genetic disease** should be clear from this account. Genetic disease means that genes are the causative factors, whereas congenital anomaly means that the disorder is present at birth. In other words, genetic diseases are not necessarily congenital and congenital diseases are not necessarily genetic.

4) Anticipation: This is a phenomenon of apparent earlier onset of a disease in succeeding generations. In many diseases, earlier age of onset is associated with increased severity leading to pro-

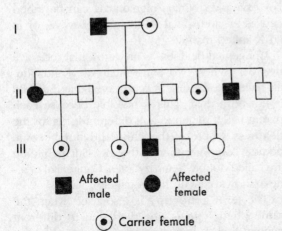

Fig. 50 X-linked recessive inheritance. A pedigree of hemophilia showing consanguinity between cousins (generation I) and an affected female (generation II).

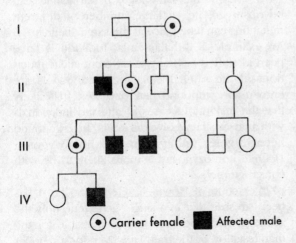

Fig. 51 Typical pedigree of X-linked inheritance in which affected males do not reproduce, e.g., Duchenne muscular dystrophy.

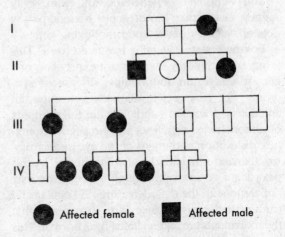

Fig. 52 Typical pedigree of X-linked dominant inheritance.

Delayed age of onset causes difficulty in deducing the mode of inheritance. If the individual is affected by any other lethal problem, it may obviate the later manifestation of the disease under consideration.

5) Penetrance refers to the ability of a gene to express phenotypically, and **nonpenetrance** to its inability. At an individual level, penetrance remains an all-or-none phenomenon. However, in a population, when, of all the individuals carrying the same gene, some do not express it, the trait is said to exhibit **reduced penetrance**. The reduced penetrance is expressed mathematically as the percentage of genetically susceptible individuals who actually show the trait.

Phenotypic expression of an abnormal gene in the form of a trait may not be of an equal degree in all individuals having that gene. This varying degree of expression, i.e., mild, moderate or severe, is called **expressivity**. Thus, in polydactyly, an individual may have only a small wartlike appendage on the side of the hand, but at the other extreme, another affected person may have a complete extra finger. In osteogenesis imperfecta, some individuals are mildly affected so that their everyday life is not disturbed, whereas others are so severely affected that they may become complete invalids with gross skeletal deformities. Most affected individuals, however, lie somewhere between the two extremes.

gressive worsening of a condition in succeeding generations. This was regarded as the normal course for many inherited disorders. However, it is now felt that the phenomenon of anticipation is apparent rather than real, being more due to a bias in the selection of cases.

Delayed age of onset reduces natural selection against a disease gene since the patient develops the disease past his reproductive age. Examples are Huntington's chorea, polycystic kidney, hemochromatosis, Alzheimer's disease, etc.

The phenomena of penetrance and expressivity suggest that expression of genes phenotypically depends at least partly upon modifying genes.

Forme Fruste. (literally, frustrated form) This is any mild clinically insignificant expression of a genetic trait in an abnormality, disease or syndrome. For example, in Marfan's syndrome, an autosomal dominant condition, the full complex of abnormalities manifests as elongated extremities, dislocation of the lens of the eye and cardiovascular abnormalities. In a family affected by this disorder, a generation, through forme fruste may appear to skip the disorder. Here, the ocular and cardiovascular disturbances are so minimal that the individuals are taken clinically as normal. This accounts for skipped generations in autosomal dominant conditions.

6) <u>Pleiotropy</u>: Pleiotropy is a phenomenon where a single gene is responsible for a number of distinct and seemingly unrelated phenotypic effects.

Each gene has the primary role of directing the synthesis of a polypeptide chain. When there is disturbance in the synthesis of such a chain because of the gene defect, there could be diverse secondary effects, if the polypeptide chain has a widespread role in the structure and function of the body.

Many genetic disorders, known as syndromes are examples of pleiotropy. A syndrome refers to a combination of manifestations that commonly occur together. Phenylketonuria is a metabolic disease, inherited as an autosomal recessive, in which the enzyme phenylalanine hydroxylase, essential for the first step in the conversion of phenylalanine to tyrosine, is lacking. This enzyme defect leads to accumulation of phenylalanine in the body, resulting in such diverse effects as mental retardation, excretion of phenylketones in the urine, and hypo-pigmentation.

Pleiotropy (one gene — several affects) seen in the form of syndromes, is quite different from genetic association and genetic linkage.

7) <u>Genetic Heterogeneity</u>: A single disease phenotype can be caused by mutations at different loci in different families in a given population.

For example, retinitis pigmentosa can be inherited as an autosomal dominant, recessive, or in an X-linked manner.

Congenital deafness is an autosomal recessive disorder. When two congenitally deaf individuals have an offspring, it is observed that the child is not born deaf. This is possible because each parent had a mutation at a different locus for the deafness whereby the child did not become homozygote for either of the loci. Such children are called double heterozygotes. Congenital deafness shows genetic heterogeneity.

The term **genocopy** is also used when the same phenotype is observed due to different genetic loci. When the same phenotype is because of environmental causes, it is referred to as **phenocopy**.

At times, at the same locus heterogeneity can be observed, i.e., a large number of different mutations can take place at the same allelic level. An example is ß-thalassemia. Individuals have been identified having two different allelic mutations at the same locus. Such individuals are known as compound heterozygotes. It is likely that the majority of cases of affected individuals with autosomal recessive disorders, are compound heterozygotes rather than true homozygotes. Definite homozygosity is more likely to be with consanguinity.

8) <u>Interaction of Nonallelic Genes</u>: So far it has been stressed that in a single gene trait, only the allelic genes concerned, are responsible for the manifestation of the trait. However, for a number of genes, their expression is dependent on other genes, i.e., genes are expressed differently on different genetic backgrounds.

For example, the ABO secretor trait represents a situation where two gene pairs act together to produce the phenotype. Secretors are those individuals who secrete the antigens A, B and H in the saliva. To be a secretor of antigen A the person should have both the genes *A* and *Se*.

9) <u>Association</u>: It is the occurrence of two or more phenotypic characters in members of a kindred group or a population, in a frequency greater than would be predicted on the basis of chance, i.e.,

non-random occurrence of two phenotypically separate traits in a population. For example, blood group O and peptic ulcer of the duodenum show significant association. The hereditary basis of peptic ulcer is not established. It is, therefore, very likely that some physiologic peculiarity, and not any genetic linkage with the blood group O, renders a person more susceptible to peptic ulcer.

10) Linkage: Mendel's law of independent (random) assortment states that during gametogenesis, the members of various gene-pairs assort independently of one another. However, this has been found to be true only when the two genes under study are located on different chromosomes, or are far apart on the same chromosome, when they assort independently of each other, i.e., chances are 50 per cent that both the genes under consideration will pass to the same gamete and 50 per cent that those two genes will pass to different gametes (the same gamete will not carry both the genes).

When the two genes are located close to each other on the same chromosome, there are greater chances that the two genes would be transmitted together to the same gamete. A little note given below explains this exception to Mendel's law of independent assortment.

For the formation of a zygote, both the gametes contribute a set of 23 chromosomes, one member of each of the 23 homologous pairs of chromosomes, i.e., the sperm brings haploid 1 to 23 (one of them being X or Y) and the ovum also brings haploid 1 to 23 (one of them being X). Each member of the 23 homologous pairs of chromosomes retains its own identity. Thus the combination of genes that an offspring receives from either of his parents is faithfully carried over in all the subsequent mitotic cell divisions from the stage of zygote onwards throughout all the body cells for the total life span. However, in the gonads where gametogenesis takes place, the meiotic cell division alters the combination of genes on a given chromosome. The two homologous chromosomes, each member derived separately from the two parents, regularly interchange genetic material during the first prophase of meiosis. When

the interchanges result in a new combination of genes on homologous chromosomes, the phenomenon is referred to as **crossing over** or **recombination**.

The phenomenon of crossing over between the members of a homologous pair, i.e., the location of the chiasma is random. This means that the frequency with which crossing over results in the dissociation of the two given loci on a single chromosome will be directly proportional to the distance between them along the chromosome. When two genes are located close to each other on the same chromosome, they tend to be transmitted together to the same gamete much more often. Such loci are termed linked loci.

The term linkage is thus defined as the phenomenon where two genes on a given chromosome are reasonably close together, whereby they do not assort independently of each other but are transmitted to the same gamete more than 50 per cent of the times. The term **synteny** refers to all genes on the same chromosomes. The syntenic genes are all the genes on any given chromosome, whereas linked genes are very closely placed genes on a given chromosome, where they do not assort independently.

Some of the examples of linkage are genes for the ABO blood groups and nail-patella syndrome, genes for antigen Xg and for partial colour blindness, of X chromosome, or genes for Lutheran blood group and for secretor trait (secretion of ABO blood group substances into saliva).

Method of Determining Linkage and Synteny

From pedigree data. When one parent is doubly heterozygous (Aa Bb) and the other parent is homozygous for the recessive allele at each locus (aa bb), this kind of mating is called double backcross. If the loci A and B are not linked, then theoretically

Aa Bb × aa bb

Aa Bb : Aa bb : aa Bb : aa bb

1 : 1   : 1   : 1

If this ratio of genotypes is altered, it would mean A and B are linked and thereby not assorting independently of each other. In a single human family with limited progeny, deviations from above mentioned proportions are difficult to note. But observations on a series of large families indicate a significant deviation from 1:1:1:1 ratio which means that A and B are assorting non-randomly, i.e., they are linked.

Phase of Linkage: The process of determining whether the linked alleles are present on the opposite homologous chromosomes is referred to as determining the phase of linkage. Family studies are necessary to determine the phase of linkage.

In a person whose genotype is Aa Bb, the two linked genes A and B may be present on the same chromosome; then the genes are said to be linked in coupling and the linkage is in *cis* configuration (Fig 53). If the two genes A and B are located one each on two homologous chromosomes, then the genes are said to be linked in repulsion and the linkage is in *trans* configuration. For example, if a mother is a carrier for two X-linked genes — a form of colour blindness and hemophilia. If the two genes are linked in coupling, any one son will receive either both the genes or none. If the two genes are linked in repulsion, any one son would receive any one of the conditions. When exceptions to this occur, the cause is recombination between the A and B loci, and the exceptional offsprings are recombinants. The physical basis of recombination is the crossing over of chromosomal material that occurs in meiotic prophase.

Study of linkage in man is difficult as progeny in humans is small in number and each generation spreads over decades. Here we have to rely on finding informative matings which have occurred by chance. These are rare. For example, in order to determine the relative positions on the X chromosome of the genes for Duchenne muscular dystrophy and hemophilia, we would need to study families where both these diseases occur together. However, these diseases are so rare, that no such family has been described where both diseases occurred together. Hence genetic linkage studies in man are made with the help of

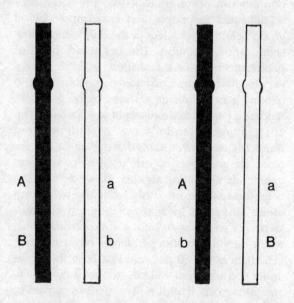

Fig. 53 Linkage may be in coupling AB/ab or in repulsion Ab/aB

marker genes in pedigrees of families with a particular hereditary disorder. Marker genes are so called because they are common in the general population with a good chance of their being present in the families under investigation. They show a simple mode of inheritance, have different frequencies in different populations and their phenotypes can be readily classified.

A study of the **autosomal marker genes** has been carried out through the following traits: blood groups, serum protein (haptoglobins, transferrins), ability to taste phenylthiocarbamide (PTC), etc. The X-linked marker traits are colour blindness, Xg blood group, Xm serum factor, glucose-6-phosphate dehydrogenase (G6PD) deficiency, etc.

In human genetics, it is difficult to distinguish between expression of close linkage and expression of a pair of alleles.

Measurement of Genetic Linkage: This can be done only in family studies. Meiosis is a must to demonstrate linkage. It means that genetic linkage can only be shown as a result of gametogenesis. Therefore, only family members can be studied to determine if linkage of genes has occurred.

The closeness of genetic linkage is expressed in centimorgans or per cent recombination as follows.

Recombination is defined as the occurrence of progeny with combinations of genes other than those that occurred in the parents due to independent assortment or crossing over. If among the offspring 80 per cent have the parental combination of genes A and B, and 20 per cent have a new combination of genes A and B not found in either parent, the genes are said to show 20 per cent recombination, i.e., they are 20 map units apart. Distances between any two genes are measured in terms of **map units**, one map unit also known as a **centimorgan cM**, being equal to one per cent of crossing over. The frequency of recombination gives the frequency of crossing over and thereby the distance, between any two loci on a given chromosome, in map units.

To summarise

1) Loci that are separated by crossing over in one per cent of gametes only are 1 cM apart;
2) Loci which never separate are linked at a genetic distance of 0 cM;
3) Loci which are separated beyond 50 c*m* units are unlinked loci because their chance of random assortment is 50 per cent like any other two loci present anywhere on two separate non-homologous chromosomes.

LOD Score: LOD score stands for logarithm of the odds. It is a statistical method of measuring linkage in family data. It is the logarithm of the ratio of two likelihoods:

i.e.,
$$\frac{\textit{Likelihood of linkage at a given distance}}{\textit{Likelihood of no linkage}}$$

For getting accurate results a large number of subjects should be studied.

LOD scores of more than 3.0 are accepted as evidence of linkage and LOD scores less than -2.0 are considered as absence of linkage.

Linkage Disequilibrium: This is non-random association of alleles at linked loci, i.e., there is a tendency for certain alleles at two linked loci to occur together more often than expected by chance. Usually linkage disequilibrium between loci diminishes with time as a result of recombination. However, it can be influenced by natural selection which acts over generations in a population. For example, some loci in the major histocompatibility complex on chromosome 6 are in disequilibrium. Presumably such allelic combinations can confer a selective advantage for immunity to some diseases. When there is random association between two linked loci, the two loci are said to be in equilibrium. Both linkage equilibrium and disequilibrium are measured at a population level and not at a family level. They vary in different populations as well.

Synteny: It is the occurrence of two loci on the same chromosome. Syntenic loci are not linked when the map unit distance exceeds 50 cM units and hence the crossing over chances between them are 50 per cent. There is random assortment as per Mendel's law.

Linkage studies are clinically useful (1) for determining precise genotype at an individual level, (2) for ascertaining the pattern of inheritance of a disease exhibiting genetic heterogeneity and (3) for do gene mapping by confirming recombination. Linkage studies are used for prenatal diagnosis, carrier detection and presymptomatic diagnosis of late onset diseases. The use of a linkage marker to provide data about a disease gene always involves uncertainty because the recombination between the marker loci and the disease loci can disturb the prediction.

11) Sex Limited Traits: A sex limited trait is a trait which is expressed in only one sex though the genes determining it are neither X-linked nor Y-linked.

Since **sexual dimorphism** forms a part of the genetic constitution, it affects the penetrance and expressivity of some genes of the autosomes, which are not themselves concerned with the determination of sex. Some such genes are sex limited in their penetrance, finding expression phenotypically in one sex only. Examples are the anatomical and physiological characteristics of the female sex, such as the width of the pelvis or the age of onset of menstruation. Similarly, sex limited male characteristics, such as type of beard growth or amount and distribution of body hair, probably depend on genes found in both sexes. An example of a sex limited dominant trait is precocious puberty in the male. Unlike X-linked recessive inheritance, sex limited traits can also be transmitted from male to male.

12) Sex Controlled or Sex Modified or Sex Influenced Traits (Table 7): When a genotype is expressed in both sexes but in a varying degree, it signifies sex controlled, sex modified or sex influenced genetic expression. For example, harelip and cleft palate are developmental genetic abnormalities, in which penetrance is incomplete, and expressivity varies from very slight external clefts to very severe clefts of the soft and hard palates. Sex influence can be seen from the manifestation that penetrance is higher in males — 60 per cent of affected individuals are males and a severe type of expression is seen more often in males. Another examples is **pattern baldness** in males.

Multiple Alleles

Alleles are said to be multiple when in a population, more than two different alleles exist at a given locus of a chromosome. In a given individual only two of these alleles occur, one derived from each parent.

Good examples are various blood groups discussed in Chapter 8. Four alleles A_1, A_2, B and O for ABO blood groups exist in the population. However, in any given individual, any two different alleles out of these or the same allele in duplicate would be present. One individual can transmit only one of these two alleles to his/her children. Blood groups represent **multiple allelism** where all the alleles happen to be normal. There can be multiple alleles where one is normal and others are abnormal (dominant or recessive). Duchenne muscular dystrophy is a disorder which is transmitted by a recessive gene situated on the X chromosome. Of the two other alleles for the same gene, one is a normal gene and the other a recessive allele expressing as a mild type of muscular dystrophy (Becker type).

NON-MENDELIAN INHERITANCE

1) Mosaicism

Somatic and gonadal mosaicism provide a pattern of non-Mendelian inheritance.

2) Uniparental Disomy and Genomic Imprinting

An individual normally inherits one pair of homologous chromosomes from each parent. But occasionally, one inherits both homologues from one parent (proven with DNA techniques). This condition is called as uniparental disomy. It could result from error in meiosis of any gamete result-

Table 7: Examples of Autosomal Phenotypes with Unequal Expression in Males and Females

Phenotype	Mode of Inheritance	Sex Difference
Baldness	Autosomal dominant in males, recessive in females	Great excess of males
Congenital adrenal hyperplasia	Autosomal recessive	More often recognised in female
Hemochromatosis	Autosomal dominant	Excess of males; loss of blood during menstruation may protect females
Perthe's disease	Autosomal dominant type	Excess of males
Myopathy limited to females	Autosomal dominant	Limited to females
Precocious puberty	Autosomal dominant	Limited to males

ing in a trisomic or monosomic individual. Disomy could result with random loss of one of the trisomic chromosomes or reduplication of the monosomic chromosome.

Uniparental disomy could result in a father with hemophilia (X-linked disease) transmitting the disease to his son (both the sex chromosomes being derived from the father).

Sometimes, the clinical features of an inherited gene depend on whether the gene was inherited from the father or the mother. This 'parent-of-origin' effect on the gene is referred to as genomic imprinting.

An example of the above is a condition of micro-deletion of short arm on chromosome 15. If the micro-deletion is of the paternal chromosome, the individual would have Prader-Willi syndrome (characterised by short stature, obesity, moderate mental retardation). But if the deletion is of the maternal chromosome, the individual has Angelman syndrome (characterised by epilepsy, ataxia, and severe mental retardation).

3) **Mitochondrial Inheritance** (Fig 54)

Certain rare disorders like hereditary blindness, Leber's optic atrophy are transmitted from a female to all her children and from a male to none of his children. Such exclusive maternal trans-

mission of the disease in humans could only be via mitochondrial DNA transmitted to the offspring via the affected ovum. Spermatozoa do not contribute any mitochondria to the zygote.

Organs susceptible to mitochondrial mutation are those where mitochondria have an important role in cellular metabolism like skeletal muscle, heart, liver and nervous system. Certain neuromuscular disorders also show mitochondrial inheritance.

POLYGENIC INHERITANCE

Some inherited traits instead of being governed by a single gene (i.e., alleles at one locus), are determined by a number of genes, each having minor effect in expression of a single trait. Such traits are known as **polygenic traits** and the patterns of inheritance is called polygenic.

Some geneticists use the term **multifactorial** as synonymous with polygenic. Others use the term multifactorial trait, where both genetic and non-genetic or environmental factors are involved in determining the trait and where both the genetic and non-genetic factors are multiple.

Polygenic traits are characterised by a **continuous variation**, i.e., they do not manifest them-

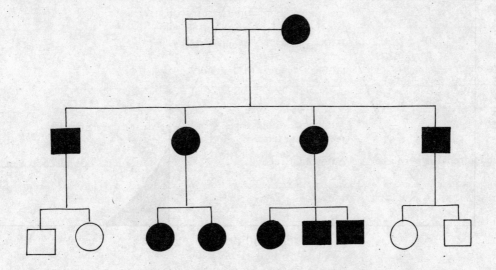

Fig. 54 Typical pedigree chart of mitochondrial inheritance.

selves as sharply defined pairs of phenotypes like black and white. If a large group of normal human beings were arranged in order of height, each would differ from his neighbours by an exceedingly small measure. The same thing is true for all the traits that can be classified according to a numerical scale like arterial pressure, pulse rate, longevity, degree of resistance to disease, age of onset of disease, IQ, refractive index of eye, dermatoglyphic ridge counts, basal metabolism, or dimension of any particular bodily structure, such as length of finger or weight of lung. Because of this, polygenic traits are also referred to as quantitative traits, and their mode of inheritance as quantitative.

Polygenic quantitative traits show a **Gaussian, bell-shaped** or **normal curve** when a specific measurement is plotted on the abscissa against a large number of persons showing that measurement on the ordinate (Fig 55). Such a distribution is possible only when the result is determined by a number of genes algebraically additive in their total effect, some acting in one direction, some in the other. If the continuous variation of human stature is largely determined genetically, it must be on the basis of the working together of a large number of genes. Each of these genes would have a small effect, so that the action of no single gene can be individually distinguished. Some of the genes increase the height, some decrease it, thus producing a final result which is the sum total of individual contributions.

The genes that determine ordinary, normal, inherited differences between normal people (differences which are as a rule so clearly quantitative) are the **basic stuff of evolution**, storing a

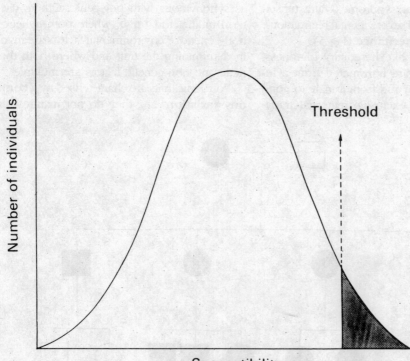

Fig. 55 Susceptibility to a given trait follows the curve of normal distribution but a threshold divides the population into the two phenotypes, normal and abnormal.

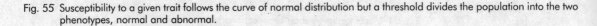

vast reservoir of potential variability, enabling the species to adapt itself to different environments, and also enabling it to change gradually and smoothly in response to changing external conditions.

Quasicontinuous Traits: For a polygenic trait having underlying continuous distribution, a threshold effect gives a discontinuous appearance. (Fig 55) Such a trait is said to be a quasicontinuous or threshold trait.

Quasicontinuous variation is very likely to be the **basis of developmental defects**. If the timing of development shows a continuous variation, extremely slow growth could lead to failure of normal development at a later stage, where punctual completion of this is vital. For example, if the ureteric bud of the mesonephric duct does not complete the development of the collecting tubule system on schedule, the kidney may become polycystic.

The concept of **threshold-controlled liability** to express specific phenotypes (i.e., susceptibility to a given trait is normally distributed, but the population is divided into normal and abnormal type by a threshold) explains the incidence of pyloric stenosis, in the population. The ratio of affected males to affected females is 5:1; the incidence in males is 5 in 1,000, but that in females is only 1 in 1,000. These findings can be accounted for if it is assumed that there are different thresholds for liability to pyloric stenosis of males and females. If in the general population, the threshold for males is lower than that for females, more males than females would be affected.

Heritability: In multifactorial diseases, it may be possible to determine the contribution of genetic factors as compared to environmental factors. The term heritability refers to the contribution of additive genetic influence in the variation of phenotypic manifestation of a condition. It can be expressed as a fraction of one or as a percentage.

Estimates of heritability are done on degree of resemblance in close relatives or calculating data on concordance rates in monozygotic and dizygotic twins.

Estimates of heritability are useful. If the role of genetic factors is high based on high percentage of heritability it would be worth trying to locate the genes. This can be done by searching for disease markers such as HLA complex or sib-pair linkage analysis. If heritability is low, it would be better to find out responsible environmental factors and take prophylactic preventive measures.

SUMMARY

Single-gene trait inheritance: Trait determined by genes at a single locus: such inheritance, from one generation to the next, follows Mendel's laws.
Autosomal dominant inheritance
1) Trait expressed in both homozygous and heterozygous states.
2) Occurrence and transmission not influenced by sex.
3) Trait transmitted by an affected person if heterozygous to half his/her children on an average and if homozygous to all his/her children.
4) Trait seen in every generation.
Autosomal recessive inheritance
1) Trait expressed only in homozygous state.
2) Occurrence and transmission not influenced by sex.
3) Seen only in siblings. Not seen in the parents, offspring or other relatives.
4) Ratio of affected, carrier, and non-affected is 1:2:1 in sibs; the recurrence risk in such a family is 1 in 4 for each birth.
5) Parents of affected child may be related consanguineously (cousin marriage).
Codominance: Phenomenon of both the alleles of a pair expressing fully in the heterozygote. Codominant gene and trait are the gene involved and the concerned trait in codominant inheritance.
Intermediate inheritance: Phenomenon where a heterozygote is neither like a homozygote with both the dominant genes nor like a homozygote with both the recessive genes.
Sex-linked inheritance: Sex chromosome X-linked and sex chromosome Y-linked.
X-linked inheritance: 1) No inheritance from father to son. 2) Father always transmits gene to daughter.
X-linked recessive inheritance
1) Always expressed by all males.
2) Females affected only if homozygous.
3) Affected male does not transmit to his sons, transmits to all his daughters.
4) Carrier female transmits to 50 per cent of her children — both male and female.
5) Trait not transmitted from male to male.
6) Trait transmitted from affected man through all his daughters to half of all his grandsons.

X-linked dominant inheritance
1) In female, trait manifests in homozygous as well as in heterozygous state.
2) Homozygous female will transmit trait to all the children.
3) Always expressed in male who transmits to all his daughters but to none of his sons.

Y-linked inheritance or holandric inheritance:
1) Males only get affected.
2) Affected male transmits the trait to all his sons but to none of his daughters.

Variation in the expressions of genes:
1) Penetrance: Ability of a gene to express phenotypically.
2) Nonpenetrance: Inability of a gene to express phenotypically.
3) Expressivity: The varying degree of phenotypic expression of an abnormal gene, i.e., mild, moderate or severe.
4) Forme fruste: Mild, clinically insignificant expression of a genetic trait in an abnormality, disease or syndrome.

Pleiotropy: A number of distinct and seemingly unrelated phenotypic effects from a single gene abnormality. Usually, because the gene concerned directs the synthesis of a polypeptide chain which has widespread role in maintaining the structure and function of the body.

Association: Occurrence of two or more phenotypic characteristics in a given population in a frequency greater than would be expected on the basis of chance.

Linkage: Phenomenon where two genes located close together on a chromosome do not assort independently of each other (as expected from Mendel's law of independent assortment) during meiosis, but are transmitted to the same gamete more than 50 per cent of times.

Recombination is the occurrence of progeny with combination of genes other than those that occurred in the parents. Recombination occurs because of independent assortment or crossing over.

Genetic heterogeneity: An identical or similar phenotype produced by different independent genes.

Sex limited traits: Genes though located on autosomes are expressed in only one sex, e.g., primary sexual characters, differing in males and females.

Sex controlled or sex-modified or sex-influenced Traits: Genes located on autosomes and expressed in both sexes but to a varying degree in each sex, e.g., secondary sexual characteristics.

Multiple alleles: In a population, there may exist more than two alleles at a given locus of a chromosome. In a given individual any two of these alleles occur, one derived from each parent.

Mitochondrial inheritance:
1) Occurrence not influenced by sex.
2) Transmission only by females, never by males.
3) Trait transmitted to all children of affected female.
4) Trait seen in every generation.

Polygenic inheritance: Phenomenon of a trait being governed by a number of genes, each contributing a minor effect in expression of that trait. Traits show a continuous variation, i.e., quantitative variation in its manifestation in a population. This can be graphically shown as Gaussian, bell-shaped or normal curve — e.g., human height, pulse rate, blood pressure, blood cholesterol.

Multifactorial inheritance: Multiple genetic and nongenetic factors involved in determining the trait.

Quasicontinuous trait: Polygenic trait continuously distributed dependent on a threshold effect for manifestation. Basis of developmental defects.

6 GENETIC BASIS OF VARIATION: POLYMORPHISM AND MUTATION

Introduction

No two individuals are identical. The phenotypic differences such as height, weight, blood pressure etc. between individuals are based on genetic differences as well as the influence of environmental factors. The genetic differences are due to changes in the DNA sequence of the genome. All such variations in DNA sequence originate from mutations. Mutations can affect germline cells or somatic cells. Most of the mutations do not result in abnormal genotype or phenotype. In fact, the genetic diseases seen in medical practice represent extreme manifestations of the more common genetic change or mutation. Each of the many variants of genes and their products exist in more than one form. When in a given population, more than two different alleles exist at a given locus, the phenomenon is known as multiple allelism. However, out of the multiple alleles, any two of these alleles only can exist in a given individual. When the frequencies of each of the multiple alleles exceed one per cent in a population and that frequency is sustained in the population without any help of mutation, such a phenomenon is known as polymorphism (phenomenon of many forms).

MUTATION

Mutation is any sudden heritable structural change in DNA. It also refers to the process by which a gene undergoes a structural change.

Mutations may be subdivided according to:

A. **Cause of mutation**
1) spontaneous
2) induced by exogenous agents

B. **Type of change brought about by a mutation**
1) genome mutations (numerical chromosomal aberrations)
2) chromosome mutations (structural chromosomal aberrations)
3) gene or point mutation (alteration in the DNA at the molecular level)

C. **Place at which a mutation occurs**
1) somatic mutations (occurring in body cells)
2) germ cell mutations (occurring in germ cells — gametes)

SPONTANEOUS MUTATION

The **spontaneous mutation rate** varies for different loci, the limits of the observed range being between one in 10,000 (1×10^{-4}) and one in 1,000,000 (1×10^{-6}) per locus per gamete, with an average of about 1×10^{-5}. Some loci, especially the **blood group loci**, are virtually not observed to mutate. At the opposite end of the range, the highest mutation rates measured in humans are those of neurofibromatosis and Duchenne muscular dystrophy, both of which are in the range of 10^{-4}. Assessment of mutation rates and conditions modifying them is one of the main fields of **mutation research** in humans.

For rare dominant mutations, the method of measurement is relatively easy.

$$\mu = \frac{n}{2N}$$

Where μ = rate of mutation, the
n = number of cases of the disorder that have been born to normal parents in a defined area over a defined time span and

N = Total number of births in the same area during the same period.

Since a new dominant trait required a mutation in only one of the two gametes, the factor $^1/_2$ is involved in calculation.

This is the direct method of estimating mutation rate. However, for accurate measurement, care should be taken to exclude **genetic heterogeneity**, i.e., whether the same phenotype is produced by mutation at more than one locus or by environmental factors.

It is difficult to determine the mutation rate of recessive genes and of X-linked genes. In recessive genes there is no demonstrable heterozygous expression. For X-linked genes, it is not possible to know whether a sporadic case of a disorder has been inherited from a heterozygous but phenotypically normal mother or whether it represents a new mutation.

Factors Influencing Spontaneous Mutation Rates:

Parental age and sex. Most mutations involving numerical aberrations of chromosomes are caused by **non-disjunction** during the first or second meiotic divisions. Non-disjunction is more common in female than in male germ cells; roughly two-third of all trisomies are due to **female non-disjunction**. Moreover, the **risk of non-disjunction** increases with increasing maternal age, especially for women above 35. A certain increase for older men is also observed. This has been demonstrated for fathers of children with **new dominant mutations**. Fathers of new mutant achondroplastic dwarfs are on an average a few years older than other fathers in the population.

Other factors influencing the non-disjunction rate appear to be **autoimmune processes** and possibly an increased tendency for **satellite association** among acrocentric chromosomes.

Gene or point mutation (Fig 56): Alteration in the DNA at molecular level: Molecular mechanisms of mutation.

Single gene mutation:

Base pair substitution: In this, one base pair is substituted by another in the DNA. This can change the amino acid sequence. Alteration of the amino acid sequence can have deleterious effects. Many of the serious genetic diseases are because of single base pair substitution. These can be of the following types:

Silent mutations: Because of the degeneracy of genetic code, many single base pair mutations do not change the amino acid sequence thereby exercising no effect. Such mutations are called silent substitutions.

Mis-sense mutations: These are type of base-pair substitutions which produce a change in a single amino acid.

Non-sense mutations: The base-pair substitutions which produce one of the three stop codons in the mRNA: UAA, UAG or UGA. This change alters the length of polypeptide either by shortening or lengthening.

Pseudogenes: Pseudogenes are copies of genes which though present cannot be transcribed due to some mutation in their regulatory, coding or promoter sites. Examples are $\psi \alpha$ and $\psi \beta$ hemoglobin gene.

Most of the abnormal hemoglobins are examples of base pair substitution. In these hemoglobins, there is just one amino acid substitution in a known position in either the α or the β peptide chain. In sickle cell hemoglobin (hemoglobin S) valine is substituted for glutamic acid in the sixth position of the β peptide chain. This is brought about by a change from GAA (or GAG) to GUA (or GUG) mRNA codons. In hemoglobin C, lysine replaces glutamic acid, again in the sixth position of β peptide chain. Here, GAA (or GAG) is changed to AAA (or AAG).

Hundreds of other abnormal variants of hemoglobin are known, some of the α chain and some of the β chain, which result in amino acid substitutions in this way. The clinical effect of such amino acid substitutions varies from no apparent effect to a completely unstable hemoglobin molecule and all its consequences.

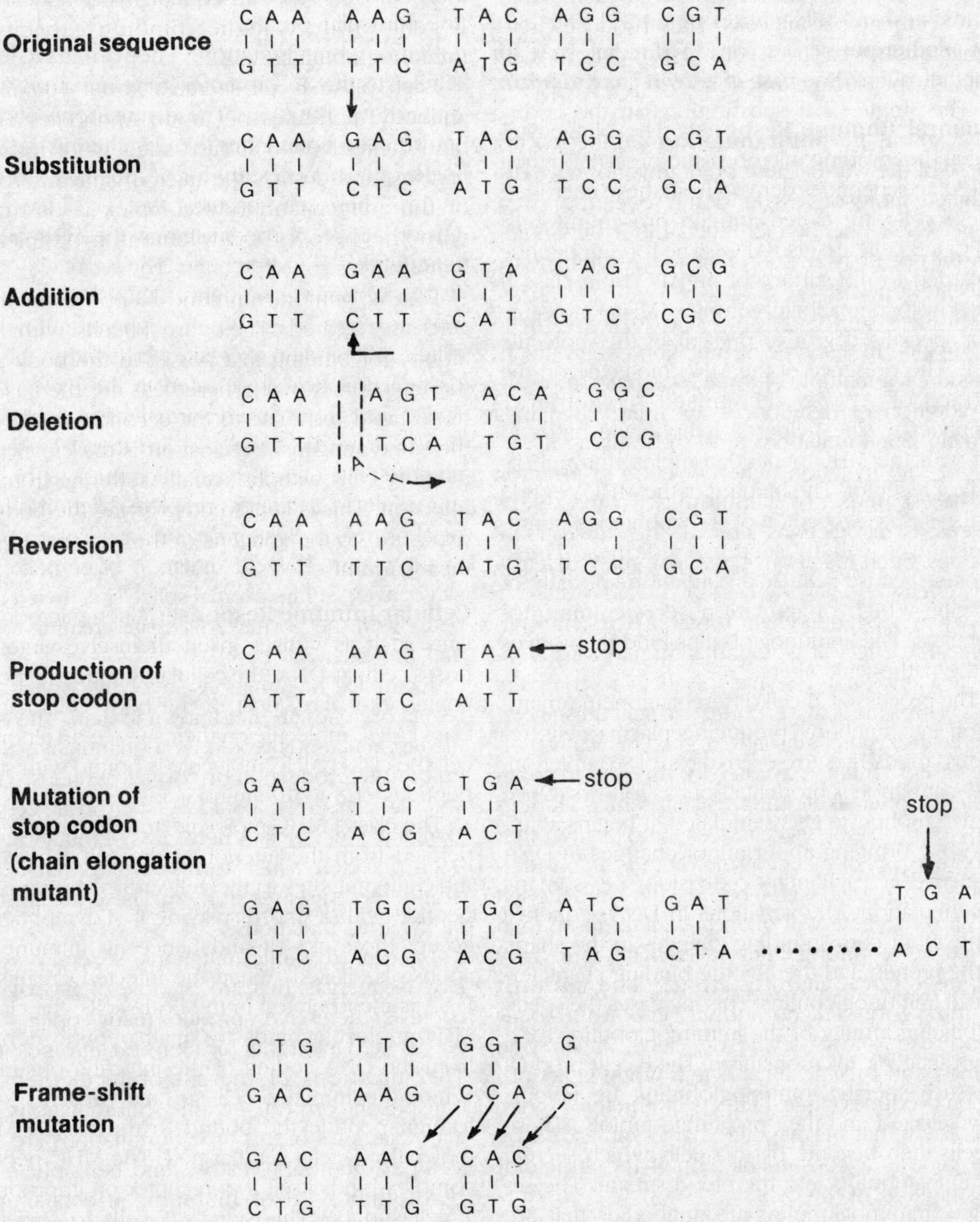

Original sequence

```
C A A    A A G    T A C    A G G    C G T
| | |    | | |    | | |    | | |    | | |
G T T    T T C    A T G    T C C    G C A
```

Substitution

```
C A A    G A G    T A C    A G G    C G T
| | |    | |      | | |    | | |    | | |
G T T    C T C    A T G    T C C    G C A
```

Addition

```
C A A    G A A    G T A    C A G    G C G
| | |    | | |    | | |    | | |    | | |
G T T    C T T    C A T    G T C    C G C
```

Deletion

```
C A A    A G T    A C A    G G C
| | |    | | |    | | |    | | |
G T T    T C A    T G T    C C G
```

Reversion

```
C A A    A A G    T A C    A G G    C G T
| | |    | | |    | | |    |   |    | | |
G T T    T T C    A T G    T C C    G C A
```

Production of stop codon

```
C A A    A A G    T A A  ← stop
| | |    | | |    | | |
A T T    T T C    A T T
```

Mutation of stop codon (chain elongation mutant)

```
G A G    T G C    T G A  ← stop
| | |    | | |    | | |
C T C    A C G    A C T
```

```
                                                                stop
                                                                 ↓
G A G    T G C    T G C    A T C    G A T              T G A
| | |    | | |    | | |    | | |    | | |              | | |
C T C    A C G    A C G    T A G    C T A  • • • • • • • A C T
```

Frame-shift mutation

```
C T G    T T C    G G T    G
| | |    | | |    | | |    |
G A C    A A G    C C A    C
```

```
G A C    A A C    C A C
| | |    | | |    | | |
C T G    T T G    G T G
```

Fig. 56 Schematic representation of different kinds of point mutation.

When a purine base (adenine or guanine) is substituted for a pyrimidine base (thymine or cytosine), this type of substitution is called **transversion**. Substitution of one purine base for another purine base or a pyrimidine base for another pyrimidine base is known as **transition**.

The single base substitutions in the coding DNA strand are **point mutations** in the strictest sense of the word. These point mutations are distributed more or less randomly over the entire gene. Their phenotypic effects differ depending on the location and kind of the resulting base substitution.

<u>Deletions or insertion of groups of three base-pairs</u>: In this type of mutation, when the alteration is a multiple of three base-pairs, it results in addition or deletion of an amino acid in a protein. Such mutations tend to be harmful.

<u>Frame shift mutation</u>: When deletion or insertion of base-pair is not a multiple of three, such insertions or deletions alter all the downstream codons. Such mutations have extremely deleterious effects.

When a peptide chain forms a part of an enzyme, the effect of gene mutation may vary from some alteration in enzyme specificity to complete loss of enzyme activity. Under such circumstances, the heterozygote is usually normal clinically as is the case with heterozygotes for the gene responsible for phenylketonuria, galactosemia, Hurler's type of mucopolysaccharidosis, and many other inborn errors of metabolism. There is a considerable safety margin with most enzymes, and though the heterozygote will often have little more than 50 per cent of normal enzyme activity, there may be no clinical manifestations. The **mutant homozygote** with no normal gene at the locus concerned, shows severe deficiency in enzyme activity and is clinically affected. When gene mutation produces clinical effects in a heterozygote, it is likely that the peptide chain synthesized by the gene is a constituent part of the structural organisation of the cell.

Mutations affecting regulator genes

<u>Promoter gene mutation</u>: This can decrease the affinity of RNA polymerase for a promoter site, which can result in decreased production of mRNA which in turn decreases the production of the particular protein.

<u>Enhance gene mutation</u>: This can have effect similar to that in promoter gene mutation.

<u>Splice Site Mutation</u>: These mutations occur at intron-exon boundaries thereby altering the splicing sequence necessary for proper excision of an intron. These may occur at the GT seqence that always defines 5' donor site or at the AG sequence that defines 3' acceptor site. They may also occur in the consensus sequences that lie near donor and acceptor sites. When such mutations take place, the excision may take place within the next exon at a splice site located in the exon. These splice sites are not used normally and remain hidden as if in the exon and are therefore termed cryptic splice sites. The use of cryptic site for splicing results in partial or complete deletion of exon or abnormal inclusion of part or all of an intron in the mature RNA. If mutation of cryptic splice site converts it into normal splice site, then it competes with the normal splice site creating abnormal proteins.

Examples of mutations involving operator or regulator genes are not known in man. The effect of such mutations would be a quantitative alteration in the production of normal peptides. The α and ß thalassemias could be such instances.

<u>Dynamic mutations</u>: A new class of mutations has been detected which forms an important cause of inherited diseases in men. These are unstable or dynamic mutations.

In some dynamic mutations, several types of DNA sequences that are capable of propagating copies of themselves, produce many copies which get inserted into other locations on chromosomes. The insertions of these mobile elements or transposons can cause frame-shift mutations. Human examples of this type of mutations are seen as type I neurofibromatosis and hemophilia A.

Another type of mutation affects tandem repeated sequences that occur within or near certain disease genes. A normal individual has about 20 to 40 tandem repeats. The number of repeats increases during meiosis or possibly early fetal development so that a newborn can have hundreds or thousands of repeats. When this occurs in certain regions of the genome, it causes genetic disease. Like other mutations, these expanded repeats are also transmitted to the carrier's or the patient's offspring. The example of diseases having such mutational basis are Huntington's disease, Fragile X syndrome and myotonic dystrophy.

The exact mechanism bringing about such expansion of tandem repeats is not known. It is likely that two single stranded breaks within the repeat sequence create DNA segment which slides as it is not anchored by a unique DNA sequence during DNA polymerisation. These expansions usually extend over a number of generations which accounts for the pattern of inheritance in these diseases and the phenomenon of anticipation.

Abnormal crossing over (Lepore-type Mutants): When unequal crossing over takes place between two closely placed loci, it results in abnormal recombination and is referred to as Lepore-type mutants. This is exemplified by **Hemoglobin Lepore** which is the result of unequal crossing over between two closely linked and very similar genes coding for ß and δ polypeptides. As a result thereof the mutant codes for non α chain having both the N-terminal portion of a normal δ and the C-terminal portion of a normal ß chain.

Abnormal Crossing Over (Gene Duplication): One type of mutation that can occur is gene duplication. It may occur by unequal crossing over and perhaps by duplication during copying of DNA. Either process gives two similar gene-loci in adjacent positions on a chromosome. Haptoglobin alleles offer an example of the origin of mutant alleles by "unequal" crossing over (Fig. 57). Haptoglobins or α globulins are types of serum protein, which are concerned with the binding of hemoglobin from aged and broken-down red blood cells. The haptoglobin molecules are composed of two kinds of polypeptide chains,

α and ß (not related to the α and ß chains of hemoglobin). A number of different haptoglobins are found in different individuals. The differences in haptoglobins are due to variations in the α chains, the ß chains being everywhere the same.

Three alleles at the Hp (haptoglobin) locus are responsible for the three main kinds of α chains found in human populations. Two of the alleles are Hp^{1F} and Hp^{1S}. They control α chains that differ from each other by a single specific replacement of one amino acid. The third allele, Hp^2 differs from both Hp^1 alleles in being nearly twice as long, i.e., a combination of two nearly complete Hp^1 chains arranged in tandem sequence. The presumed origin of such an allele is shown in Fig. 57. It is likely that a Hp gene of normal length underwent crossing over with its allele in the homologous chromosome, but at a non-homologous site. The result would be a partial duplication, of the original Hp allele, thus forming the Hp^2 allele. In later generations individuals would arise as homozygotes for Hp^2. In gametes of such individuals the two Hp^2 alleles can pair in two ways, either equally so that the left half of the duplicated gene in one chromosome would pair with the left half of the other and likewise the two right halves with each other, or unequally so that the left half of the gene in one chromosome would pair with the right half of the gene in the other. In the former case crossing over within the paired section would not alter the alleles but in the latter, an almost triplicated gene Hp^{21} would arise as well as a reverted allele of single length. Hp^{21}, a rare Hp allele, is found in several different types among humans.

Chromosomal deletions and other types of chromosomal anomalies account for other types of gene mutation.

It must be emphasised that mutations may occur in somatic as well as germ cells. A mutation that occurs in a germ cell is discovered when this cell or its progeny forms gametes, thus transmitting the mutant gene to the next generation. Fig. 58 shows **somatic mutation**. If one gene in a cell of a very early embryo mutates, further divisions of unmutated and mutated cells would

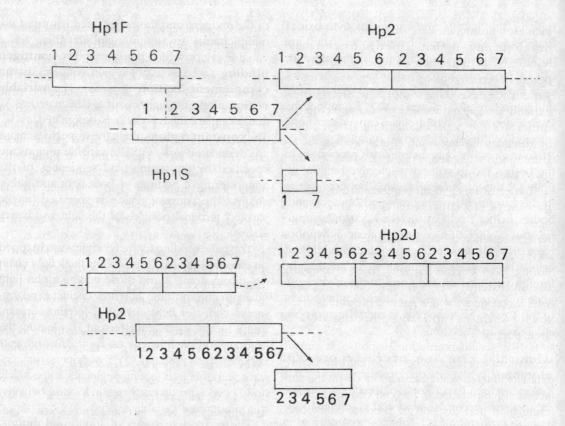

Fig. 57 Presumed origins of the haptoglobin alleles of nearly twice (upper figure) and thrice (lower figure) the length of the original genes by means of unequal or nonhomologous crossing over.

build up in an individual whose tissues would comprise partly of mutated and partly of unmutated cells.

Mutation Rates: It is estimated that many mutations are neutral. It is expected that each new zygote has about 100 new base pair combinations not present in the genome of either parent. Most of this variation is not in coding sequences but is located in extragenic sequences or in non-coding heterochromatic regions of the chromosomes.

The mutation rate has been estimated for a number of inherited disorders. The median gene mutation rate is approximately 1×10^{-6} mutations per locus per generation, but the rate can vary from 10^{-4} to 10^{-7} mutations per locus per generation. This is based on gene size or presence or absence of mutational 'hot spots' in the genome.

It has been estimated that at least six per cent of all persons born have some tangible genetic defect. It has also been calculated that each individual in population carries three to five lethal equivalents. A lethal equivalent is a gene which when homozygous is lethal to the individual.

Induced Mutations: The mutational change may occur **spontaneously**, i.e., without exposure to mutagenic agents, or it may be induced by such agents. The **mutagenic agents** include (1) penetrating ionising radiation such as X-rays, gamma rays from radium and other radioactive substances, neutrons from nuclear reaction, and (2) chemicals like mustard gas and various nitrogen or sulphur-mustard compounds, formaldehyde, nitrous acid, etc. They produce mutations only in cells on which they act directly and are not specific for particular loci or groups

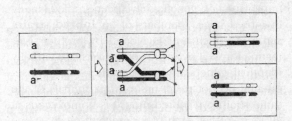

Fig. 58 Somatic mutation a cell of genotype a a^- undergoing mitosis, involving crossing over of alleles a and a^-. The resulting daughter cells have a genotype a a and a^- a respectively.

of loci. It is not known whether frequency of spontaneous mutation rises with the age of a person.

If a gene in the heterozygous state is advantageous, it is preserved and increased in proportion in a population, even if that very same gene when homozygous, is severely detrimental. The classic example is the resistance to malaria offered by the sickle cell trait. HbC, thalassemia, G6PD deficiency and Fy allele of the Duffy blood group are also thought to provide protection against malaria.

Mutation is one of the basic phenomena of life. It is very likely that all life on our planet goes back to one common origin. It could have developed from the first group of molecules, in which a primitive, information-carrying unit cooperated with an energy-gaining device, into the multiplicity of organisms of today, but through many constantly recurring mutations.

It is reasonable to suppose that **spontaneous mutations** have been taking place, pouring new genes into the gene pool continuously ever since life existed on earth. Individually, most of the mutations cause little harm; in fact, they are **beneficial**, providing as they do the **basis of evolution**. However, the harmful mutant genes, accumulated over generations and in the aggregate, either in heterozygotes or homozygotes or in polygenic combinations, decrease the **fitness** of the population.

Family patterns of disease due to mutant genes of severe (large) effect: The diseases due to **mutant genes** can be divided into **dominant**, **recessive and X-linked**. It has been suggested that the polypeptide products of the genes involved in dominant conditions make up structural proteins, whereas those concerned in recessive conditions make up enzymes. The X-linked conditions are determined by mutant genes located on the X chromosome.

Dominant conditions. A characteristic pedigree would show that the first case in the family appears **sporadically** as a result of **fresh mutation**. An affected child is born to normal parents and has normal siblings. Thereafter there is an average 1:2 risk to the offspring of those affected. Examples are von Willebrand's disease, hypokalemic periodic paralysis, and Huntington's chorea.

When the condition reduces fitness to zero (i.e., patient begets no children), all cases would be sporadic, i.e., they would have no similarly affected relatives, e.g., Apert's type of acrocephalo-syndactyly.

Recessive conditions. The family pattern of recessive conditions commonly shows siblings of affected person to be also affected but it is unusual for anyone else in the family, including half-siblings and offspring to be affected. Another feature of the pedigree of recessive conditions is a raised frequency of first cousin or other **consanguineous marriages** among the parents of the patients.

X-linked conditions. The typical family pattern of X-linked conditions depends on the fact that women heterozygous for the mutant gene are likely to transmit the disease to half their sons, and half their daughters are likely to be heterozygotes (**carriers**). When a man survives and has children, all his daughters are heterozygotes, but none of his sons are affected and none of them can transmit the mutant gene. A substantial proportion of patients with severe X-linked conditions appear as sporadic cases. In some instances the mother is not a heterozygote but mutation occurs during the formation of her ova.

GENETIC VARIATION

Genetic diversity manifests itself as changes in the staining pattern of chromosomes, as protein variations or as nucleotide changes in DNA.

Chromosomal Heteromorphism: Normal karotypes of individuals of the same sex are similar. It means that morphology of chromosomes in all humans of the same sex is the same. However, occasionally variations in chromosome morphology or staining are detected. This phenomenon is called heteromorphism. It represents differences in the amount or type of DNA sequences at a particular location along a chromosome. Normal homologs differ in size by many millions of base pairs. The major difference is usually in the amount of heterochromatic DNA sequences.

The most commonly observed examples of heteromorphism are the heterochromatic regions of the Y chromosome long arm and pericentric regions of chromosomes 1, 9 and 16. They can all be easily detected by banding techniques for staining chromosomes. Other methods of detecting heteromorphism is the use of a specific DNA probe for heteromorphic satellite DNA sequences or restriction enzyme treatment of metaphase chromosomes to identify differences in satellite sequences.

Protein Variations: Mutations can bring about changes in proteins without having any deleterious effect on the survival of the individual. At times, the change in amino acid sequence can have only an insignificant effect on the three dimensional structure and function of a protein. Mutations of such kind create individuals having more than one version of a particular protein in a population. When such multiple alleles are created for a given locus and where the variation in phenotypic expression at protein level can be detected, the phenomenon is called multiple allelism. When there are multiple alleles at a locus and where the rarest of the genes has the frequency exceeding one per cent and is sustained in the population without the help of any new mutations, the phenomenon is called **polymorphism**.

The most common examples of polymorphism are the various blood groups. The protein polymorphic systems have been now detected with the aid of protein electrophoresis.

Protein Electrophoresis: Detection of Variations at Protein Level: Protein electrophoresis technique detects single amino acid difference in a given protein because of a change in electrical charge of the protein. Because of the change in the electrical charge, the same protein from different individuals migrates at different rates through electrically charged gels. This technique is used for detecting variations in serum proteins, hemoglobins and enzymes.

On screening populations for a large number of different human enzymes and proteins by electrophoresis, about a third of them show polymorphic genotype. With such high degrees of genetic variation and polymorphism, it becomes evident that thousands of such polymorphisms are inherited. Each one of them is more or less independent of the other in inheritance. The result is an infinite combination of genotypes and phenotypes. Thus the chemical makeup of each enzyme and protein is unique.

Inherited Variation and Polymorphism at the DNA Level: It is estimated that humans vary at approximately 1 in 300 bp. So about 10 million polymorphisms can exist among 3 billion bp constituting human genome. Variations at blood group levels and protein levels can detect a very small proportion of these polymorphisms. With the availability of new molecular techniques, thousands of new polymorphisms at DNA level have been detected.

The molecular techniques for detecting polymorphisms are restriction fragment length polymorphisms (RFLPs) and variable number of tandem repeat polymorphisms (VNTRs).

Restricted Fragment Length Polymorphisms (RFLPs): Bacterial enzymes restriction endonucleases cut DNA at specific recognised sites. These sequences are known as restriction sites or recognition sites. Variation in genomic DNA sequences show the presence of additional or absence of usual cleavage sites. These give differing lengths of restriction fragments made visible by southern blotting and hybridisation to a cloned DNA probe. As there are several hundred restriction enzymes available, it permits extensive examination of nucleotides in the immediate vicinity.

There are thousands of possible combinations of probes and restriction enzymes that can reveal variations of a given cloned DNA probe. The variations detected for restriction sites at DNA level are called restriction fragment length polymorphism. The different fragment lengths constitute codominant alleles at DNA level.

RFLPs are a useful tool for studying genetic variation and diagnosing genetic disease.

Variable Number of Tandem Repeat Polymorphisms (VNTRs): This is a form of RFLP. It is because of the presence of minisatellites throughout the genome. Minisatellites are regions in which the same DNA sequence is repeated over and over again in tandem. The genetic variation measured is for the number of repeats in a region and hence the term variable number of tandem repeats or VNTRs.

VNTRs are detected by the same technique as RFLPs. Special probes are used that hybridise only to a given minisatellite region. RFLPs show polymorphisms in terms of presence or absence of a restriction site whereas VNTRs reveal polymorphisms based on different numbers of repeats present between two restriction sites. The number of these repeats vary in population considerably. It may be anywhere from 2 to 20 or more. Therefore, these polymorphisms reveal a high degree of genetic variation which is useful for mapping genes using the technique of linkage analysis.

DNA Fingerprinting: More than conventional fingerprinting, DNA fingerprinting has potential for precise individual identification.

Principle: When sufficient number of polymorphisms in a given individual are studied, the probability that any other individual can have the same alleles at every locus is virtually nil. Only identical twins show an indistinguishable pattern.

Procedure: The DNA left at the scene of a crime in the form of blood or hair is typed for a series of VTNRs and/or microsatellite polymorphisms after amplifying DNA with PCR approach. This DNA is compared with that of the suspect. If the alleles in the sample and the suspect match, then the suspect is implicated.

Zygosity of Twins or Multiple Births: Monozygous twins have identical alleles at all loci tested whereas dizygotic twins differ from each other at a substantial number of loci, as would singleton siblings.

Genetic Markers: A genetic marker refers to a locus having polymorphism with easily recognisable alleles and which can be used in genetic studies, at family level or population level. The marker can be a gene, or restriction enzyme site such as RFLPs, VTNRs, microsatellite repeats or any characteristic of DNA that allows different versions of a locus or its products such as blood groups to be distinguished from each other and followed through families.

Genetic markers can be used for:

1) Determining zygosity of twins or multiple births.

2) To test paternity. Samples from the child, the mother and the putative father are tested. In general, genetic markers can exclude but not prove paternity with certainty. Paternity is excluded if neither of the two alleles of the putative father is present at a locus. Paternity is also excluded if the putative father lacks an allele that is present in the child but not in the mother.

3) Forensic medicine: Genetic markers are used to determine the genetic origin of blood, semen or tissue specimens available at the scene of crime. Even a small amount of DNA or proteins gives valuable clues through genetic markers characterising the victim or suspect, or identifying missing persons by comparing the person and his close biological relations.

4) Blood groups — ABO, MN, Rh — for preventing mismatched transfusions.

5) Tissue typing — HLA complex — for successful organ or tissue transplantation.

SUMMARY

Mutation: It is any sudden heritable structural change in DNA.
Classification:
1) According to the cause, (a) spontaneous; (b) induced by exogenous agents.
2) According to type of change (a) genome mutations (numerical chromosomal aberrations), (b) chromosome mutation (structural aberrations in chromosome), (c) gene or point mutation (alteration in DNA at the molecular level).
3) According to site of mutation (a) somatic (occurring in body cells), (b) germ cell mutations.

Extraneous agents which induce mutations are called mutagenic agents and include (a) ionising irradiation like X-rays, (b) chemicals like mustard gas, formaldehyde, etc., and (c) some viruses.

Spontaneous mutations, presumably occurring continuously since the inception of life on earth are the source of new genes which have provided a basis for evolution. Individually, a mutation may cause little harm, but an accumulation of a number of harmful mutation genes over several generations and in the aggregate would tend to decrease biological fitness of a population.
Mutation:
Subclassification of *gene* or *point mutation.*
According to the site of point mutation:
  1. Affecting structural gene.
  2. Affecting promoter gene, enhancer gene, splice site.

According to the type of base-pair affection:
  1. Silent mutation
  2. Mis-sense mutation
  3. Non-sense mutation
  4. Chain elongation mutation
  5. Frame-shift mutation

Dynamic or unstable mutation:

DNA sequences which can propagate copies of themselves and get inserted on other structural genes are called dynamic or unstable mutation. The tandem repeats could even remain in their original site and produce deleterious effects. Such sequence repeats tend to occur during meiosis or early embryonic development.

Genetic polymorphism:

Multiple forms in a population, due to differences at genetic level is termed as genetic polymorphism. The frequency of each of the multiple forms must be greater than one per cent.

Measures of genetic polymorphism:

  1) Blood groups: Variation in blood groups is a result of antigens that occur on the surface of RBCs.
  2) Protein electrophoresis: detects variation in genes which encode for serum proteins. Serum proteins with slight variation in amino acid sequence will migrate at different rates in an electrically charged gel.
  3) RFLPs: are variations in DNA sequence at specific restriction sites. The variation in DNA fragment length are seen by sorting the fragments by electrophoresis.
  4) VNTRs: are a form of RFLPs where the variation in DNA is due to different number of repeat DNA sequence in different individuals.

7 POPULATION GENETICS

Introduction

A population is to a human geneticist what *E. coli*, *Drosophila* or mice are to an experimental geneticist. Since human generation time is of the order of twenty-five years, human genetics is not amenable to direct laboratory observations. However, an entire human population manifesting an infinite range of **genetic variability** of different traits is available for instant observation, through the application of **mathematical** and **statistical techniques**.

Known phenotypes can lead us to knowing the related genotypes, from which the frequencies of different alleles in a given population can be readily ascertained on the basis of the **Hardy-Weinberg law** or principle. The law states that in a randomly mating population, if the frequency of a pair of alleles determining a particular trait is represented as p and q such that p + q = 1, then the three genotypes would be expected to occur in the frequencies of p^2, 2pq and q^2. Further these frequencies will tend to remain constant from generation to generation in a very **large inbreeding population**, provided factors like natural selection, mutation, etc., do not disturb this equilibrium.

Population genetics has sometimes been called **bean-bag genetics**, since if identical black and white beans are mixed in a known proportion in a bag and drawn out two at a time by random chance without looking, the frequencies with which both whites, one black and one white and both blacks are likely to occur, would be as mentioned for p^2, 2pq and q^2.

Twins are a special category of a human population. They may be identical or fraternal. Genetic studies can help to ascertain their **zygosity**, i.e, whether they are monozygous or dizygous. Monozygotic twins, in particular, are a rich source of genetic material, whereupon different environmental effects can be studied.

Population studies have been extended to a detailed analysis of **dermal ridge patterns** on the palms, fingers, thumbs, the soles of the feet and the toes. These are known to be inherited in a polygenic manner and have shown characteristic variations in a number of chromosomal abnormalities.

POPULATION GENETICS

Population genetics is the study of genes in populations. It deals with the distribution and behaviour of genes and with how gene and genotype frequencies are maintained or changed. The change in the gene and genotype frequencies is the basis of evolution. Hence the study of population genetics also incorporates the study of factors concerned in human evolution.

Gene Frequencies in Populations: The Hardy-Weinberg principle is the basis of population genetics. It was put forward independently by Pritish mathematician, **G. H. Hardy**, and a German physician **W. Weinberg**, in 1908.

The Hardy-Weinberg law states that if two alleles (A and a) occur in a randomly mating population with the frequency of p and q, respectively, where p + q = 1, then the expected proportions of the three genotypes would be AA = p^2, Aa = 2pq, and aa = q^2 (Table 8). The proportion remains constant from generation to generation in an infinitely large, inbreeding population. **Mutation, selection, migration** and **genetic drift** can disturb the **Hardy-Weinberg equilibrium**.

If the two genes A and a are in proportion to p and q, the sperms and ova will contain them in the same proportions, and with random mating, the various gametic combinations, would be:

Male   Female
A(p)a(q)   ×   A(p)a(q)
    AA (p^2) + Aa(pq) + Aa(pq) + aa(q^2)

Therefore, the frequencies of the various offspring from such matings would be p^2 (AA), 2pq(Aa) and q^2(aa).

Table 8: Relationship of Gene Frequency to Genotype Frequency

Gene Frequencies		Genotype Frequencies		
p	q	p^2 A/A	2pq A/a	q^2 a/a
0.5	0.5	0.25	0.50	0.25
0.6	0.4	0.36	0.48	0.16
0.7	0.3	0.49	0.42	0.09
0.8	0.2	0.64	0.32	0.04
0.9	0.1	0.81	0.18	0.01
0.99	0.01	0.98	0.02	0.0001
0.999	0.001	0.998	0.002	0.000001

If the progeny were to mate among themselves, the result would be

AA(p^2) Aa(2pq) aa(q^2) × AA(p^2) Aa(2pq) aa(q^2)
AA/AA   = p^2 × p^2 = p^4
AA/Aa   = p^2 × 2pq   = 2p^{3}q
AA/aa   = p^2 × q^2 = p^{2}q^2
Aa/AA   = 2pq × p^2 = 2p^{3}q
Aa/Aa   = 2pq × 2pq   = 4p^{2}q^2
Aa/aa   = 2pq × q^2 = 2pq^3
aa/AA   = q^2 × p^2 = p^{2}q^2
aa/Aa   = q^2 × 2pq   = 2pq^3
aa/aa   = q^2 × q^2 = q^4
i.e., Total = p^4+4p^{3}q+6p^{2}q^2+4pq^3+q^4
            = p^4+2p^{3}q+p^{2}q^2+2p^{3}q+4p^{2}q^2
              +2pq^3+p^{2}q^2+2pq^3+q^4
            = p^2(p^2+2pq+q^2)+2pq(p^2+2pq
              +q^2)+q^2(p^2+2pq+q^2)
            = p^2(p+q)^2+2pq(p+q)^2+q^2(p+q)^2
            = p^2+2pq+q^2, since p+q = 1

This shows that the proportions of the various genotypes remain the same in the second generation as they were in the first. If one continues to calculate for many generations, the result would be the same. The relative proportions of the genotypes would remain constant from one generation to another, and would occur in the proportions p^2 : 2pq : q^2.

Based on this equation it is possible to find out the frequency of the various genotypes in the population if the frequency of one of the homozygotes is known. If the frequency of an autosomal trait is 1/40.000

q^2 = 1/40.000
q = 1/200
and, p = 1 − 1/200 = 199/200
The frequency of carriers = 2pq

$$= 2 \times \frac{199}{200} \times \frac{1}{200}$$

$$\cong 1/100$$

This also illustrates the fact that in the general population carriers are more frequent than affected individuals.

Factors affecting Hardy-Weinberg Equilibrium: The Hardy-Weinberg equilibrium is altered if there is non-random mating. **Random mating (panmixis)** ensures that the frequencies of the different kinds of matings are determined only by the relative frequency of the genotypes in the population. In practice, the requirement of random matings is not commonly fulfilled. The preferential selection of a mate with a particular genotype is common and such a mating is referred to as **assortative or non-random mating**. Preference for a mate of the same genotype is positive assortative mating and preference for a mate of a different genotype is **negative assortative mating**.

Consanguinity implies marriage between two blood relatives who have at least one common ancestor in the preceding five generations, i.e., up to their great great grandparents. If consanguinity in a community is traditional then it tends to disturb the Hardy-Weinberg equilibrium by reducing the frequency of heterozygotes and increasing relatively, the frequency of affected homozygotes.

Mutation. Hardy-Weinberg equilibrium assumes that there is no mutation. Usually some mutations do occur at all loci but their effect is nullified due to reduced fitness of affected individuals. Thus the Hardy-Weinberg equilibrium is maintained. However, if there is a disproportionately high mutation rate at a particular locus then it leads to a steady increase in the number of mutant alleles in a given population.

Natural selection is an important factor operative in evolution. The **Darwinian theory of biological fitness** is considered to be the relative ability of an organism to survive and transmit its genes to the next generation. It is determined by the number of offspring who reach reproductive age. Fitness is unity (or 100 per cent) if a person has at least two such offspring. In the modern era, survival of the fittest is interpreted as operative through the action of selection of new genotypes which have arisen by mutation or recombination. Autosomal dominant genes are always expressed and are exposed to the scrutiny of selection, in contrast to autosomal recessive genes. As a result, the effects of selection are more obvious and can be more readily measured for dominant genes than for recessive ones.

Genetic drift is the fluctuation of gene frequencies in small populations due to new settlements formed by members of an older group. **Gene flow** is a gradual diffusion of genes from one population to another by **migration** and **miscegenation**.

Factors Influencing the Prevalence of Genetic Disease in a Population: Some genetic disorders show a high incidence in some populations than in others. The possible factors responsible for this are as follows:

1) **Founder effect.** When a population size is small then some of the rare autosomal recessive disorders show high incidence. This high frequency usually results from a founder effect as also the social, religious or geographical isolation of the group. A founder effect is also seen in autosomal dominant disorders. Because of the limited number of sexual partners available to the group, the mere fact of one or more founder members carrying the rare alleles allows the same to be established at relatively high frequencies.

2) **Heterozygote advantage.** When a serious autosomal disorder despite its effect of reducing physical fitness, prevails in large population, the possibility is that the heterozygotes have advantage over others. For example, the carriers of sickle cell **anemia** and **ß-thalassemia** have evident advantage of reduced susceptibility to Plasmodium falciparum malaria. Another mechanism speculated is that the sperm carrying a mutant gene for a condition like cystic fibrosis tends to be more viable than the others.

Applications of Hardy-Weinberg Equilibrium:
1) **Estimation of carrier frequencies.** Gene frequency and carrier frequency can be calculated (approximately) by knowing the disease incidence and mode of inheritance. During genetic counselling, rishs may thusbe calculated and explained.

2) **Estimation of mutation rate.** Depending on differences in disease incidence in parents and children, males and females, and the effects of the disease on physical fitness, it is possible to calculate approximately the mutation rate. A knowledge of mutation rate gives an idea of gene size, structure and the effects of mutagens on the genes.

Dermatoglyphics: Dermatoglyphics is the study of patterns of the ridged skin of the palms, fingers, soles and toes. Dermatoglyphics form an important part genetics of because:
1) Characteristic combination of pattern types are found in Down's syndrome and other chromosomal disorders. Dermatoglyphics and their correlation to genetic disorders have been superseded by newer and more accurate methods of chromosomal analysis. However, such methods are still not easily accessible at many places in various parts of the world and dermatoglyphics are still used to diagnose of many chromosomal disorders.

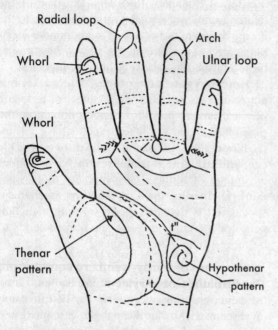

Fig. 59 The nomenclature of the dermatoglyphics of the palm and fingers. There are four digital triradii (a, b, c and d) and an axial triradius t (t" indicates its distal location, t'" indicates location further distal to t"). Thenar, hypothenar and digital patterns are shown.

2) Dermatoglyphic traits are genetically determined.

3) They provide a useful means of measuring resemblance between twins in the determination of twin zygosity.

The patterns studied are:
1. The flexion creases of the palm.
2. Dermal patterns (Fig. 59)
   a. Fingerprints
   b. Palmar patterns
   c. Plantar patterns.

1) **The flexion creases.** The 'heart,' 'head' and 'life' lines of palmistry are formed at the same time as the dermal ridges. They also affect the course of dermal ridges. A single transverse crease (**simian crease**) in place of the usual two creases is found in 1 per cent of Caucasians and in a larger percentage of Asian. In Down's syndrome and other chromosomal abnormalities, single flexion creases are very common. Simian creases

are also more common in abnormal individuals, such as children with congenital malformations.

2) **Dermal patterns.** (a) Fingerprints. They are classified according to Galton's system as **whorls, loops or arches** (Fig. 60). A **triradius** is a point from which three ridge systems course in three different directions at angles of about 120□. A whorl has two triradii, a loop has one and an arch has none. Loops are subclassified as radial or ulnar, depending upon whether they open to the radial or ulnar side of the finger. In a fingerprint formula, the patterns are conventionally listed as: left 5,4,3,2,1; right 1,2,3,4,5. The size of a finger pattern is expressed as the **ridge count**, i.e., the number of ridges that come across a line drawn from the triradial point to the pattern core. An arch has a count of zero, as it has no triradius. The total ridge count (TRC) of the 10 digits is used as a dermatoglyphic parameter. The frequency of the different patterns varies from finger to finger.

b. **Palmar patterns.** The four digital triradii, near the distal border of the palm and an axial triradius, commonly placed over the fourth metacarpal near the base of the palm, provide the landmarks for palmar patterns.

Normally, the axial triradius is situated near the base of the palm, somewhere along the fourth metacarpal. It is displaced distally in Down's syndrome and other chromosomal disorders. Its location is measured as the "atd angle" or in terms of the total length of the palm. An atd angle greater than 57° is more common in patients with Down's syndrome and several other chromosomal syndromes, than in the general population (Fig. 61).

In a normal palm the ridges commonly course obliquely towards the proximal portion of the ulnar side. Interdigital patterns of loops or whorls are formed, if the recurving ridges are present between the digital triradii. Hypothenar and thenar patterns may be present.

c. **Plantar patterns.** These patterns are difficult to obtain and hence not much is known about them. In various clinical syndromes, well-defined

L oop

Triradius

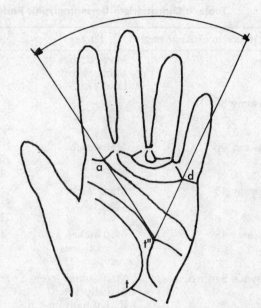

Fig. 61 Measuring the atd angle of the palm. If there is more than one axial triradius, the distal one is used. Usually the angle measures about 60°. Angles of more than 75° are common in cases of Down's syndrome where the axial triradius is shifted distally.

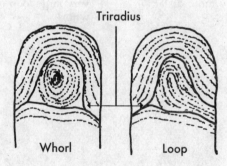

Triradius

Whorl   Loop

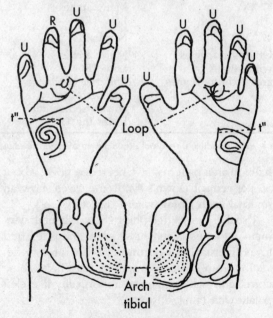

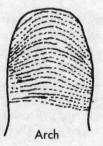

Arch

Fig. 60 Different types of fingerprints. The magnified picture of the loop shows rows of sweat pores. For counting ridge the line drawn from the triradius to the core of the loop is used.

Fig. 62 Typical dermal patterns in Down's syndrome, many ulnar loops, radial loop on 4th digit, axial triradius t" giving atd angle of 80° and tibial arch in the sole.

Table 9: Characteristic Dermatoglyphic Pattern seen in some Chromosomal Abnormalities

Chromosomal Abnormality	Fingers	Palms	Soles
5p–	Many arches Many whorls Low TRC	Thenar pattern t^{II} Single flexion crease	Openfield
Trisomy 8	—	t^{I} or t^{II} Unit or bilateral single flexion crease	—
Trisomy 9p	Many arches	t^{II} Absence of fusion of the sub- digital triradii b and c	—
Trisomy 13	Many arches Low TRC	t^{I} or t^{III} Single flexion crease Thenar pattern	large pattern, arch fibular or loop tibial
Trisomy 18	6–10 arches (also on toes) very low TRC	Single flexion crease	—
Down's Syndrome	Many ulnar loops (usually 10) Radial loop on 4th and/or 5th digits	t^{II} Single flexion crease	Arch tibial or small loop distal
45.X	Large loops or whorls High TRC	t slightly more distal	very large loop or whorl
47.XXY	Many arches Low TRC	t slightly more proximal	—
47.XYY	Normal	Normal	Normal
Other syndromes with extra X and Y chromosomes	Many arches Low TRC; The greater the number of sex chromosomes, the lower the TRC		

t = axial triradius; t^{II} = distal displacement of axial triradius; t^{III} = extreme displacement; TRC = Total Ridge Count.

hallucal area patterns have been described. About 50 per cent of Down's syndrome cases show an unusual **arch tibial** pattern (Fig. 62).

Usually, dermatoglyphics show bilateral symmetry. At times asymmetry is seen, and is referred to as **fluctuating asymmetry**. This random deviation from bilateral symmetry may have some correlation with congenital abnormality like cleft palate with family history.

Clinical Applications:

1) **Chromosomal abnormalities.** The various chromosomal disorders are often associated with some unusual dermatoglyphic patterns (Table 9).

The differences are mainly seen in (a) the Total Ridge Count (TRC) which may be higher or lower (b) the flexion creases of palm, which may be represented by a single crease and (c) the position of the axial triradius which tends to get displaced distally. However, any of the abnormal dermatogylphic features, on its own, carries no significance unless it is associated with other abnormal clinical features.

2) **Congenital malformations.** Congenital malformations involving limbs are associated with gross distortion of the dermatoglyphic patterns.

SUMMARY

Population genetics: Studies the distribution and behaviour of genes in population.

Hardy-Weinberg Law: Give gene frequencies in populations, enunciated independently by Hardy and Weinberg. It states that if two alleles (A and a) occur in a randomly mating population with the frequency of p and q respectively, where $p + q = 1$, then the expected proportions of the three genotypes would be $AA = p^2$, $Aa = 2\,pq$ and $aa = q^2$. The proportion remain constant from generation to generation in an infinitely large, inbreeding population.

Factors affecting Hardy-Weinberg Law: Mutation, natural selection, migration and genetic drift.

Dermatoglyphics: Study of patterns of the ridged skin of the palms, fingers, soles and toes.

Palm: Flexion creases, palmar patterns — four digital triradii and an axial triradius.

Fingers: Fingerprints — whorls, loops, arches; triradius: the point from which three ridge systems course in three different directions at angles of 120°; finger patterns expressed as ridge count, i.e., the number of ridges that come across a line drawn from the triradial point to the pattern core.

Sole: Plantar pattern — studied less often.

Usefulness of dermatoglyphics: Study of chromosomal disorders and congenital malformations. Both are associated with some unusual dermatoglyphic patterns.

8 IMMUNOGENETICS AND BLOOD GROUPS

Introduction

Immunogenetics is the branch of genetics concerned with the inheritance of **antigens** and the **antibodies** which react with them in a variety of ways. Antigen–antibody or **immune reactions**, enable the detection of a number of genetic traits. The various blood groups refer to the **surface antigens** carried by the red cell plasma membrane. Their reacting antibodies found in the plasma, may either occur naturally or be induced by antigenic invasion.

The classification of blood groups into the **ABO system** and the **Rh-system** is of paramount clinical significance. Apart from their determination in the all too frequently resorted to **blood transfusions**, the blood groups have also contributed to an understanding of many genetic principles such as multiple allelism, codominance, genetic polymorphism, immune reactions and the study of genetic linkage.

The immunoglobulins being proteins, represent a class of specifically inherited molecules. They are manufactured by **plasma cells**, which are concerned with a wide range of antigen–antibody reactions involved in **humoral immunity**. Another group of specialised **lymphocytes** is originally produced in the thymus and is then widely distributed in various other lymphoid organs. These are involved in **cellular immunity** and are mainly concerned in the rejection or elimination of grafted tissue from a source other than one's own body. Since organ transplants are becoming commonplace, a study of different immune-deficiency disorders and their inheritance is of obvious importance.

IMMUNOGENETICS

Immunogenetics deals with the genetic aspects of antigens, antibodies and their interactions. It involves the combination of immunologic and genetic techniques, whereby genetic characteristics are detected by immune reactions.

Four areas of immunogenetics are of medical significance:
1) blood groups and clinical problems related to blood group incompatibilities
2) organ transplantation
3) immune deficiency diseases and
4) autoimmune diseases.

Definitions of some of the terms commonly used in immunology given below, help in the understanding of immunogenetics.

Antigen. A substance which elicits cellular and/or antibody response by immunocompetent cells and reacts specifically with the cells/antibody so produced.

Antibody. An immunoglobulin, a specific complex protein produced in response to the introduction of a specific antigen and reacts selectively with that antigen.

Immune reaction. The specific reaction between an antigen and its specific antibody.

Immunological homeostasis. The characteristic condition of a normal adult, who has certain antigens and the ability to react to antigens, by producing cells/antibodies, but who does not produce cells/antibodies to one's own antigens.

Autoimmunity. Immunity against one's own self. In certain conditions an individual forms antibodies against one or more of his own antigens.

Immunological tolerance. The inability to respond to a specific antigen because of previous exposure to that antigen, especially during embryonic life.

Hybrid. The progeny of a cross between two genetically different organisms.

Allotypes. Genetically determined differences in antigens.

Incompatibility. The donor and host are said to be incompatible if, because of genetic differences, the host rejects cells transplanted from the donor. In maternal–fetal incompatibility, the mother forms antibodies against fetal cells that enter her circulation.

When a foreign organism is encountered by the body, it responds with the first line of defence, i.e., innate immune system formed by phagocytes and the complement system. This innate immune system recognises general features of the invading microorganisms.

After the first line of defence, a more specialised adaptive immune system comes into play. This system is designed to recognise the features of the invading microorganisms and of foreign antigens so as to mount a more specific and aggressive immune response.

The **immune response** can be divided into two parts: (1) **humoral, antibody or immunoglobulin**, and (2) **cellular**. In general, antibodies effect the destruction of bacteria, viruses and other microorganisms. The antigen-antibody reaction depends on mutually interlocking sites which vary with the antibody and which are specific for each antigen-antibody pair. An example of cellular immune response is that of lymphoid cells producing killer cells to reject a transplant.

Fig. 63 schematises the working of the immune system. During the development of an individual, lymphoid precursor cells take one of the two alternative pathways. One path involves formation of the thymus gland, and differentiation into small lymphocytes found in the cortical regions of lymph nodes and spleen. These lymphocytes are responsible for cellular immunity (transplantation immunity, delayed hypersensitivity). The other path involves differentiation of precursor cells into plasma cells responsible for the synthesis of immunoglobulins; and found in Peyer's patches in the intestine.

The T cells or thymus lymphocytes interact

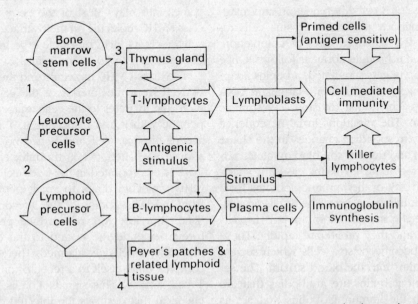

Fig. 63 Scheme showing the mode of functioning of the immune system. Block at 1 — reticular dysgenesis; at 2 — Swiss-type agammaglobulinemia at 3 — Di George syndrome; at 4 — Bruton type of agammaglobulinemia.

directly with the infected cells to get rid of the microorganisms or other foreign cells. The B lymphocytes or B cells on maturing become antibody secreting plasma cells. They produce circulating antibodies. The T cells help B cells in their antibody producing function.

Humoral Immune Response: The phagocytes engulf the invading microbes and present on their cell sufaces peptides derived from these microbes. These cells are called antigen presenting cells (APCs). B cells are also APCs. The foreign peptide is carried to the surface of an APC by a class II major histocompatibility complex (MHC) molecule in a specialised groove present in the molecule itself. The presence of the MHC molecule on the surface of APC is recognised by helper T lymphocyte. The helper T lymphocyte binds itself with the MHC peptide complex, through its surface receptor. The binding of the MHC peptide to the surface receptor of T lymphocyte stimulates the T cell to secrete cytokines. These cytokines cause cellular proliferation specially of B cells, which on mutation secrete immunoglobulins. The immunoglobulins bind themselves to the pathogenic agents.

The process of B cell differentiation and maturation into antibody producing plasma cells requires about five to seven days of completion. The maturation is brought about as follows. Once the B lymphocyte gets stimulated, it begins adaptation by bringing about minor changes in DNA sequence at each mitotic division, i.e. somatic hypermutation. The variations in DNA sequence bring about corresponding changes in the shape of the protein and thereby the binding characteristic of immunoglobulins. This increases the specific binding affinity of the immunoglobulins for a given antigenic microorganism. The B cells producing such specific immunoglobulins are favourably selected and they proliferate rapidly. These B cells then become plasma cells which secrete immunoglobulins into the blood stream. The secreted immunoglobulins are antibodies that are identical with the immunoglobulins that act as receptors on the B cell surface. To sum up, adaptation by immune system involves an initial selection of B cells whose receptors can bind with the pathogen and subsequent hypermutation of B cells produce higher binding capacity of immunoglobulins.

Each plasma cell secretes about 10 million antibody molecules per hour. Antibodies either bind themselves to surface antigens of microorganisms and destroy the microorganism directly, or the antigen–antibody complex is destroyed with the help of complement proteins and lymphocytes.

During humoral immune response, memory cells are created. These are B cells with high affinity for binding that persist in the body after the infection is over. These cells are the basis of more rapid response to the second exposure to the same antigens. Vaccination is the creation of memory cells without actually suffering from the infection. This is achieved by giving the body an exposure to the antigens of the bacteria, free of their harmful effects.

Cellular Immune Response: When microorganisms such as viruses insert themselves into the host's cellular DNA, the cellular immune response comes into play. Most of the body cells have a class I MHC molecule on their surface. In a normal cell the class I MHC molecule is bound with small peptides of 8 to 10 amino acids.

The class I MHC molecule and the peptide are derived from the interior of the cell. The MHC molecule migrates to the cell surface carrying the peptide with it and displaying it. T lymphocytes accept these as self and hence no immune response is elicited. When the infected organism's DNA is incorporated in the body cells, the class I MHC molecule binds to small peptide derived from the DNA coding of the infecting organism. When the infected cell surface presents such foreign peptide the bound to the class I MHC molecule, T cells get alarmed. The MHC peptide complex binds itself to a receptor on appropriate T cell surface. This signals T cells to secrete a chemical that destroys the infected cell. Because of this ability of T cells to destroy a cell, such type of the T cells are known as cytotoxic T lymphocytes or killer T lymphocytes. They are also known as CD_8 T cells because of the presence of CD_8 molecule on their surfaces. The helper T cells have a CD_4 molecule on their cell surfaces and hence are also known as CD_4 T lymphocyte. Each cytotoxic T lymphocyte can destroy one infected cell every one to five minutes.

To begin with, only a very small proportion of the body's T cells will have selective binding affinity for the infecting organism's peptide. But as in the case of B lymphocytes and humoral antibodies, helper T cells by secreting cytokines stimulate the proliferation of the cytotoxic T lymphocytes. These can selectively bind to the infected cells. The circulating dendritic cells present the foreign peptides on their cell surfaces and migrate to secondary lymphoid tissues where most of the T cells reside helping to alert the appropriate T cells to infection.

For the cellular immune response, a similar mechanism operates. When a foreign histocompatibility antigen matches an antibody on the surface of a lymphoid cell, the cell commences differentiation and division to produce killer cells that attack the antigen.

Fig. 63 gives sites of hypothetical blocks — 1, 2, 3, 4 — in various immunological deficiency diseases. The different immunological deficiency diseases known so far are discussed later in this chapter.

Immunoglobulins

Immunoglobulins are serum proteins which act as antibodies, an important **defence mechanism** against microorganisms. Each immunoglobulin (gamma globulin) molecule is made up of four polypeptide chains: **two identical light** and **two identical heavy chains** held together by **disulfide bonds**. The light chains are of two types, kappa (K) and lambda (λ), the two differing in amino acid sequence. The light chains are alike in all classes of immunoglobulins. The heavy chains differ in each immunoglobulin.

An immunoglobulin has a special structural-functional organisation to suit the varying nature of the antigens and the rather fixed nature of the complement. Any immunoglobulin thus, has a variable region which is concerned with **antigen binding** and a constant region concerned with **complement fixation** (Fig. 64). The **variable region** along the light chain is designated as V_L and along the heavy chain is designated as V_H. The **constant regions** along the respective chains are designated as C_L C_H. The variable regions are specified by the amino acid sequences of the amino terminal portions of both light and heavy chains. The constant region is specified by the carboxy terminal portions of the light and heavy chains.

The genes coding for heavy chains are mapped on chromosome 14. Those coding the k light chain on chromosome 2 and those coding alpha light chain on chromosome 22. Three distinct gene segments code for light chains: C for the constant and V for the variable region and J for joining the constant and variable regions. Four gene segments code for heavy chain, C,V,T segments for constant, variable and joining segments respectively and D codes for diversity region located between the joining and variable regions.

There are five types of immunoglobulins, namely, IgG, IgM, IgA, IgD and IgE. Each has a different H-chain designated respectively as γ, μ, α, δ and ϵ. Both the L-chains are common to all immunoglobulins. The molecular formula of each immunoglobulin is $\gamma_2 k_2 \gamma_2 \lambda_2$ for IgG, $\mu_2 k_2 \mu_2 \lambda_2$ for IgM, $\alpha_2 k_2 \alpha_2 \lambda_2$ for IgA, $\delta_2 k_2 \delta_2 \lambda_2$ for IgD and $\epsilon_2 k_2 \epsilon_2 \lambda_2$ for IgE. All the immunoglobulin types are found in a normal individual.

Immature lymphocytes produce only IgM, but as they mature, a rearrangement of heavy chain gene called class switching occurs. This produces the four other major classes of immunoglobulins, each of which has different amino acid sequences, charge size and carbohydrates content. Each class gets localised in selective parts of the body and each responds to a different type of infection.

In a population, the genetically determined variants of the immunoglobulins are:
1) *Gm* system associated with the H-chain of IgG.
2) *Am* system associated with the H-chain of IgA.

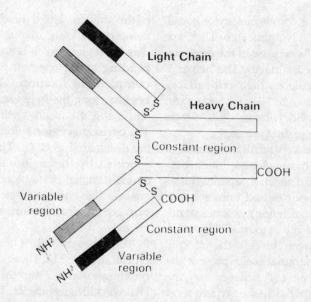

Light Chain

Heavy Chain

Constant region

COOH

COOH

Variable region

Constant region

Variable region

Fig. 64 An immunoglobulin molecule, consisting of both light and heavy chains with their respective variable and constant regions. The constant regions activate complement and phagocytes. The variable regions bind to antigen.

3) *Inv* system associated with the kappa L-chain.
4) *Oz* system associated with the lambda L-chain.

The *Gm, Am* and *Inv* groups are controlled by multiple alleles at a single autosomal locus. The frequencies of the different alleles differ in various racial groups. The Gm and Inv traits are polymorphic.

Complement: After the formation of an antigen–antibody complex, the lysis of the antigen-bearing cell is brought about by a sequential series of reactions, which are dependent on proteins known collectively as complement. The complement is effective only after the antigen-antibody complex is formed. It brings about destruction of the antigen–bearing cells by facilitating phagocytosis. The complement is active in the destruction of microorganisms, the production of inflammation and the rejection of implanted tissue.

Hereditary deficiencies of almost all the components of the complement system are known, each associated usually with an autoimmune disease or increased susceptibility to infection. The most common genetic disorder related to the complement is deficiency of the inhibitor of the activated C_1 component. This is the cause of hereditary angioneurotic edema, an autosomal dominant disorder.

Several components of the complement show polymorphism. So far, all the components that have been mapped are shown to be on chromosome 6, closely linked to the HLA complex.

Basis of Diversity of Immunoglobulins and T Cell Receptors: As the host immune system cannot be ready in advance with all possible immunoglobulins and T cell receptors, it may be required to combat foreign microorganisms invading it during its lifetime, mechanisms have been suggested as operative in generating diversity at both levels —immunoglobulins and T cells.

An individual has 100 to 200 different V segments, six different J segments and 30 different D segments located contiguously in his germline genes. This allows significant diversity.

Somatic recombination of VJ segments of light chain and VTD segments of heavy chains is done during B lymphocyte maturation. This is done by selective deletion of the DNA sequences by enzyme recombinases encoded in RAG_1, and RAG_2 genes in V,J,D segments before they are transcribed into mRNA. This cutting and pasting process is known as somatic recombination, whereby mature B lymphocytes vary in their rearranged immunoglobulin DNA sequences. As there are many possible recombinations of single V,J,D segments, a large number of different types of antibody molecules can be produced.

Variations occur in the V,D and J segments in the site where they are joined. The number of nucleotides may be deleted or added at the junction joining the regions. This adds to the capacity required to produce varied type of antibodies.

At the time of B maturation, the lymphocyte undergoes somatic hypermutation. The mutation rate of the genes coding for immunoglobulins increases with each cell division. This produces alteration in DNA sequence coding for immunoglobulins. Somatic hypermutation of the V, D and J genes results in significant antibody diversity.

A random combination of different heavy and light chains in immunoglobulin gives added variation to antibodies.

Putting all mechanisms in operation it has been calculated that the body has potential to produce 10^{10} to 10^{14} distinct antibodies.

Similarly, T cell receptors also need to be varied. T cell receptors are heterodimers composed of either an alpha and beta chain or a gamma and delta chain. The genes coding for alpha, kappa and delta chains are mapped on chromosome 14 and those for beta and gamma on chromosome 7. A given T cell can have either alpha-beta receptor or a gamma-delta receptor. As in case of immunoglobulins, multiple germline gene segments, somatic recombination and junctional diversity produce T cell receptor diversity. The mechanism of somatic hypermutation does not operate in the genes coding for T cell receptors as they have to retain tolerance of normal self antigens and recognise MHC molecules.

Transplantation: Tissue and organ transplantation is a modern development. Except for corneal and bone grafts, the greater the antigenic dissimilarity between the donor and the recipient, the greater are the chances of **graft rejection** by the host. Homograft rejection does not take place in identical twins or in those nonidentical twins, where mixing of placental circulation had taken place *in utero*.

The mechanism of rejection is the immune response. The implanted tissue is antigenic to the host, which reacts by the production of T effector lymphocytes. These invade the tissue surrounding the graft and reject the graft.

When a graft from a donor is introduced into the host (recipient), the regional lymph nodes of the host respond to the foreign tissue by cellular proliferation. The important cells in this response are small lymphocytes of two types, **T cells and B cells**. T cells are thymus dependent cells, and are important in cell-mediated reactions such as tissue rejection. T cells are sensitive to the antigens on the surface of the implanted cells. They respond by proliferation and differentiation to form blast cells (lymphoblasts). **Blast cells** produce **T effector cells, T suppressor cells** and **T helper cells**. **Primed T effector cells** reach the graft site and bring about rejection. T helper cells are seen as circulating lymphocytes and assist the B cells in response to various antigens. T suppressor cells inhibit the response of B cells to some antigens. Primed cells are antigen sensitive memory cells, responsible for subsequent rapid response to the same antigen.

B cells are equivalent to cells derived in **birds** from the lymphoid organ called the **bursa of Fabricius** at the distal end of the alimentary canal. B cells produce humoral antibodies. B cells are sensitive to bacterial and viral antigens, and are transformed by antigenic stimulation into plasma cells, which mature by proliferation and differentiation. The plasma cells of one clone synthesise only one antibody.

Types of Graft:
Autograft. A graft made of the host's own tissues.

Allograft. A tissue graft from a donor to a host with a different genotype, host and donor being members of the same species.

Isograft. A tissue graft between two individuals having identical genotypes, as between identical twins, or between members of an inbred strain of animals.

Xenograft. A graft between members of different species, e.g., from ape to man; this type of graft is rejected more rapidly than an allograft.

Allograft reaction. The allograft reaction or primary response is the process by which a host rejects an allograft. The graft at first may appear to be accepted and blood supply to it may be established, but within a few days, the duration depending on the antigenic differences between the host and the donor, the graft dies and is sloughed off.

After rejection of one graft the host rejects a second graft from the same donor more rapidly by a process called secondary-set-response or **hyperacute response**. This type of response is brought about by the primed antigen sensitive cells (**memory cells**) of the T series. The secondary-set-response is rapid and stronger than the primary response.

Graft versus host reaction. When the graft from the donor has **immune-competent cells**, such cells react against the antigens of the host. This is the graft versus host reaction. The graft versus host reaction comes in the way of bone marrow transplantation, because the donor tissue containing immune-competent cells reacts against the antigens of the host with serious and often fatal consequences.

Development of immune competence. Sometime before birth, the immune system matures to elicit the immune response. The fetus develops **tolerance** to all the antigens to which its immune system is exposed to in the fetal life. Thus the fetus *in utero* not only develops tolerance to its own antigens — **immunological homeostasis** — but is also ready to accept the cells from a genetically different donor to allow them to persist and proliferate, making itself a **chimera** with lifelong tolerance to tissues from that donor. This phenomenon is known as **acquired tolerance**. Some dizygotic twins who happen to exchange *hemopoietic* stem cells *in utero*, have a population of blood cells derived from the co-twin as well as their own. Such a person — **twin chimera** — throughout postnatal life accepts tissue from the co-twin.

Autoimmunity — **autoimmune disease** — is an exception to immunological homeostasis where an individual produces antibodies against antigens of self origin.

Transplantation genetics. The principles of transplantation genetics have been studied largely in inbred mice. Members of an **inbred strain**, some of which are developed by brother-sister mating for well over 100 generations, are virtually identical genetically — **isogenic** — and consequently do not reject tissue from animals of the same strain. An inbred mouse is homozygous at all loci, so that each of its progeny receives one copy of each of its genes. Thus an F_1 (the first generation progeny of a mating) does not regard tissue from either parent as foreign; and therefore does not show immune response of rejection against it. However, if an inbred mouse from one strain is mated with an inbred mouse from another strain, the F_1 hybrid has antigens from the other parent and hence its tissues are not accepted by either parent strain.

In the mouse, there are 25 to 45 **histocompatibility loci (H loci)**, each of which has several alleles. The loci are known as H-1, H-2 and so forth; the alleles at a locus are designated $H\text{-}2^a$, $H\text{-}2^b$ and so on; and the corresponding tissue antigens (H antigens) are H-2^a and H-2^b. The major histocompatibility complex (MHC) is the highly complex H-2 locus, which determines powerful antigens that produce a strong T cell response.

In general, in mice, one member of a given inbred strain accepts tissues of another member of the same strain. However, in some mouse strains, females reject tissue from males of the same strain. The antigens responsible for exciting the immune rejection response is determined by a gene located on the Y chromosome. This antigen is known as the H-Y antigen. The H-Y is weak in comparison to the H-2 antigens. The H-Y locus in humans and other mammals seems comparable.

The major histocompatibility complex includes a series of about 80 genes located on the short arm of chromosome 6. The MHC is classified into three groups: Class I, Class II and Class III.

The class I MHC molecules are composed of a single heavy glycoprotein chain encoded by loci on chromosome 6 and a single light chain called β_2-microglobulin encoded by a gene on chromosome 15. Class I MHC molecules are found on the surface of nearly all body cells and they bind with cytotoxic T cell receptors. [The most important of the Class I loci are labelled HLA and include HLA-A, HLA-B and HLA-C.] The Class I MHC molecules present foreign peptides on the surface of infected cells. They bring about transplant rejection as the foreign MHC molecules (not self) stimulate host's cytotoxic T cells to bring about destruction of foreign cells.

Class II MHC molecules are found only on the surface of the immune system's antigen presenting cells — phagocytes and B lymphocytes. It includes genes coding HLA-DP, DQ, and DR. It also includes gene coding for peptide transporter proteins (TAP 1 and TAP 2) which help to transport peptides into the endoplasmic reticulum, before migration to the cell surface.

Both Class I and Class II MHC molecules guide helper and cytotoxic T cells to specific cells which are not self or foreign and need to be eliminated from the body.

The Class III MHC region includes about 36 genes. The important ones among them code for complement proteins. Other genes are not involved in the immune response.

MHC molecules show great polymorphism. Class I and class II MHC molecules vary greatly among individuals in humans. But, in a given individual the same class I and class II molecules are found in all the body cells. This is necessary for allowing T cells to recognise self versus nonself. In contrast, in the same individual the immunoglobulins and T cells after VDJ recombination differ from cell to cell. This gives capacity to the individual to respond to a large number of varying infective agents.

The immunoglobulin, T cell receptors and MHC genes are members of a single gene family.

The HLA Complex. The HLA–**human leucocyte antigen** — complex is the major histocompatibility complex of man. It is comparable to the H-2 locus of the mouse.

The HLA system consists of a group of closely linked loci which includes what are known as class I molecules A,B,C,E,F and G and class II

Table 10: Proportion of Genes in Common

Relationship to Proband	Proportion of Genes in Common
Parent, child, sibling	1/2*
Dizygotic twin	1/2
Monozygotic twin	1
Grandparent, grandchild, uncle, aunt, nephew, niece	1/4
First cousin	1/8*
Second cousin	1/32

* JBS Haldane once announced that he would lay down his life for two brothers or eight cousins. His reasoning; the survival of two full siblings (each with about half of his genes identical to Haldane's) or the group of cousins (each with about an height of his genes the same as Haldane's) made the decision genetically acceptable.

molecules D related or DR, DQ, DPA1, DPA2, DNA, DOB, DQB2 and DQA2.

It is highly polymorphic. The number of alleles known for HLA-A is 32, HLA-B is 55, HLA-C is 14 and HLA-D is more than 85. This results in a large number of phenotypic variations and hence two unrelated individuals are unlikely to have identical HLA phenotypes.

HLA loci are mapped on chromosome 6. The loci are closely placed on the chromosome. The close linkage results in their being inherited as

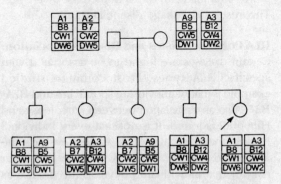

Fig. 65   Pedigree chart of inheritance of HLA haplotypes. A haplotype consists of four loci (HLA-A, HLA-B, HLA-C and HLA-D), each with different antigenic specificities. Since haplotypes are transmitted as units, a child has only one haplotype in common with each of his parents, but there is a one-in-four probability that any two siblings will match exactly.

one block. The term haplotype is used to indicate the set of HLA alleles an individual has on each member of chromosome 6 pair.

Several loci related to complement synthesis, the Chido and Rodgers blood group loci and some enzyme loci, are also located on chromosome 6.

The four HLA loci are designated HLA-A, HLA-B, HLA-C and HLA-D. Each locus has a number of alleles. The set of HLA genes on one chromosome constitutes a haplotype, each with four HLA determinants, for a total of eight HLA antigens. Since haplotypes are transmitted as units, a child has only one haplotype in common with each of his parents, but there is a one in four probability that two siblings will match exactly (Fig. 65). Table 10 gives the antigenic similarity between different members of a family.

For this reason a brother or sister is selected over parents and parents over unrelated donors for organ transplantation. It may be mentioned here that the genes for immunoglobulins, T cell receptors and HLA complex belong to the same family. The immunoglobulins and T cell receptors vary in the same individual but the HLA complex is fixed in an individual and varies from individual to individual.

Though crossing over is known within HLA complex, certain alleles tend to occur together more often than can be accounted for by chance. This results in linkage disequilibrium.

HLA Polymorphisms and Disease Association: Certain diseases are found to be associated with specific HLA types. Most common studied example is that of ankylosing spondylitis and HLA-B27. Also an association between narcolepsy and HLA-DR2 is found. It is not that every individual having the particular HLA allele develops the associated disease. There is however a greater risk for that individual to develop the disease as compared to the general population.

The probable explanation for the association are either close linkage of HLA complex and susceptibility gene, or cross reactivity of antibodies to environmental antigens with specific HLA antigens or abnormal recognition of self antigens

because of either defects in T cell receptors or antigen processing.

H-Y Antigen: This is a Y-linked histocompatibility antigen. It is important for testicular differentiation and function. The structural gene for H-Y antigen in humans has been mapped on chromosome 6. There is a possibility of presence of a regulatory gene for H-Y antigen on the Y chromosome. A separate sex determining region SRY has been isolated on the Y chromosome which is likely to be the testis determining gene. The H-Y antigen does not seem to play a significant role in tissue transplantation.

Matching tests for donor selection. The histocompatibility, or antigenic similarity between donor and recipient can be determined by matching them for antigens of the ABO blood groups and HLA antigens which are present on various tissues including leucocytes. The matching is done by serological tissue typing and by the mixed lymphocyte culture (MLC) test, in which lymphocytes from donor and recipient are mixed *in vitro.* **Serological tissue typing** is usually carried out by observing the cytotoxic effect of specific antisera on blood lymphocytes collected from the prospective donor and recipient of organs or tissues that are to be transplanted. The MLC test consists in culturing together approximately equal numbers of lymphocytes from two individuals for 5 days. The number of *blast* cells seen in the culture seems to be directly related to the degree of incompatibility between the histocompatibility antigens of the two individuals.

Immune Deficiency Diseases. Most of the immune deficiency diseases are genetically determined. They are the outcome of some form of abnormality in some component of immune response.

The immune deficiency diseases are classified as follows:
1) Swiss-type agammaglobulinemia, where Ig synthesis is depressed. It is an autosomal recessive disease and leads to severe combined immunodeficiency as both B and T cells are absent or greatly reduced.

2) Bruton-type agammaglobulinemia is an X-linked recessive trait. As IgG H-chains and kappa L-chains are synthesised by autosomal genes, it is likely that this disorder is due to a mutation of a particular locus on the X chromosome which normally acts as a regulator gene for the autosomal loci responsible for Ig synthesis.

3) Dysgammaglobulinemias, where only one or two types of immunoglobulin groups are deficient, the remaining being normal or elevated.

4) Hypogammaglobulinemias, where Ig levels are reduced but not totally absent.

5) Ataxia telangiectasia (autosomal recessive) is characterised by an abnormality of Ig and is associated with a hypoplastic thymus and low levels of IgA.

6) Wiskott-Aldrich syndrome (X-linked recessive) is characterised by an abnormal Ig, and low levels of IgM.

All the immunoglobulinopathies are associated with increased susceptibility to infections and its consequences.

Autoimmune Disease. Autoimmunity is the immune response to specific antigens of an individual's own self. Normally such a response does not occur, i.e., a state of immunological homeostasis exists, but this may be disturbed by changes in the antigen–antibody relationship. Exposure to a foreign antigen resembling a self-antigen may result in the formation of a **new antibody** capable of combining with the **self-antigen**. For example, some streptococci on entry into the human body, produce an antigen similar to some of the histocompatibility antigen specific to the cells of the human heart. Hence the antibody formed in response to an infection by those streptococci, apart from attacking the streptococci, also attacks human heart cells. Such an attack may be the causative factor in cardiac damage in rheumatic fever. In rheumatoid arthritis, there is an **autoantibody** produced which combines with normal antibody in plasma. To put it differently, the autoantibody is an anti-antibody in cases of rheumatoid arthritis and is known as the **rheumatoid factor**. Autoimmune diseases affect connective tissue more often. Many of them constitute the so-called collagen diseases.

Based on some observations made on patients of autoimmune disorders and their relatives, it may be tentatively stated that the tendency to form antibodies against self-antigens has a genetic basis.

BLOOD GROUPS

The study of blood groups is important since apart from the boon of blood transfusions, it has contributed to the understanding of many genetic principles such as multiple allelism, codominance, polymorphism, immune reactions and linkage.

The term blood group is restricted, as a rule, to the **red cell antigens**. The notations used for blood groups are mainly of three types:

Table 11: Genotypes, Gametes and Phenotypes Possibly Formed the Three Allelic Genes A, B and O

Genotype	Gametes	Phenotype (Blood Group)
AA	A	A
AO	A or O	A
BB	B	B
BO	B or O	B
AB	A or B	AB
OO	O	O

1) Alternative alleles are designated by letter sequence (e.g., *A, B* and *M, N*).

2) Alternative alleles are designated by capital and small letters (e.g., *C* and *c, K* and *k* and *S* and *s*). The small letter does not necessarily signify a recessive trait.

3) Alternative alleles are designated by a symbol with superscript (e.g., Fy^a and Fy^b and Lu^a and Lu^b).

The system followed now is to refer to a blood group after the person in whom the antibody was first recognised (e.g., Duffy and Kidd); and some part of this name is used to designate the gene-ocus concerned (e.g., *Fy* for Duffy, *Jk* for baby J. Kidd).

ABO Blood Group System: Landsteiner discovered the ABO blood groups — the first blood group system to be discovered. There are **four major phenotypes — AB, A, B and O**, which indicate the presence or absence of corresponding antigen/s on the red cell with O group individuals having neither antigen A nor B. The inheritance of ABO blood group follows the principle of multiple allelism. There are three main alleles designated as 1^A, 1^B and 1^O at the *ABO* locus. The blood group antigen–antibody reaction is described as **isoagglutination**, hence the gene symbol 1. However, the genes are also referred to as *A, B* and *O*, without the *1*. The antigens A and B of the red cells have naturally occurring antibodies anti-A (α) and anti-B (β) in the serum, respectively, such that α coexists with group B without interacting and β with group A, α and β occur with group O but are absent in individuals with group AB. This natural occurrence of antibodies is unique to the ABO system. Of the alleles *A, B* and *O, A* and *B* are codominant while *O* is recessive to both *A* and *B* (Table 11).

Table 12 shows blood group phenotypes and their relationship with genotypes, serum antibodies, and agglutination reactions within the ABO blood group system.

Table 12 shows that the blood group can be determined by an **isoagglutination reaction**, observed with the naked eye as clumping of red cells. The table also gives an idea of compatible and incompatible blood transfusions. Though theoretically group O individuals appear as **universal donors** and group AB individuals as **universal recipients**, it is preferable to transfuse a patient only with blood of his own ABO group.

Numerous subtypes of ABO groups have been recognised, e.g., A_1 and A_2, and correspondingly A_1B and A_2B. About 85 per cent of individuals of A group have A_1 subgroup.

The antigenicity of these groups depends upon the three-dimensional arrangement of certain sugar residues added to a series of precursor glycolipids in RBCs, and glycoproteins in body fluids like saliva. These are added by the action of several enzymes known as transferases which are controlled by various genes including *A,B,O* alleles. *Le* (Lewis) gene changes a precursor substance into Le^a substance. Its recessive allele has no such action and thereby leaves the precursor substance unchanged. The locus H has alleles *H* and *h*, *H* gene transforms Le^a substance into an H substance, the presence of which is essential. For the phenotypic expression of genes A and B. The allele O, an amorph, leaves the H substance unchanged.

It has been shown that the ABO locus is closely linked with the locus for nail-patella syndrome (autosomal dominant, manifested as dystrophy of nails, absence or reduction of patella with or

Table 12: Blood Groups

Phenotype	Genotype	Antigens on Red Cells	Antibodies in serum	Reactions with other blood groups			
				O	A	B	AB
O, α and β	OO	neither A nor B	Anti-A (α) Anti-B (β)	—	+	+	+
A, ß	*AA* *AO*	A	Anti-B (β)	—	—	+	+
B, α	*BB* *BO*	B	Anti-A (α)	—	+	—	+
AB, O	*AB*	A_1 B	Neither (O)	—	—	—	—

without other bone dysplasias, and nephropathy) and the locus for adenylate kinase (a polymorphic red cell enzyme which occurs in muscles as myokinase).

Several associations have been suggested between blood groups and susceptibility or resistance to some diseases, e.g., Group A and gastric ulcer, Group O and duodenal ulcer.

The Bombay Phenotype: The precursor of A and B antigens is H substance or H antigen. *A* and *B* genes act on H substance to modify it to the corresponding antigen, whereas the O gene, an **amorph** or **inactive gene**, keeps H substance unaltered. Most individuals have a gene *H* required for the development of H substance from a precursor. Persons of Bombay phenotype are homozygous for its inactive allele (amorph) *h*. When H is not formed, the enzymes determined by *A* and *B* genes have no substrate on which to act, so that h/h individuals cannot make the A or B antigen even if they have the *A* or *B* gene.

Anti-H antibody is found naturally in serum of subjects of Bombay phenotypes who have genotype *hh*. Because of anti-H antibody, individuals having Bombay phenotypes cannot form A or B antigen even if they carry genotype *AA/AO/BB/ BO*. The RBCs of such individuals, in spite of genotypically having *A* or *B* gene, cannot be agglutinated by anti-A, anti-B or anti-H, as their sera contain all three antibodies. This leads to misjudging of blood groups in individuals having Bombay phenotype, which is however very rare. The Bombay phenotype was discovered first in Bombay in 1952.

Secretion of Blood Group Substance: A, B and H antigens of the A, B, O blood group system are also found in other tissues besides red cells. Most individuals also secrete them in a water-soluble form in a number of body fluids. The gene *Se* or **'secretor' gene** determines the ability to secrete; its allele *se* has no known function. **Secretors** (78 per cent of population) of H, A, and B are *Se/ Se* or *Se/se* and non-secretors are *se/se*.

Fig. 66 shows the steps involved in the synthesis of H, A and B antigens. The Lewis genes

(*Le*) are involved in the synthesis of Le^a and Le^b substances in secretions and plasma.

Table 13 shows the relationship between ABH antigens on the red cells, and the antigens in the saliva of **secretors** and **non-secretors**.

Table 13

Blood group	Secretors		Non-secretors	
	Red cells antigen	Saliva antigen	Red cells antigen	Saliva antigen
O	H	H	H	—
A	A	A and H	A	—
B	B	B and H	B	—
AB	A & B	A, B and H	A & B	—

The Rh Blood Group System: The Rh blood group system was discovered by Landsteiner and Wiener in 1940. The Rh antigen is named after Rhesus monkeys as they were used in the experiments which led to its discovery. Exact genetic interpretation of the Rh locus is not clear. The two systems of nomenclature in current use are those of Fisher and Race, and of Wiener (Table 14).

According to the Fisher and Race postulation, the Rh blood groups are determined by a series of three closely linked genes, *C*, *D* and *E*, with

Table 14: The Rh Blood Group System

Fisher and Race Gene Notation	Wiener Gene Notation
CDe	*R^1*
cDe	*R^0*
cDE	*R^2*
CDE	*R^Z*
Cde	*r'*
cde	*r*
cdE	*r"*
CdE	*ry*

allelic form *c, d* and *e*. There are eight different possible combinations of these six genes (*Cde, cde, cDE, cDe, cdE, Cde, CDE,* and *CdE*). Their frequencies vary in different parts of the world. **No naturally occurring antibodies are known**. Antibodies found in humans after antigenic stimulation, are labelled as anti-LW after Landsteiner and Wiener. Each person has two *Rh* gene complexes on two homologous chromosomes, so that the total number of possible combinations of the eight gene complexes becomes 36. Rh-negative persons are homozygous *d/d* (*C* and *E* are not taken into consideration). However, *Cde, cdE, CdE* are rare as compared to *cde*, so that a large majority of Rh-negative individuals are *cde/cde*. Wiener has postulated a single locus with a large number of alleles. Table 14 gives the Fisher and Race gene notations and Wiener gene notations.

Rh null blood group. Rh null individuals have no Rh antigens. They are comparable to Bombay phenotypes of the ABO blood group system. They do not have a precursor, which is needed as a substrate for formation of the antigens of Rh system. They are homozygous, for a rare gene X^0r, whose allele X^1r is responsible for synthesis of a precursor of both Rh and LW antigens (Rh null people also lack LW). The Rh null phenotype is very rare and was first found in an Australian aborigine.

The -D-/D- Genotype: This is a rare Rh blood type, where the C and E series of antigens are missing and only D is present. This was attributed to a deletion of that part of chromosome which carries the C and E loci. (It should be noted that the order of the genes on the chromosome is now believed to be *DCE* and not *CDE*). However, the genotype is more likely to be due to a separate suppressor gene like X^0r.

Rh Incompatibility, Erythroblastosis Fetalis or hemolytic disease of newborns (HDN) is characterised by jaundice and anemia due to hemolysis and the presence of erythroblasts in the blood stream normally found only in bone marrow. The presence of **circulating erythroblasts** accounts for the name of the disease.

The **genesis** of erythroblastosis is as follows: There are no naturally occurring specific antibodies against Rh antigen in serum but antibodies are produced in Rh-negative persons by introduction of Rh-positive cells. When an Rh-negative woman carries an Rh-positive fetus, and a break occurs in the placental barrier separating maternal and fetal blood streams, the Rh antigen from the fetus finds its way into the maternal blood stream to excite the production of an antibody. This antibody does not react with the red cells of the Rh-negative mother, since they do not carry the antigen. However, the antibody finds its way through placenta to the Rh-positive fetus, where immunological reaction takes place between the antibody and the red cells of the fetus, culminating in erythroblastosis fetalis.

Most cases of clinically recognised hemolytic disease of the newborn are due to anti-D (anti-Rh) antibody. However a few occur due to anti-A, which are often difficult to diagnose. Such cases tend to be mild and require no treatment. Hemolytic disease in the newborn is rarely caused by other blood group antibodies like anti-K or anti-Fy[a]. Antibodies like Anti-Le[a] and anti-Le[b] are found in the serum of pregnant women but these antibodies are IgM globulins and do not cross the placental barrier.

Prophylaxis against Rh Immunisation. Rh sensitisation usually occurs at the time of delivery or abortion. Clinical trials have shown that primary immunisation of the mother to the Rh antigen on fetal cells can be prevented by giving an injection of Rh-immunoglobulin to the mother at the time of abortion or delivery.

MNSs Blood Group System (Landsteiner and Levine, 1927): This system is not important clinically in blood transfusion or in maternal–fetal incompatibility. However, it is important medico-legally in cases of **disputed paternity** or identity establishment elaborated in genetic counselling.

Originally the antigens recognised were M and N, dependent upon a pair of codominant alleles. There is no naturally occurring antibody in serum against these antigens. Later on Ss subdivisions of MN groups were discovered. It appears

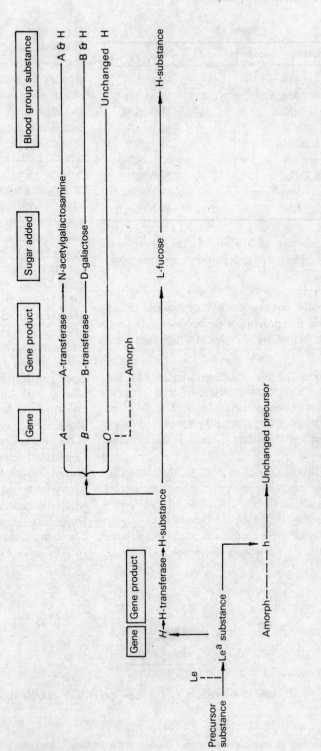

Fig. 66 Schematic representation of the steps involved in the synthesis of H, A and B antigens..

Table 15

Blood Group Phenotype	Genotype
MS	M/M/S/S
Ms	M/M/s/s
MNS	M/N/S/S
MNs	M/N/s/s
MNSs	M/N/S/s
NS	N/N/S/S
Ns	N/N/s/s
MSs	M/M/S/s
NSs	N/N/S/s

that combinations of MN and Ss are inherited as units. Table 15 gives the phenotype and the genotype.

All the remaining blood groups are not significant clinically, but are studied for a wider understanding of the principles of genetics. They are mentioned below in the order in which they were discovered.

P Blood Group System (Landsteiner and Levine, 1927): There are four recognisable phenotypes and corresponding genotypes P_1 = p^1/p^2, p^1/p^t, p^1/p; P_2 = p^2/p^2, p^2/p; P = p/p; and pk = p_1/p_2 lacking an independent dominant gene as in the Bombay phenotype.

Lutheran Blood Group System (Callender et al, 1946): The phenotypes and the corresponding genotypes are Lu (a + b–) = Lu^a/Lu^a; Lu (a+ b+) = Lu^a/Lu^b; Lu (a– b+) = Lu^b/Lu^b; and Lu (a– b–) = silent Lu gene or a dominant suppressor gene affecting the expression of all genes at Lu locus.

The Lutheran blood group system was the first example studied of autosomal linkage and autosomal crossing over in man — the Lutheran secretor linkage. The locus for myotonic dystrophy is also linked to the Lutheran and secretor loci.

Kell Blood Group System (Coombs et al, 1946): Originally the Kell blood group system was described as having two alternative phenotypes: Kell positive (K+) and Kell negative (k–) determined by a pair of allele K and k. Several new antibodies have since been discovered. The Kell system is sometimes found to be responsible for hemolytic disease of the newborn.

Lewis Blood Group System (Mourant, 1946): The common phenotypes and corresponding genotypes are Le (a+ b–) = Le (a+) or Le (a– b+) = Le (b+) Le (a– b–) is rare and Le (a+ b+) is not observed in adults.

Lewis blood group system interacts with the ABO and secretor systems. It is likely that the Lewis substances are not primarily red cell antigens but antigens of the body fluids such as plasma and saliva and that the antigens only get absorbed on to RBCs from the plasma (Fig. 67). The presence of Le^a and Le^b antigens in the serum and saliva is determined by a pair of allelic genes, Le and le. Persons whose red cells are Le (a+ b–) do not secrete ABH substances in saliva, and persons whose red cells are Le (a– b+) always secrete ABH substances.

Duffy Blood Group System (Cutbush et al, 1950): There are three allelic genes at the Duffy locus, Fy^a, Fy^b and Fy^a. The Duffy locus was the first

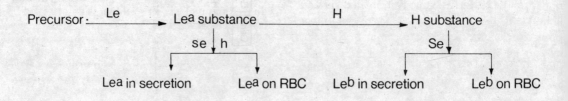

Fig. 67 Schematic representation of the steps involved in the synthesis of the Lewis blood group antigens and its relationship to the ABO blood group system and *secretor* locus.

locus to be assigned to a particular chromosome, chromosome No. 1.

Kidd Blood Group System (Allen et al, 1951): There are three allelic genes at Kidd locus, Jk^a, Jk^b and Jk. Anti-Jk^a is responsible for hemolytic disease of the newborn and for some transfusion reactions.

Diego Blood Group System (Layrisse et al, 1955): Di^a antigen is suggested to be a specific marker for Mongolians. The phenotypes are Di (a+) and Di (a–) for the genotypes Di^a/Di^a or Di^a/Di, and Di/Di respectively.

I Blood Group System (Wiener et al, 1956): This system is different from the other blood group systems. Almost all adults are I positive. In fact, I antigen was believed to be a public antigen possessed by all members of the human species. The fetal antigen i is strong at birth and decreases in strength thereafter, whereas the adult antigen I is poorly developed at birth and increases as i decreases. Very rarely are adults I negative.

In many blood disorders in the adults, like thalassemia major, the red cells are agglutinated by both anti-i and anti-I.

Yt (Cartwright) Blood Group System (Eaton et al, 1956): The phenotypes and corresponding genotypes are Yt (a+ b–) = $Y1^a/Y1^a$; Yt (a+ b+) = $Y1^a/Yt^b$; and Yt (a– b+) = Yt^b/Yt^b. About 98 per cent of the population are Yt (a+).

Xg Blood Group System (Mann et al, 1962): This blood group system is of special interest to geneticists. As the Xg locus is on X chromosome, it is used as an X-linked marker.

The Xg locus on the X chromosome appears not to participate in X inactivation like other X-linked loci. The Xg locus has been useful in mapping the X chromosome. It is an informative marker in some cases of X chromosome aneuploidy. It allows the calculation of the population frequency of X-linked genes. Table 16 gives the phenotypes and genotypes.

Table 16: Phenotypes and Genotypes

Sex	Phenotype	Genotype
Male	Xg (a+)	Xg^a/Y
	Xg (a–)	Xg/Y
Female	Xg (a+)	Xg^a/Xg^a
	Xg (a–)	Xg/Xg

Dombrock Blood Group System (Swanson et al, 1965): The known phenotypes and corresponding genotypes so far are Do (a+ b–) = Do^a/Do^a; Do (a– b+) = Do^b/Do^b. Approximately 64 per cent of northern Europeans are Do (a+).

Blood Group Chimeras: A person with blood cells of two different genotypes derived from two different zygotes is called a blood group chimera. In blood group chimeras, the **exchange of hemopoietic cells** takes place in fetal life, prior to the development of immune competence.

The foreign cells do not stimulate the host to form antibodies against them, so they persist in the host's bone marrow and remain throughout life. If the hemopoietic cells above are exchanged and not the germ cells, the host will transmit to his offspring only his own blood group.

The possible mode of origin of blood group chimeras is sharing of their circulations in prenatal life by dizygotic twins or dispermic chimeras, formed by fusion of dizygotic twin zygotes or early embryos. Such possibilities are rare and hence the incidence of blood group chimeras is very low.

SUMMARY

Immunogenetics is looking at immunology through genetic glasses, and *vice versa*. An individual's immunologic constitution is determined by his antigens, antibodies, lymphocytes, plasma cells and blood group (both ABO and Rh), through which he interacts with microbes, transfused blood, or a transplanted organ. Some genetic principles have been derived from the study of such interactions.

Immune response in humans can be cellular and/ or humoral. The humoral response is by production of antibodies by plasma cells. There are 5 classes of antibodies, IgG, IgM, IgA, IgD and IgE. Each is a Y-shaped molecule with two heavy chains (H) and two light chains (L). The L chain could be K or L variety. The H chain are of 5 types (as per their names).

The DNA segment coding for the antibodies sequentially are a constant (C) region, K and L light chains and various types of heavy chains, a variable (V) region, a diversity (D) region of the heavy chains, and a joining (J) region.

Complement system consists of a series of inactive proteins getting sequentially activated in a cascade (similar to clotting mechanism) to phagocytose microorganisms.

The cellular immune response is capable of destroying infected cells within the body. Pathogens within a cell alter the class I MHC molecule on the cell surface. These are recognised by cytotoxic T killer lymphocytes which destroy the cell.

Antibodies or immunoglobulins need a system of complements for successful functioning. Hereditary deficiencies of various elements of the complement system lead to a form of autoimmune disease (destructive immune action against one's own self), and increased susceptibility to infections. All components of the complement system mapped so far are on chromosome 6, closely linked to the HLA complex.

The major histocompatibility complex (MHC) lies on the short arm of chromosome 6. It is divided into three classes: class I, class II and class III. Class I molecules present foreign peptides on the surface of infected cells and are responsible for transplant rejection.

Class II molecules are present only on the surface of antigen presenting cells of immune systems, phagocytes and B cells. Class I and II guide helper T cell and cytotoxic T cells in recognising self from non-self.

Class III region codes for complement protein. MHC loci are inherited en bloc as a haplotype.

Transplantation genetics — part of immunogenetics — is studied largely in inbred mice. A mouse has 24 to 45 histocompatibility loci or H loci, each with several alleles, and known as H-1, H-2,

and so on. The H-2 locus is the MHC determining antigens that evoke a strong T cell response in a donor. The Human Leucocyte Antigen or HLA complex is the MHC in man, comparable to the H-2 locus in mice. The HLA complex comprises 4 loci (HLA-A, HLA-B, HLA-C, HLA-D) and is located on chromosome 6. The greater the similarity between the HLA complex of donor and of recipient, as also between their blood groups, the greater the chances of a successful transplantation.

Immune deficiency diseases — agammaglobulinemias, dysgammaglobulinemias, hypogammaglobulinemias, — are immunoglobulinopathies that lead to increased susceptibility to infections. Autoimmune disease arises when antibodies and immune-competent lymphocytes attack an individual's own tissues. Rheumatoid arthritis, rheumatic myocarditis, and collagen disorders are probably autoimmune in nature. Autoimmunity is currently held responsible for the ageing process.

Blood groups. Knowledge of blood groups accounts for what is the most successful and frequent tissue transplant the world over — *blood transfusion.* Study of blood groups has also contributed to the understanding of many genetic principles such as multiple allelism, codominance, polymorphism, immune reactions and linkage. It also facilitates organ transplantation.

The term blood group refers to red cell antigens Major blood group systems are ABO and Rh. Generally, group O persons are universal donors and AB individuals are universal recipients. However a patient should preferably be transfused with the same blood group. Blood group antigens are also found in other tissues, besides red cells. Most individuals secrete them in body fluids, notably in saliva and these are called secretors. Those not secreting are called non-secretors. Rh incompatibility underlies *erythroblastosis foetalis* or hemolytic disease of newborn. An Rh negative mother reacts against her Rh positive fetus leading to hemolysis anemia, jaundice, etc. Therapy consists of appropriate transfusion of blood to the newborn.

9 DEVELOPMENTAL GENETICS

Introduction

This branch of genetics deals with the mechanisms which activate or inactivate certain genes at appropriate times during embryogenesis, and fetal and postnatal life. All the cells of a multicellular organism have the same set of genes as the zygote from which they are derived, yet each cell type differs greatly from other differentiated cells. At a given time only a part of the total genome remains active and this active region determines the nature of differentiation. Differentiation does not depend on differences in the genes present, but on the variations in the activity of the genes.

Experimental evidence for genetic control in development is:

1) If a nucleus from the intestinal epithelium of a tadpole is introduced into an anucleated unfertilised egg, the egg can develop into a normal adult frog.

2) The enzyme cystathionine synthetase is normally synthesised by the liver but not by skin cells. However, in tissue culture, skin fibroblasts become capable of synthesising this enzyme.

This evidence shows that all genes are retained in all cells and that the genes remain inactive in the cells when their activity is not needed. The process of **cell specialisation** and **differentiation** involves the **differential activity of genes** present in all cells, rather than the selective elimination of unwanted genes.

3) In amphibian eggs, the ribosomes used in the early part of embryonic development are those manufactured during oogenesis; and no new ribosomes are synthesised till the gastrula stage of development.

4) When the nucleus from an adult neurone is transplanted into the cytoplasm of an anucleated unfertilised egg, the transplanted nucleus adopts the functions typical of the normal host cell nucleus.

This shows that the egg cytoplasm is capable of influencing the activity of genes in the nucleus.

5) The chromosomes in the salivary glands of certain insects are enlarged and have distinctive patterns of transverse bands representing sites of different genes. During larval development certain bands swell and show puffiness in a characteristic sequence at certain sites on specific chromosomes. Puffing is associated with the synthesis of RNA. It is suggested that these swelling are derepressed (activated) genes. Puffiness in one region and its absence in another illustrates the sequential **derepression** and **repression** of genetic loci during development.

6) Ecdysone, a hormone produced by the prothoracic glands of insect larvae, is responsible for moulting of the larvae. **Ecdysone** injected into young larvae induces the same sequence of puffing which occurs during larval development. This is an instance of a chemical substance bringing about derepression. In humans, random inactivation of the X chromosome (Lyon hypothesis) probably represents a similar mechanism of repression-derepression.

7) The phenomenon of **embryonic induction**, where one tissue determines the fate of another, e.g., the ability of the chordamesoderm to induce the overlying ectoderm to differentiate into neuroectoderm, is brought about by a chemical agent called the inducer. Experiments to study the nature of the inducer and the process of induction, suggest that the substance which diffuses out of the chordamesoderm and acts as

an inducer on the ectoderm contains RNA. The process of induction is due to the gene product of one cell diffusing out of that cell and then inducing changes in the adjacent cells. It seems that the active principle in embryonic induction is a nucleoprotein.

8) In a *dwarf* mouse the mutant gene — recessive in homozygous state — brings about growth retardation because of a poorly developed pituitary. Implantation of normal pituitary cells restores the mouse to normal size. This illustrates the influence of a hormone on growth and development.

9) If a *pygmy* mouse has a mutant gene, implantation of normal pituitary does not restore the normal growth. Pituitary cells from pygmy mice are effective in restoring normal growth in dwarf mice. This means that the *pygmy* mutant produces sufficient growth hormone, but its tissues are refractory to the hormonal effects.

In humans, comparable conditions either due to defective synthesis of the growth hormone or a peripheral unresponsiveness to the growth hormone are seen.

10) In *Drosophila*, several lethal mutants have been studied, e.g., *lethal giant larvae, meander and translucida*. Each of these **mutant genes** alters the normal course of events at a **specific time in development**. This illustrates that there are lethal mutants which interfere with normal development resulting in death during development. It also suggests that the normal alleles of these mutants bring about normal development. During normal embryogenesis, the developmental changes are a result of many genes acting in an orderly sequence and any disturbance in that activity, either because of genetic mutation or because of environmental agents (e.g., radiation) known as **teratogens,** can result in **congenital malformations**.

11) It has been shown that if chromosomal DNA is freed of its histone, the amount of RNA synthesis goes up. This suggests that in the intact chromosome histones inhibit DNA-dependent RNA synthesis.

12) Many enzymes are shown to exist in multiple molecular forms known as isozymes or **isoenzymes**, e.g. lactic dehydrogenase isozyme patterns show progressive changes during fetal and postnatal development. Similarly the change from fetal to adult hemoglobin during late fetal and early postnatal life (Figs. 87, 88) reflects changes in the activity of specific genes.

Based on these observations, it has been suggested that the sequence of events during embryonic development is a result of **genetic switches**, i.e., a particular effector substance sets in a sequence of developmental processes by switching on or off certain genes. Repressed genes get activated if they are responsive to the effector. This may bring about switching on to new developmental pathways. Some derepressed genes may produce enzymes responsible for changes brought about in the metabolism of adjacent cells and tissues.

Some of the details available on the genetic control of human development are outlined below.

Genes Controlling Development: There is no direct evidence available to show exactly which genes control human development. Whatever information is available is from the work on *Drosophila* and other organisms. It is hoped that genetic insights from experimental animals will explain genetic control of human development, on the basis of homology.

Three gene-families have been shown to be important in mammalian embryogenesis. These genes code for proteins that act as transcriptional regulators.
1) Homeobox or Hox genes.
2) Paired-box or Pax genes.
3) Zinc finger genes.

Homeobox or Hox Genes: In mammals 38 genes containing homeoboxes have been established. They are very similar to the homeoboxes of Drosophila. These genes are seen in four clusters as A (mouse chromosome 6, human chromosome 7) B (mouse chromosome 11, human chromosome 17) C (mouse chromosome 15, human chromosome 12) and D (mouse chromosome 2, human chromosome 2). Hox genes are numbered in each cluster cephalocaudally.

Hox genes control the developing ectodermal and mesodermal derivatives but none of the entodermal organs. Hox codes have been identified for four different locations.

1) an axial code, specifying somites along cephalocaudal axis.
2) a branchial code specifying neuronal and neural crest development in branchial region.
3) an organogenesis code.
4) a limb code.

In each Hox cluster there is a direct linear correlation between the position of the gene and its temporal and spatial expressions which implies that these genes play an important role in early embryogenesis.

Paired-Box or Pax Genes: Pax genes belong to a family of regulatory genes. The paired-box is a highly conserved DNA sequence coding approximately 130 amino acids. Genes which contain a paired-box are known as Pax genes and were identified first in Drosophila. There is strong evidence to suggest that they code DNA-binding proteins which control transcription and play an important role in animal development.

Eight Pax genes have been identified in humans through homology. In humans mutation in Pax 3 is shown to be the basis of Waardenburg syndrome an autosomal dominant disorder characterised by deafness, white forelock and iris heterochromia. Mutation in Pax 6 causes: absence of iris. Alternation in arrangements because of translocation in Pax 3 is seen in alveolar rhabdomyosarcoma. It is likely that different mutations involving Pax 3 may be responsible for varied unrelated human disorders.

Zinc Finger Genes: When there are finger-like projections formed by amino acids positioned between two cystine residues which form a complex with a zinc ion, it is referred to as zinc finger. The genes which code for a number of DNA binding proteins contain zinc fingers. They play an important role in the regulation of development.

There is now evidence to show that mutation of zinc finger gene on chromosome 7 is responsible for Greig cephalopolysyndactyly malformation. This autosomal dominant syndrome is characterised by cranial and hand abnormalities of supernumerary and/or webbed digits.

Genetic Basis of Dysmorphology: Dysmorphology is abnormal physical development or morphogenesis. The term dysmorphology is not synonymous with teratology. The term teratology refers to the study of the environmental causes of congenital anomalies.

Development of gene mutations is likely to be the basis for various congenital malformations. As mutations in the genes controlling development would disturb the transcription regulatory control, explaining thereby the phenomenon of pleiotropy whereby a single gene can exert multiple and varied effects.

Dysmorphology is now classified by international working group as follows:

1) **Malformation.** It refers to a primary morphologic defect of an organ or body part resulting from an intrinsically abnormal developmental process (e.g. cleft lip, ASD, VSD or polydactyly).

2) **Dysplasia.** It refers to a primary development defect involving abnormal organisation of cells and tissues. This is usually seen in all parts of the body wherever that particular dysplastic tissue is present (e.g. osteogenesis imperfecta). Most dysplasias are caused by single gene defects and are associated with high recurrence risks for siblings and/or offspring.

3) **Sequence.** Basically there is a single primary defect but it leads to a number of structural abnormalities (e.g. Pierre Robin sequence, a disorder in which a primary defect in mandible development leads to a small jaw, and secondary drooping of tongue and cleft palate).

4) **Syndrome.** It refers to a consistent pattern of multiple primary malformations because of a single underlying cause. The underlying cause can be chromosomal abnormality as in Down's syndrome or single gene abnormality as in Meckel's syndrome characterised by polydactyly, encephalocele and polycystic kidneys.

All these types of malformations are primary

events in embryogenesis and histogenesis. The two types mentioned below are secondary to another cause acting on the part of the body.

5) **Deformation.** It refers to alteration by mechanical force of form, shape or position of an otherwise normally formed body part. This is likely to operate during the fetal period and not during embryogenesis.

The mechanical force can be extrinsic as in oligohydramnios resulting in club foot or congenital dislocation of foot. It can be an intrinsic muscular one as in congenital myotonic dystrophy.

6) **Disruption.** It refers to a morphologic defect of an organ, part of an organ, or a large region of the body resulting from external factors disturbing the normal developmental process. Such factors are usually ischemia, infection and trauma. By definition, disruption is not genetic although occasionally genetic factors can predispose to disruptive events. For example, a small proportion of amniotic bands are caused by an underlying genetically determined defect in collagen which weakens the amnion making it more liable to tear or rupture.

In general approximately 6 per cent of all recognised congenital abnormalities have a chromosomal basis. Single gene defects account for about 7.5 per cent of all congenital malformations.

Genetic Basis of Hydatidiform Mole: Hydatidiform mole, partial or complete, is an abnormal conception in which the placenta shows proliferating abnormal tissue. Chromosomal analysis of tissue from partial moles shows triploidy wherein DNA study shows that 46 of them are paternal in origin and 23 are maternal in origin. The doubling of paternal chromosomes can be due to either dispermy, i.e., fertilisation by two sperms or due to duplication of a haploid sperm chromosome set by endoreduplication. In such cases the fetus rarely survives to term. Triploid conceptions only survive to term if additional chromosomal complement is maternal in origin in which case the hydatidiform mole does not occur.

In a complete hydatidiform mole there are 46 chromosomes and all are solely paternal in origin. A complete mole arises by fertilisation of an empty ovum by either two sperms or a single sperm undergoing endoreduplication. The complete mole can undergo malignant change to become choriocarcinoma.

Varied Chromosomal Expression Based on its Parental Origin: Experimental studies in mice have shown that maternal chromosomes are a must for the zygote to develop into an embryo and paternal chromosomes are a must for extraembryonic tissues to develop. The observations on hydatidiform mole suggest that a comparative situation prevails in humans whereby paternally derived gene are essential for differentiation of trophoblast and maternally derived genes are essential for early embryonic development.

Sex Differentiation: (Fig. 68). An embryo would develop into a female in the absence of the Y chromosome (see 45 X Turner syndrome). Presence of the Y chromosome leads to maleness re-

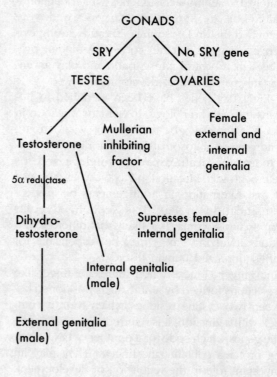

Fig. 68 Sex Differentiation

gardless of the number of X chromosomes (47, XXY — Klinefelter syndrome, 48, XXXY, etc.).

The sex determining region of the Y chromosome (SRY gene) is responsible for the undifferentiated gonad to become the testis. If there is mutation in the SRY gene, a 46, XY individual develops ovaries and becomes a female. As a corollary, if there is translocation of the SRY gene on to the X chromosome, a 46, XX individual develops testis and becomes a male.

The Sertoli (sustentacular) cells of the testis produce a Mullerian Inhibiting Factor (MIF) which inhibits the paramesonephric (Mullerian) ducts at around 6 weeks of intrauterine life. Absence of MIF secretion results in female internal genitalia (fallopian tubes, uterus and vagina).

The interstitial (Leydig) cells of the testis secrete testosterone which promotes the mesonephric (Wolffian) ducts to form the male internal genitalia (epididymis, vas deferens, seminal vesicles).

Testosterone is converted to dihydrotestosterone by the enzyme 5 α-reductase. Dihydrotestosterone brings about the development of male external genitalia in the 12–14th week of intrauterine life (i.e., enlargement of the genital tubercle to form the penis and fusion of the genital swellings to form the scrotum). Deficiency of the enzyme 5 α-reductase and/or of androgen receptors results in female external genitalia despite a normal testis and male internal genitalia (Male pseudohermaphroditism). In female embryos with congenital adrenal hyper-plasia, the external genitalia could be like that of a male (female pseudoherma-phroditism).

Twins: Humans and other large mammals, normally bear only one offspring at a time. Multiple births result from the simultaneous intrauterine development of two (or more) embryos. The commonest form of multiple births is twinning — the birth of a pair of fetuses. Multiplicity above two becomes rarer as the number of fetuses increases. The overall incidence of twinning is 1:80–90 births, and that of identical twinning is 1:270 births.

Twins provide important study material in genetics. Galton in 1875 had drawn attention to the importance of twin studies for comparison of the effects of heredity and environment, or nature and nurture. Twins are said to be **concordant** for a given trait if both exhibit the trait. For diseases presumably caused by genetic factors, **monozygotic twins** show a higher concordance rate than **dizygotic twins**. If monozygotic twins do not show full concordance for a given condition, it can be concluded that nongenetic factors also play a part in its.

Classification of Twins: (Fig. 69).

1) Like, true, identical, uniovular, or monozygotic.
2) Unlike, false, non-identical, fraternal, binovular or dizygotic.
3) Conjoined twins, i.e., double monsters and Siamese twins.

1) **Identical or homozygous twins** are derived from a single fertilised ovum, whereby each member of the pair acquires an identical chromosomal constitution. Developing from a single blastocyst, they are usually contained within a common chorionic sac and share a common placenta. The umbilical cord and the amniotic cavity also may not be separate. The twins have identical physical features, the same sex and the same blood group. Monozygotic twinning is a hereditary characteristic.

Monozygotic twins though genetically identical can be discordant for a single gene trait or chromosomal abnormality because of a postzygotic somatic mutation or non-dysjunction. Monozygotic female twins show discrepancy in X chromosome inactivation.

Uniovular but **dispermatic twinning** has also been reported. Here, either the mature ovum, the secondary oocyte, or the primary oocyte undergoes an equal cytoplasmic division instead of throwing off a small polar body. Each of these three variants has different degrees of genetic dissimilarity depending upon the stage at which such a division occurs.

Dispermy represents a rare condition which is the converse of twinning. It may provide a triploid or a tetraploid constitution to the zygote depending upon whether two sperms fertilise a single haploid or diploid ovum, or a haploid ovum which has fused with its polar body. Thus in the same individual two genetically dissimilar sets of cells could occur.

2) **False twins** are about three times more common than true twins, but this ratio may be reversed, as for example in the Japanese population. They are due to the simultaneous fertilisation of two ova from the same or different ovarian follicles by separate sperms. Each has its own chromosomal constitution, chorionic sac, and placenta. The sex and blood group may or may not be the same. The physical features show resemblance, but are not identical. Dizygotic twinning is also partly a hereditary trait.

3) **Conjoined twins** are a variety of true twins who are joined with each other to a small or large extent. Such 'double monsters,' are known as **Siamese twins**. They arise from the incomplete separation of the two embryos developed from a single zygote. (occurring more than two weeks after conception). The incidence is 1 in 50,000 pregnancies.

Siamese twins are named so after Chang and Eng, who were born conjoined at the upper abdomen, in Siam (present-day Thailand) in 1811. They made a successful living out of their travelling shows in USA where they settled, married and fathered a large number of children despite remaining conjoined until they died within a few hours of each other at the age of 61 years.

The Disappearing Twin: Ultrasonographic studies during early pregnancy have shown that twin pregnancy is more common at conception. Resorption of one of the twins takes place. Disappearance of one member of a twin may be responsible for some otherwise confusing discrepancies noted between prenatal cytogenetic findings and the karyotype of the newborn.

Dizygotic twins with different fathers though theoretically possible are very rare. However, their existence has been confirmed by genetic marker studies.

Heterokaryotypic Twins: Monozygotic twins with different karyotypes have been reported though

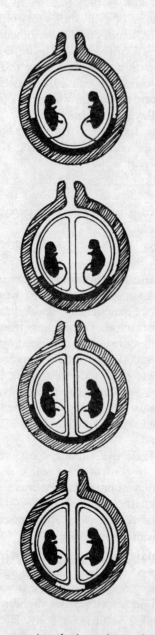

Fig. 69 Scheme to show fetal membranes in twins. First, dizygotic or monozygotic twins with separate amnions, chorions and placentae. Second, dizygotic or monozygotic twins with separate amnions and chorions but single placenta. Third, monozygotic twins with single chorion and placenta but separate amnions. Fourth, monozygotic twins with single amnion, chorion and placenta

rare. These cases arise postzygotically. They are like chromosomal mosaics in whom there are at least two cell lines derived from a single zygote.

Determination of twin zygosity. The determination of zygosity of a twin pair helps in furthering research in genetic and developmental disorders in twins. It also helps in the selection of donors in cases of transplantation of tissues and organs. In transplantation, a monozygotic co-twin is the most useful donor, whereas a dizygotic co-twin is genetically like any other sibling.

Zygosity is determined by the examination of the placenta and fetal membranes, and by using various genetic markers indicating the similarities and differences between the co-twins.

The analysis of polymorphic systems such as the blood groups, HLA antigens and other biochemical markers is carried out. Now zygosity is determined more specifically and easily by determining highly polymorphic molecular markers which are identified by DNA fingerprinting.

Chimerism. A chimera is an individual whose cells have arisen from more than one fertilised egg, as in the following examples:
1) Conjoined twins.
2) Anastomosis of placental blood vessels in twin pregnancies, resulting in the mixing of blood and mixed cell-lines.
3) In a leukemic patient, repopulation of bone marrow from a donor, following suppression of the host marrow by irradiation.
4) Rarely, somatic cells throughout the body may indicate their chimeric origin. If the two types of cells are XX and XY, the individual's sexual differentiation may be abnormal.

Scope and Limitation of Twin Studies: The twin method has helped to give genetic interpretation to many complex human traits. However, though it gives an idea about genetic predisposition to a given disorder, it cannot give any detail about the genes concerned, their pattern of inheritance, or their mode of action. Another important factor is the bias of ascertainment. MZ twin pairs who are concordant for a disease draw more attention, whereas discordant MZ or DZ pairs are less likely to be reported.

The Dolly Phenomenon: Cloning implies the formation of a colony of macro-organisms possessing identical genotype (genetic constitution). In bacterial culture, cloning is a rule, and hence we call such clones are referred a bacterial colony.

In higher organisms formed from bisexual gametes, the force of variation imposes unfailing uniqueness. Exceptions are provided by monozygous twins that supposedly share the same genotype. The nine-banded armadillo regularly gives birth to monozygous octuplets — a set of 8 members that develop from a single zygote. Hence the largest natural clone does not exceed 8, and is seen in only one mammalian species.

Fiction writers have fantasized the creation of human clones. Such cloning would provide a large number of humans genetically and phenotypically identical to one another. Aldous Huxley portrayed this very dramatically in his *The Brave New World,* and *The Brave New World Revisited.*

After a lot of experimentation and expenses, a first step has been taken in mammalian cloning. Dolly, a sheep, was born from a sheep ovum fertilised by the diploid nucleus of an intestinal cell. The diploid nucleus of the fertilised ovum was removed and replaced by the nucleus of a somatic cell. While this has drawn attention attention worldwide, it is still far cry from the dream of producing identical mammals or humans on an assembly line.

SUMMARY

Developmental genetics studies the mechanisms involved in cell proliferation and cell differentiation which result from 'differential' gene activity, both in space and in time to give rise to an embryo from a zygote.

It has been suggested that the sequence of events in embryonic development is a result of 'genetic switches.' A gene product or effector substance could possibly set in a sequence of developmental processes by switching on or off certain genes.

Three developmental gene-families act as factors controlling the transcription. They are homeobox (Hox) genes, paired-box (Pax) genes and zinc finger genes. These genes initiate and regulate the sequential process of development.

Dysmorphology is classified into malformation,

dysplasia, sequence, syndrome, deformation and disruption.

Paternal chromosomes are responsible for trophoblastic development (and formation of hydatidiform mole in paternal diploidy) and maternal chromosomes for embryonic development.

A testis-determining factor (TDF) located in the sex-determining region on the Y chromosome (SRY) stimulates the gonad to develop into testis. The testis liberates MIF to inhibit female internal genitalia, and testosterone to promote male internal genitalia. Dihydrotestosterone brings about the development of male external genitalia.

Twin: Birth of a pair of fetuses simultaneously.

Classification:

1) Like, true, identical, uniovular or monozygotic; derived from a single fertilised ovum; share a common placenta and have identical physical features, the same sex and same blood groups.

2) Unlike, false, nonidentical, fraternal, binovular or dizygotic; due to simultaneous fertilisation of two ova by separate sperms. Each of the twins has its own chromosomal constitution, chorionic sac, and placenta. They may or may not be of the same sex.

3) Conjoined twins: true twins joined to one another to a varying extent, arising by incomplete separation of two embryos developed from a single zygote.

Usefulness of study of twins: 1) Research in genetic and developmental disorder; 2) Comparison of effect of heredity and environment in causation of diseases; 3) Transplantation — selection of donors.

Chimera: An individual whose cells have arisen from more than one fertilised egg.

10 MEDICAL GENETICS

Human genetics is the science of heredity and variation. It is the study of the genetic basis of normal and abnormal structure and function of the human body. This encompasses investigations at the molecular, cellular, biochemical, individual and population levels.

Medical genetics is the branch of human genetics concerned with determining the genetic basis of human diseases, classified as single gene disorders, chromosomal disorders and multifactorial disorders. Medical genetics also includes the diagnosis, treatment and prevention of genetic diseases. It also involves genetic counselling.

As research in the field of molecular biology progresses an increasing number of diseases are seen as genetic diseases, both in the pediatric age group and in adults. Medical genetics is now also relied upon increasingly for greater efficiency in the prevention and treatment of human diseases.

In this chapter in the section 'Abnormal Chromosomes', we shall discuss the disorders which have a basis in chromosomal anomalies. The pattern of inheritance and types of disorders due to single gene defects and multifactorial inheritance have been already discussed in the chapter titled 'Modes of inheritance.'

In the section 'Pharnacogenetics', the genetic basis of variation or abnormal response to drugs is discussed. At the end of this chapter, a general model of the genetic basis of human disease is given.

ABNORMAL CHROMOSOMES

Abnormal chromosomes are the vehicles of inherited abnormalities. The abnormalities may be either numerical or structural or both, and may occur during mitosis or meiosis. Structural aberrations result from single or multiple breaks along the chromosomal length. The broken fragments are then either destroyed (deleted) or rearranged in various ways or shifted (translocated) to other chromosomes. Such chromosomal mutations may occur spontaneously, i.e., without an apparent cause, or be triggered by external agents, e.g., ionising radiation or some drugs.

It is only through the abnormal gametes formed at meiosis that chromosomal anomalies can be passed on from one generation to the next.

The usual forms which occur as structural abnormalities are **deletion, duplication, translocation, inversion, isochromosomes** and **ring chromosomes**.

Abnormal chromosome numbers result almost invariably from the phenomenon of non-disjunction during the first and/or the second meiotic divisions. Common examples of such anomalies include **Down's syndrome, Turner's syndrome** and **Klinefelter's syndrome**.

The causes of chromosomal aberrations are not precisely known. However, it is observed that certain factors predispose to such aberrations. These include ionising radiation, viruses, chemical carcinogens, late maternal or paternal age, and possibly a few specific genes themselves.

The normal functioning of the genetic system of an individual is dependent upon the constancy of hereditary material carried in the chromosomes. Sometimes changes do occur in chromosomes, which are brought about spontaneously or by external agents such as X-rays. Chromosomal aberrations are either numerical or structural, and may affect either autosomes, sex chromosomes, or both, in the same karyotype.

The vast majority of chromosomal abnormalities occurring at conception are lethal, either in early pregnancy or later, and only a small proportion of all such abnormalities get exhibited as live births. This is an example of natural selection at work, mediating quality control in human reproduction.

The abnormalities, in structure or number of chromosomes, can arise at any time in any cell of the body, during one's lifetime. The abnormality affecting the somatic cell has no consequences on the progeny of an individual. However, if the abnormality affects gonadal cells or arises during gametogenesis, it will be passed on to the progeny via the gametes. The zygote resulting from such a gamete will pass on the abnormality to all the cells of the body. Such a person becomes a **carrier** of the anomaly. In general, any person who has a chromosomal abnormality within his gonadal cells, which will have an effect on gametogenesis, is referred to as a carrier of chromosomal abnormality.

Chromosomal abnormalities constitute a major group of genetic diseases. About 60 chromosomal anomaly syndromes are known and they are collectively more common than all the Mendelian single-gene disorders put together. The incidence of chromosomal anomalies is about 2 per cent in pregnancies in women above 35 years of age.

Structural Abnormalities

Changes in the arrangement of the chromosomal material generally occur following breaks in the chromosome. The breaks are produced either spontaneously or are induced by such external factors as radiation, chemicals or viruses. There is some evidence that chromosomal breaks occur more frequently than chromosomal aberrations; this means that broken chromosomes often unite according to the original configuration, leaving behind no trace of the break.

Structural rearrangement can remain balanced if the chromosome set retains the normal complement of genetic information; it can become unbalanced if there are additional or missing genes. Some rearrangements are stable and are pass through subsequent cell division unaltered, whereas others are unstable. The rearrangement becomes stable only when all normal structural elements which include a single functional centromere and two telomeres are present. In unbalanced rearrangements, the phenotype is usually affected. Any alteration that disturbs the normal balance of functional genes results in abnormal development. In balanced structural rearrangement, if chromosomal breaks disrupt a gene, it would lead to mutation. However, usually there is no phenotypical abnormality since all genetic information is present, although packed differently. Such carriers of balanced rearrangements produce a high frequency of unbalanced gametes and therefore have an increased risk of having abnormal offspring with unbalanced karyotypes. The chromosomal breaks tend to disrupt a gene leading to mutation.

Deficiency or Deletion: (Fig. 70). Deletion is the loss of a portion of a chromosome. If there is a single break in the chromosome, only the terminal portion of the chromosome is deleted. If there are two breaks in a chromosome, the interstitial portion between the two breaks is deleted, followed by the union of the broken ends of the chromosome. The deleted portion, if it lacks a centromere, is an acentric fragment, which because it has no centromere, fails to move on the spindle, and is eventually lost during a subsequent cell division unless the deleted fragment gets attached to the same or another chromosome. Deletion of part of a chromosome is often referred to as partial monosomy.

Deletions have been indicated by a minus sign (–) after the arm of the chromosome involved. 5p–, for example, means that the short arm of 5 is shorter than usual. It is now indicated after the Paris Conference (1971), by the addition of 'del' before the chromosome number, instead of minus sign to distinguish a simple deletion from other instances where the shortening was part of other

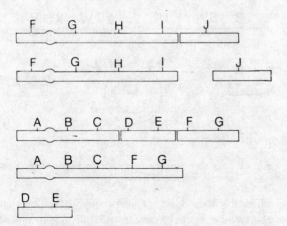

Fig. 70 Deletion, terminal and interstitial chromosomes with sites of break indicated. Deletion of J (terminal) and DE (interstitial) are shown.

aberrations, such as translocation or pericentric inversions. The full karyotype of the above example may be stated as 46,XY, del (5p) without a minus sign. If the break-point bands are known, they are added in another parenthesis; thus 46, XY, del (5) (p13) would indicate the terminal deletion of the segment, distal to the 5p 13 band.

The consequences of a chromosomal deficiency depend on its length and the role of the genetic material involved. In Drosophila, where minute deficiencies can be detected and measured accurately, deletion in some areas of even a single chrommere may be lethal, whereas, for other areas, loss of even fifty chromomeres may be compatible with life, if the organism is heterozygous for that deficiency. In a hetero-zygous deficiency, one chromosome is normal, but its homologue is deficient. By and large experiments on animals with a homozygous deficiency, indicate that they usually do not survive to an adult stage because a complete set of genes is missing. This suggests that most genes are indispensable, at least in a single dose, for the development of a viable organism. Deletions are important in investigations of gene location for determination of the presence and position of unmatched genes.

The common example of deletion in humans is the *cri du chat* syndrome, in which part of the short arm of chromosome 5 is deleted.

In humans, Turner's syndrome is an XO condition resulting from the deletion of a whole chromosome. This is the most evident and the most frequent chromosomal deficiency in man, compatible with life and related to the X chromosome.

Microdeletion: Deletions described so far are relatively large and can be seen under the microscope without special staining. With the advent of high resolution banding and FISH, a number of microscopic deletions are being noticed which were previously too small for detection (Table 17). Some of these deletions involve loss of only a few genes at closely placed loci, resulting in what are known as contiguous gene syndromes.

Ring Chromosome: A ring chromosome is a type of deletion chromosome. If two breaks occur in a chromosome at its two ends, and both the ends get lost, the two sticky broken ends of the chromosome unite to form a ring (Fig. 71). Ring chromosomes are basically deficiencies and therefore the consequences will depend on the length and the role of the genetic material lost. In addition, the carrier of such a chromosomal aberration, will produce abnormal gametes as shown in Fig. 72. Crossing over between a ring chromosome and its homologous chromosome produces a dicentric chromosome. Moreover, during mitosis, ring chromosomes often get interlocked, instead of there being free rings with one centromere each.

Ring chromosomes have now been found in every chromosome group. Many of them have not been associated with any consistent syndrome, except that mental retardation is a consistent feature. Ring X chromosomes have also been seen. The carriers of ring X chromosome may show features of Turner's syndrome and are quite often sex chromatin positive.

Translocation: The most frequently observed abnormality in the structure of a chromosome is a break at two places. If the two breaks are on nonhomologous chromosomes, the chromosomes may exchange pieces, forming a **reciprocal translocation**. When two homologous chromo-

Table 17: Microdeletion Syndromes

Syndrome	Chr. involved	Clinical features
Williams	7	Developmental disability, characteristic facies, supravalvular aortic stenosis.
Langer-Giedion	8	Characteristic facies, sparse hair, exostosis, mental retardation.
WAGR	11	Wilm's tumor (kidney tumor), aniridia (absence of iris), genitourinary malformations, retardation of growth and development.
Retino-blastoma	13	Tumor of the retina presenting in infancy.
Angelman	15	Mental retardation, microcephaly, seizures, characteristic gait.
Prader-Willi	15	Mental retardation, short stature, obesity, hypotonia, characteristic facies, small feet.
Rubinstein-Taybi	16	Development of disability, characteristic facies, broad thumbs.
Miller-Dieker	17	Lissencephaly, characteristic facies.
Di George	22	Cardiac malformations involving cardiac outflow tract, thymic and parathyroid hyperplasia.
Sbprintzen	22	Cardiac malformations involving cardiac outflow tract, cleft palate, characteristic facies.

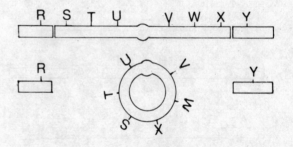

Fig. 71 Ring chromosome formation follows two terminal breaks, fragments R and Y get deleted.

somes are involved, the exchanged segments are non-homologous.

Reciprocal translocation is the most commonly encountered aberration in well-studied organisms with more than one chromosome pair. Since breakages are usually random in these cases, the chances are greater that the two breaks will be on different chromosomes rather than on the same chromosome. It is not surprising therefore that the two-break reciprocal translocation is the most commonly encountered structural abnormality in human chromosomal analyses.

Reciprocal translocations may be **homozygous** when both members of a chromosomal pair have exchanged segments with another pair. If only one member each of both the pairs has exchanged segments, then it is a **heterozygous reciprocal translocation**. All human carriers of reciprocal translocations have proved to be heterozygous for the aberration. As shown in Fig. 73 one member of each pair maintains the normal arrangement and the other member of the pair is involved in the translocation. Since the genetic material is present in normal amount, such a **translocation heterozygote** is said to be **balanced**.

A translocation may not always lead to an abnormal phenotype. However, the carriers of reciprocal translocation are characterised by low fertility. This reduced fertility is because, during gametogenesis, in order to exchange material by crossing over, the four members of the two pairs involved exhibit a characteristic cross figure as shown in Fig. 74. This tetrad reaches the equator of the spindle during the first meiotic division, oriented in different ways in relation to the poles. As shown in Fig. 74, the distribution of segregation is random, and at least two-thirds of the gametes of the carriers of a reciprocal translocation would have an unbalanced chromosomal complement. The formation of gametes would be in the proportion of one normal, one abnormal with

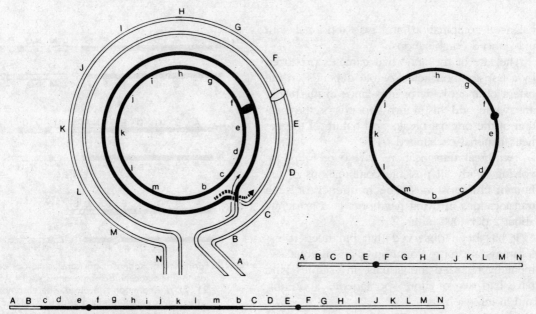

Fig. 72 Crossing over during meiosis I in ring chromosome. Note that one abnormal dicentric chromosome results. The sister chromatids of ring chromosome and its homologous chromosome remain unchanged as they are not involved in crossing over. The result would be 3 abnormal gametes, one bearing a dicentric chromosome, the other bearing no chromosome and the third one a ring chromosome; as also one normal gamete bearing a normal homologous chromosome.

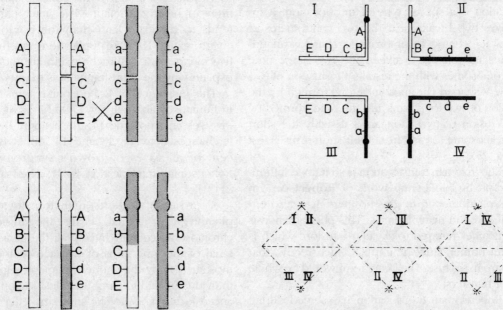

Fig. 73 Reciprocal translocation. Two pairs of nonhomologous chromosomes, with two sites of break in one member of each pair, is shown above and reciprocal interchange of fragments between only one member of each pair (heterozygous) is shown below.

Fig. 74 Gametogenesis in reciprocal translocation showing a cross configuration during crossing over. Abnormal gametes are (I II), (III IV), (I III), (II IV). Normal gamete is (I IV). Abnormal but balanced is (II III). These are chance results due to random assortment.

balanced combination, and two abnormal with unbalanced combinations.

The fate of the abnormal gametes produced by a translocation heterozygote depends on the extent of aneuploidy or imbalance in the resultant zygote; and this in turn depends on the location of the original breaks and nature of the genetic material exchanged.

Two-break translocations have been found involving nearly all possible combinations of the human chromosomes. The frequency of such translocations in living newborns is consistently about 2 per 1000 births.

It has been observed that balanced translocations are more common in institutionalised mentally retarded individuals, in couples who have had two or more spontaneous abortions, and in infertile males.

Simple Translocation: When a segment of the chromosome is transferred to a different part of the same chromosome or to another chromosome, it is referred to as simple translocation. This is an extremely rare event, if it occurs at all.

Robertsonian Translocation: Robertsonian translocation is a special type of translocation. It involves two breaks near the two centromeres of two acrocentric chromosomes. There is an unequal interchange between the two acrocentric chromosomes with the resultant formation of two new V-shaped chromosomes; one formed by the fusion of two long arms and the other formed by the fusion of two short arms. Usually the short chromosome formed from their short arms is lost (Fig. 75).

Robertsonian translocation is so named in honour of the pioneering work of **Robertson**, on this phenomenon in grasshoppers. It is also encountered in many animals. This phenomenon is sometimes referred to as centric fusion, which is a misnomer since it implies, incorrectly, that centromeres fuse. The better term would be whole arm transfers.

Robertsonian translocation has served during evolution to produce differences in chromosome number and morphology. In many organisms, the chromosomal area on both sides of the

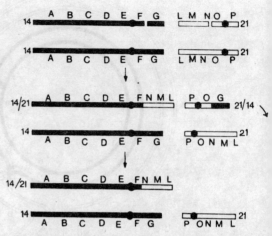

Fig. 75 Formation of Robertsonian translocation or centric fusion. The acrocentric chromosomes 13, 14, 15 and 21, 27 are commonly involved. The chromosome formed by fusion of two long arms (A B C D E F N M L) persists, whereas the chromosome formed by fusion of two short arms (P O G) is lost during subsequent cell divisions, as it is essentially made up of constitutive chromatin which lags behind in duplication.

centromere consists largely of the relatively inert heterochromatin; hence the fragment produced by fusion of the short arms consists almost entirely of heterochromatin. The heterochromatin tends to replicate later than the predominant euchromatin. The late replication and the relative inertness of heterochromatin are thought to explain why the short fragment is frequently lost.

The incidence of Robertsonian translocation in humans is about 1 per 1,000 births. It usually involves chromosome 14, the majority being interchanges between 13 and 14. About two per cent of all cases of Down's syndrome have Robertsonian translocation 14/21, 22/22 or rarely 21/21.

A carrier of Robertsonian translocation is phenotypically normal, because the translocation chromosome contains nearly all the genetic material of the long arms of two acrocentric chromosomes. Only the shorter fragment is lost. The individual is said to carry the translocation in balanced location, as he/she shows no effect of the lost short fragment.

However, during gametogenesis, in a carrier of Robertsonian translocation, imbalance results.

During meiosis, as seen in Fig. 76, the translocation chromosome pairs with two normal homologous chromosomes, showing modified trivalent or cross figure, for crossing over. Because of random segregation two-thirds of the gametes tend to be abnormal, accounting for many stillbirths and abortions. The rest produce viable progeny, but half of them become the carriers of balanced Robertsonian translocation.

Philadelphia Chromosome — Ph[1]: **Nowell** and **Hungerford** discovered that patients with chronic myelogenous or myelocytic or granulocytic leukemia (CML) have a G chromosome, the long arm of which is shorter than in the usual chromosome. This chromosome was named the Ph[1] (Philadelphia) chromosome after the city of its discovery. This represented the first specific association between chromosomal aberration and cancer.

The chromosome involved is chromosome number 22. Ph[1] is not a simple deletion. The detached piece gets translocated to the tip of the long arm of a number 9 chromosome. Those patients of CML, who lack G deletion, invariably lack the extra material on 9q as well. In about five per cent of Ph[1] positive cases, the extra material is on a chromosome other than number 9; and in about one per cent of Ph[1] positive cases, no extra material can be detected elsewhere.

About 85 per cent of those diagnosed as cases of CML are Ph[1] positive. Ph[1] positive leukemics are mosaics for it, as only the bone marrow stem cells of the granulocyte, thrombocyte and erythrocyte series show the aberration. Lymphocytes and other body cells are normal. Apparently, the chromosomal anomaly is not present at conception, but is acquired later in specific hemopoietic tissue.

It is not certain whether Ph[1] is the cause or the effect of the disease. It may also be noted that those patients of CML who do not show Ph[1] are believed to have a different disease.

Insertion: An insertion is a type of **insertional translocation, shift** or **transposition** in which a chromosome segment drops out as a result of two breaks, but becomes inserted at a single break elsewhere in the chromosome set (Fig. 77).

In case of insertion, there is merely a change in order of genetic material and hence no effect is seen on the phenotype of the individual. However, during gametogenesis as shown in Fig. 77, duplications or deficiencies result when crossing over involves the insertional segment, or a balanced condition, if crossing over does not cover the insertional segment.

Isochromosomes: A new type of chromosome may arise from a misdivision at the centromere. The centromere divides perpendicular to the long axis of the chromosome instead of parallel to it. If this misdivision occurs in a submedian centromere (e.g., that of an X chromosome), the chromosome instead of dividing into identical halves, divides into a long and short chromosome, both with metacentric centromeres; these are isochromosomes — chromosomes with identical arms, partly duplications and partly deletions of the normal chromosome (Fig. 78).

Fig. 78 shows that isochromosomes could also result from a wholearm centric fusion, e.g., in early anaphase, between the strands that were sister chromatids until that stage.

At meiosis the isochromosome pairs with itself or with a normal homologue.

Isochromosome for the long arm of the X chromosome implies absence of all, or most of the short arm(s); and since the short arm appears to contain the genetic material necessary for normal sexual development, the individuals with long arm isochromosomes phenotypically manifest 45,XO like individuals with Turner's syndrome. The only difference is the presence of the chromatin body, which is relatively larger; there is also a somewhat lower frequency of webbing and cardiovascular defects. An additional significant difference is that these individuals exhibit a tendency to develop chronic lymphocytic inflammation of the thyroid, also known as Hashimoto's thyroiditis.

An isochromosome for the short arm of the X chromosome, 46Xi(Xp) has a double dose of genetic material essential for normal sexual development; hence the individuals with this

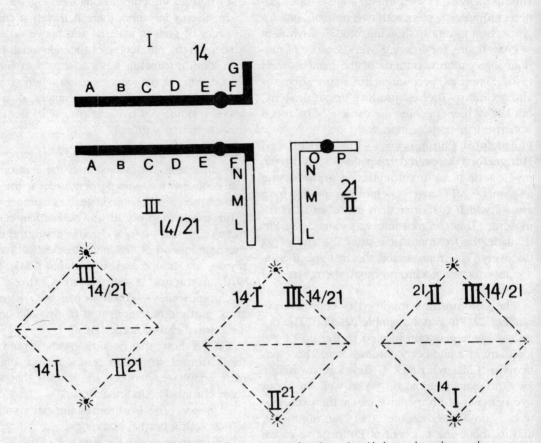

Fig. 76 During gametogenesis, the chromosome with Robertsonian translocation pairs with the two homologous chromosomes whose long arms it represents. Because of random segregation the resultant possible gametes and outcome are as follows :

1) 14,21	Normal	4) 14	21 monosomy
2) 14/21	Normal carrier	5) 21	14 monosomy } lethal
3) 14/21, 21	Down's syndrome	6) 14, 14/21	14 trisomy

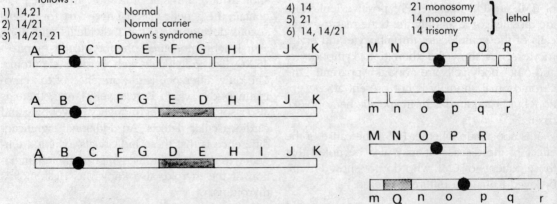

Fig. 77 Insertion. On the left, three breaks are shown. The fragment D E is shown 'inserted' within the same chromosome, after reversal to E D, or as originally broken as D E. This results in a disarrangement of loci.

On the right three breaks are shown, but here, the fragment marked Q gets inserted into the other member of the homologous pair between loci m and n. Again a disarrangement of loci takes place.

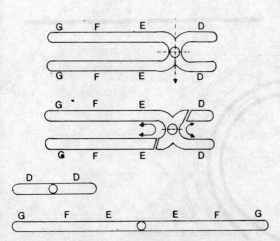

Fig. 78 Isochromosome formation. Two mechanisms are shown. In the first, the centromere splits transversely and results in the formation of two abnormal chromosomes. Each is metacentric and has an exact duplicate of its loci.

In the second, two breaks are shown, one in the short arm of one chromatid and the other in the long arm of the sister chromatid, both breaks being very close to the centromere. The broken fragments interchange places on the sister chromatids where they get reunited. This again results in the exact duplication of loci on the short and the long arms.

isochromosome do not show an external manifestation of Turner's syndrome. They have streak gonads and resemble those, in whom there has been deletion of the long arm of the X chromosome.

Isochromosomes of the autosomes are most numerous for the acrocentric or nearly acrocentric chromosomes. Many are actually centric-fusion translocations between homologous chromosomes, as a result of which all the offspring tend to be trisomic or monosomic. The result depends on which chromosome happens to be involved. Most of the autosomes are lethal in both monosomic and trisomic conditions. However, for a chromosome like 21, where trisomy (Down's syndrome) is viable, a high frequency of trisomic siblings are expected in the progeny of a carrier of such an aberration.

Inversion: When two chromosomal breaks occur on the same chromosome and the segment

between the two breaks reforms after rotating through 180°, an inversion is formed. This may take two forms: (1) **paracentric inversion** if the inverted segment does not include the centromere and (2) **pericentric inversion** if the involved segment includes the centromere region (Fig. 79).

The incidence of pericentric inversion is about one per 7,500 births, about a fifteenth the incidence of translocation of all types. Usually a change in the gene order produced by an inversion does not lead to an abnormal phenotype. However, the effect is seen during gametogenesis. As shown in Figs. 80 and 81, the carriers of inversion produce unbalanced gametes, and are therefore reproductively inferior to the general population, unless some mechanism exists to reduce crossing over in such cases.

Duplication: It is the presence of a portion of a chromosome more than once in a gamete or more than twice in a zygote.

1) Duplication results from gametogenesis in a carrier of translocation, of inversion or of ring chromosome (Figs. 72, 74, 80, 81).

These duplications do not usually have as drastic an effect as deficiencies of comparable size. Thus, a small duplication is rarely lethal, even

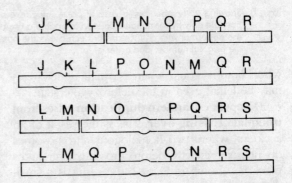

Fig. 79 Inversion. Two breaks are shown. In the first the centromere is not involved. The broken fragment MNOP gets reversed and rejoins the other two fragments. This is known as paracentric inversion.

In the second, the middle fragment which includes the centromere, gets reversed and reattaches to the other two fragments. This is known as pericentric inversion.

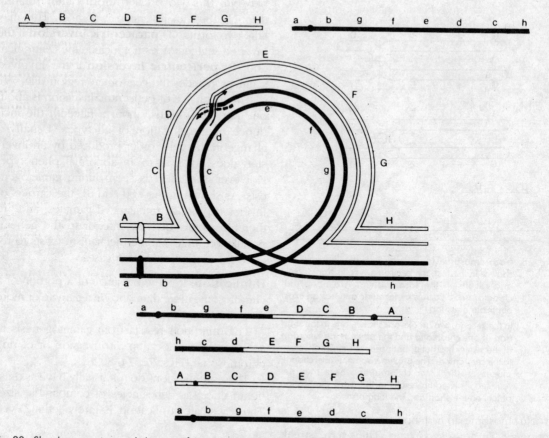

Fig. 80 Showing gametogenesis in case of paracentric inversion. Since some loci are mismatched, crossing over becomes possible only by formation of a loop to enable a rematch of the 'inverted' loci. Of the four gametes, so formed, two are abnormal with an increase or decrease in the number of loci (duplication and deletion) and the other two retain the original number and order of loci.

when homozygous, whereas small deficiencies may be lethal even in the heterozygote state.

2) **Repeat** or **tandem duplication** arises from **unequal crossing over**. This is the result of an accident, where two homologous chromosomes do not pair exactly before crossing over takes place. As shown in Fig. 82, the result is a small deficiency on one chromosome and a small duplication on its homologous member.

Being small, the duplication is likely to be an evolutionary mechanism for the acquisition of new genes. With the normal genetic material present adjacent to it, the duplicated area is dispensable. It may mutate to produce a new substance without the danger of the cells being deprived of their normal product. Thus duplicated genes evolve into genes having quite different functions from those from which they originated. Examples are hemoglobin loci, Lepore hemoglobin, and haptoglobins (Fig. 57).

Mosaicism: Usually, numerical or structural anomaly is present in all cultured cells of an individual. At times two or more karyotypes are observed and such a phenomenon is called mosaicism.

The causes of mosaicism are:

1) Non-disjunction in early postzygote mitotic division.

2) Chromosome structural anomaly arising in early postzygotic mitotic division.

The effects of mosaicism on development depends on the time of occurrence of the anomaly. It also depends on the proportion of various chromosome complements present and the tissues affected. The assessment of the effect of mosaicism at the laboratory level based on antenatal studies is difficult. This is because the proportion of the different chromosome complements observed in the tissue being analysed such as amniocytes or lymphocytes may not be representative of all body cells.

In laboratory studies geneticists have to carefully differentiate between the mosaicism truly present in an individual and pseudomosiaicism which arises in the laboratory. The distinction is not easily made.

Mosaicism is more common in chorionic villus culture studies and poses a problem in interpretation in prenatal diagnosis. It is difficult to assess phenotypic effects of mosaicism. Clinically normal mosaic persons are generally not assessed. There is no adequate study on follow-up of prenatally diagnosed mosaic fetuses. In general a mosaic with trisomy is less affected than non-mosaic trisomy.

Marker Chromosomes: Occasionally in chromosome cultures, very small chromosomes are seen in mosaic state besides normal chromosome complement. They are called supernumerary chromosomes. However, they also represent structural rearrangement. So far, the available cytogenetic tools are unable to give their precise identification and hence their clinical significance is not known. The cat-eye syndrome is considered to be due to supernumerary chromosome representing part of the long arm of chromosome 22. Patients with this syndrome have coloboma of the iris and anal atresia commonly been seens to have

Abnormalities in Chromosomal Number: The number of chromosomes is fixed for a given species. In the human, the diploid number in somatic cells is 46 and haploid number is 23. The cause for aberrations in chromosomal numbers in almost all cases is non-disjunction during meiosis I and/or meiosis II, or mitosis.

Euploid is any number which is an exact multiple of the haploid number. The normal species number is **diploid**. However euploid numbers may be abnormal. 3N (**triploid**) and 4N (**tetraploid**) **chromosome numbers are uncommon in man. Most of these are lethal and hence seen only in early abortuses**. The term **polyploid** refers to any multiple of the basic haploid chromosome number, other than the diploid; thus 3N, 4N and so on. The term **aneuploid** refers to a chromosome number which differs by one or more, from an exact multiple of the haploid number, e.g., 2N–1 or 2N+1, where N is the haploid number of chromosomes. The term **heteroploid** is used for any chromosome number, other than the normal, whether it is euploid or aneuploid.

Clinical Syndromes due to Chromosomal Aberrations: Some of the known syndromes due to autosomal aberrations are: (Table 18)
1) Down's syndrome (trisomy 21, mongolism)
2) Trisomy 18
3) D trisomy (trisomy 13)
4) *Cri du chat* syndrome
Those due to anomalous sex chromosomes are: (Tables 19, 20)
5) Mosaicism
6) Turner's syndrome (ovarian dysgenesis)
7) 47,XXX (triple X) and other X polysomies
8) 47,XXY (Klinefelter's syndrome)
9) 47,XYY
10) Intersex

Table 19: A Classification of Various Disorders of Sexual Development

1) Seminiferous tubule dysgenesis (Klinefelter's syndrome) XXY, XXXY, and others

2) Ovarian dysgenesis (Turner's syndrome) XO

3) Pseudohermaphrodite

   a) male pseudohermaphrodite (XY) testicular feminisation syndrome

   b) female pseudohermaphrodite (XX) adrenogenital syndrome

4) True hermaphrodite
XX, XX/XY, XX/XO and others

Table 18: Characteristics of Most Important Syndromes due to Autosomal Aberrations

Syndrome	Characteristics	Syndrome	Characteristics
4p monosomy	Severe growth retardation Severe encephalopathy Microcephaly 'Greek warrior helmet'	8 trisomy	Long face Thick, everted lower lip Osteoarticular anomalies
4p trisomy	Aplasia of the nasal homes 'Boxer nose' in the adult	9p trisomy	Brachycephaly Bulbous nose Unilateral grin Worried look
Partial 4q trisomy	Absence of the nasal bridge 'Cut de poule' or pursed mouth	Partial 9q trisomy	Small face Beaked nose Microretrognathia Hypotrophy Long fingers with abnormal position
Partial 4q monosomy	Deformed ears Snub nose	9p monosomy	Trigonocephaly Palpebral fissures slanted upward and outward
5p monosomy ('cri du chat syndrome')	*In the infant* Characteristic cry Microcephaly Moonlike face Hypertelorism *In later years* Narrow face Small mandible, effacement of the angles of the jaw	Partial 10q trisomy	Long upper lip High bossed forehead Broad, flat face Narrow palpebral fissures Joint laxity
5p trisomy	Hypotelorism Large mandible	10p trisomy	Severe growth retardation Dolichocephaly Turtle's beak Osteoarticular anomalies
Partial 6p trisomy	Blepharophimosis Bulbous nose Small mouth	Partial 11q trisomy	Fleshy nose Protuberant philtrum Microretrognathia Flexed limbs
Trisomy 6qter	Hypertelorism Bow-shaped mouth Micrognathia Short neck with unusual webbing	Partial 11q monosomy	Trigonocephaly Coarse features
Partial 7q trisomy	Discrete facial dysmorphism	Partial 12p monosomy	Growth retardation Microcephaly Narrow forehead Pointed nose Micrognathia
Monosomy 7qter	Microcephaly and flattening of the occiput Bulbous nose Palpebral fissures slanted upward and outward Redundant subcutaneous tissue		

Syndrome	Features
13 trisomy	Harelip Microphthalmia Hexadactyly Early death
Partial trisomy	Microstomia
13q proximal	Micrognathia Increased nuclear projections of neutrophils Abnormal embryonic hemoglobin
Distal	Microtrigonocephaly Long curly eyelashes — bushy eyebrows Polydactyly Congenital heart defect
Distal 13	Greek profile
monosomy (deletion or ring)	Rabbit-like, forward slanting incisors Absent or hypoplastic thumbs Bony syndactyly IV-Vth metacarpals
Partial trisomy 14q-proximal	Hypotelorism Prominent nose Unusual large and mobile mouth Thin lips
Proximal 15 trisomy	Oval face High cheekbones Deep orbits
18 trisomy	Deformed ears Micrognathia Occipital protuberance Overlapping fingers High frequency of arches (dermatoglyphic) Narrow pelvis Rocker-bottom feet Considerable growth retardation Premature death
18p monosomy or 18p-syndrome	Small size Round face Broad, detached ears Wide mouth Dental anomalies
Partial 18q monosomy or 18q-syndrome	Depressed midface Carp-shaped mouth Strongly folded ears High frequency of whorls (dermatoglyphic)
21 trisomy	Hypotonia Round flat face Palpebral fissures slanted upward and outward Brushfield spots on the irises Small ears Flat nape of the neck
r(21) syndrome	Hypertonia Protuberant nasal bridge Palpebral fissures slanted downward and outward Protuberant occiput Large ears
r(22) Syndrome	Doe eyes Low-set eyebrows

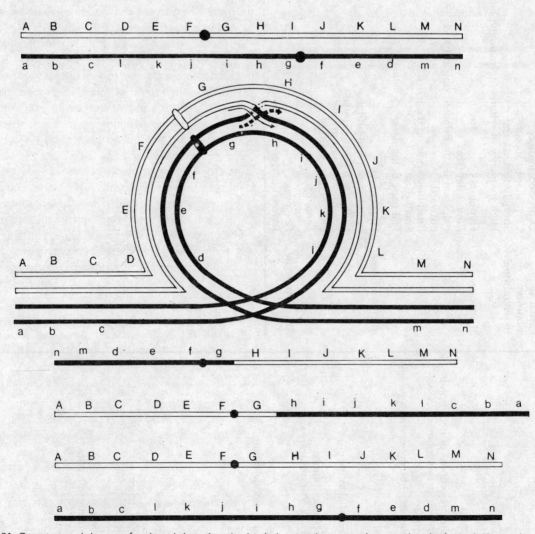

Fig. 81 Gametogenesis in case of pericentric inversion. Again, during crossing over, a loop needs to be formed. The resulting gametes with deletion, duplication and retention of original number of loci respectively are shown.

Down's syndrome (trisomy 21, mongolism):

This is the best known of the syndromes with chromosomal anomalies. It was also the first syndrome to be described in humans. (Fig. 83). The incidence of trisomy 21is 1.45 per thousand. This frequency is constant in different ethnic or socioeconomic groups. The sex ratio is approximately 3 males to 2 females.

Clinical features. Children with Down's syndrome can be usually identified at birth, or shortly thereafter, by mental retardation: (IQ, 25 to 50), brachycephaly, presence of epicanthal folds, oblique palpebral fissure, speckled iris, low bridge of nose, protruding furrowed tongue lacking a central fissure, and small stature. The voice is guttural, low-pitched; articulation is generally defective. Puberty occurs at a normal or slightly delayed age in both sexes. Secondary sexual characteristics are weakly manifested. Females with Down's syndrome can be fertile, although

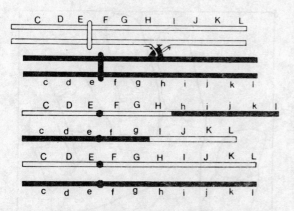

Fig. 82 Shows the phenomenon of unequal crossing over, resulting in duplication — deletion effect on two of the chromosomes. In the first (top), the locus H is duplicated. In the next, the locus H gets deleted. The remaining two retain the original number of loci

pregnancies are not frequent. Their progeny comprise an equal number of non-trisomic and trisomic children. The non-trisomic children, even with normal karyo-type, are mentally deficient. In males with Down's syndrome, no case of fertility has been reported.

A number of associated anomalies are seen in cases of Down's syndrome. They include congenital heart defects, congenital duodenal obstruction, hypotonia, hyperlaxity of ligaments, dislocation of patella, *pes varus*, strabismus and congenital cataract. The individuals with Down's syndrome have an **increased risk of developing leukemia**.

Dermatoglyphics. The hands are very characteristic, being short and broad, with single palmar crease (**simian crease**) (Fig. 84) and **clinodactyly (incurving)** of the fifth finger. The hands also have characteristic dermal patterns, including a distal axial triradius. The feet show a wide gap between first and second toes, with a furrow extending backward along the plantar surface. The hallucal area shows characteristic dermal patterns.

Cytogenetics. Down's syndrome involves **trisomy for chromosome 21**, but about four per cent of the patients have this extra chromosomal material, not as a separate chromosome,

but as a **translocation** of the long arm of chromosome 21 on to either a D (14 or 15) or another G chromosome (21 or 22). A patient with a Dq Gq translocation has 46 chromosomes in all, including the translocation chromosome This karyotype is effectively trisomic for chromosome 21 and its phenotype is indistinguishable from standard trisomy 21. About one per cent of Down's syndrome patients are mosaics, usually with a mixture of 46 chromosome and 47 chromosome cell lines.

The risk that a woman who has already had a child with Down's syndrome, would have another at a later pregnancy, varies with various factors: the woman's age (higher incidence with **late maternal age**), the karyotype of her child (higher risk with D/G translocation), karyotype of her husband (**carrier of translocation**), and her own karyotype (carrier of translocation) and the family history with respect to Down's syndrome.

Trisomy 18 (E Syndrome): A syndrome of multiple congenital malformations associated with trisomy for an E-group chromosome, no. 18. It is more severe than Down's syndrome, most of the affected infants dying by the age of six months.

D Trisomy (Trisomy 13): This is less commonly seen, as anomalies associated with this trisomy are more severe. The commonly associated anomalies are those of the central nervous system, heart, viscera, genitalia and dermal pattern, cleft lip and palate, and polydactyly.

Cri du chat syndrome: This syndrome is due to partial monosomy: deletion of a portion of the short arm of chromosome 5 (5p–). It is so called because of a fancied resemblance of the infant's cry to the mewing of a cat. The affected children show mental retardation, microcephaly, characteristic facial appearance with marked hypertelorism, and characteristic dermal patterns in the palm and the sole.

Syndromes due to Sex Chromosomal Anomalies:
Mosaicism: Some chromatin-positive males are mosaics, usually 46,XY/47,XXY (Table 20). Some females with Turner's syndrome also show mosaicism.

Fig. 83 Down's syndrome. Note typical mongoloid facies.

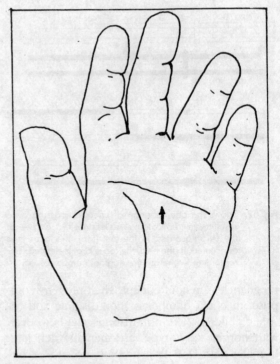

Fig. 84 Down's syndrome. The hand showing single palmar (Simian) crease.

Table 20: Human Sex Chromosomal Anomalies

Male	Female	Gynandric
XXY	XO	
XXXY	XXX	
XXXXY	XXXX	
XYY	XXXXX	
XXYY	XY	
XXXYY	XYY	
XX		
Mosaics		
XY/XXY	XO/XX	XO/XY
XY/XXXY	XY/XXX	XO/XYY
XXXY/XXXXY	XX/XXX	XO/XXY
XY/XXY/XXXY	XXX/XXXX	XX/XY
XXXX/XXXXY/	XO/XX/XXX	XX/XXY
XXXXXY	XX/XXX/	XX/XXYY
	XXXX	XO/XX/XY

Turner's Syndrome (Ovarian Dysgenesis): These phenotypically female patients have 45 chromosomes with only a single X and are chromatin-negative. Those patients of ovarian dysgenesis who are chromatin-positive are mosaics with 45,X/46,XX/47,XXX cell lines or have one normal and one structurally abnormal X.

Table 21: Associated Features of Turner's Syndrome

General
Cubitus valgus
Short metacarpals or metatarsals, usually the fourth
Deformities of the medial tibial condyle
Ostèoporosis

Head and face
Epicanthal folds
High-arched palate
Abnormal teeth
Visual abnormalities, usually strabismus
Auditory defects, usually due to inner ear defects

Neck
Webbed neck
Short, broad neck with low hairline

Chest
Shield chest with apparently widely spaced nipples

Cardiovascular
Coarctation of the aorta or ventricular septal defect

Renal
Horseshoe kidney
Duplicated or otherwise anomalous ureters
Unilateral renal aplasia or hypoplasia

Gastrointestinal
Telangiectasis

Skin and lymphatics
Pigmented naevi
Lymphedema of hands and feet

Nails
Hypoplasia or malformation

Table 22: Turner's Syndrome and other Forms of Gonadal Dysgenesis

Karyotype	Description
45,X	XO, Monosomy for X chromosome
46,X,i(Xq)	Isochromosome for the long-arm of X; or iso-X
46,X,del(Xp) or 46,XXp–	Deletion of the short arm of X
46,X,del(Xq) or 46,XXq–	Deletion of the long arm of X
46,x,r(X)	Ring X
46,X,i(Xp)	Isochromosome for the short arm of X
46,X,i(Yq)	Isochromosome for the long arm of Y
46,X,t(X,X) or 46,X ter rea(X,X)	X-X translocation terminal rearrangement
46,X,t(X, Autosome No.) or 46,X,t(X,Y)	X-autosome or X-Y translocation

Approximately one in every 2500–3500 newborn girls has a chromosomal aberration that leads to **gonadal dysgenesis** or **Turner syndrome**. Embryos with the karyotype 45,X are exception-ally prone to abort. About a fifth of chromosomal abnormalities which lead to first trimester abortions are accounted for by 45,X.

Clinical features. (Fig. 85) Patients with Turner's syndrome usually have a short stature with webbing of the neck, low hairline at the nape of the neck, characteristic facial appearance, wide chest with broadly spaced nipples, poorly developed breasts, juvenile external genitalia and female internal sexual organs with ovary represented by a streak of connective tissue. Commonly associated features are edema of the extremities, coarctation (narrowing) of the aorta and cubitus valgus (reduced carrying angle at the elbow). Axillary and pubic hair are usually present. Primary amenorrhea may be the presenting feature (Table 21).

Cytogenetics. The karyotype 45,X is responsible for about 40–60 per cent of patients with Turner's syndrome. Other karyotypes leading to Turner's syndrome involve structural aberrations of the X and Y chromosomes and mosaicism. Table 22 gives some of the commonly found karyotypes in the Turner's syndrome.

The Xg blood groups in 45,X patients and their parents can reveal whether the single X is paternal or maternal in origin. In about 75 per cent of patients, the single X present is from the mother and in about 25 per cent it is from the father. Maternal-age has no effect as there is for Down's syndrome and other aneuploids. Structurally, abnormal X chromosomes are often paternal in origin. There may be an increased risk of structural aberrations with increasing paternal age.

47,XXX (Triple X) and other X Polysomies: 47,XXX types are usually normal in external appearance, but may be mentally subnormal or psychotic. They have two sex chromatin bodies in their somatic cells. Whenever they have borne children, all of them have been normal. Patients with four or five X chromosomes are also physically normal but show severe mental retardation.

47,XXY (Klinefelter's Syndrome): (Fig. 86). The patients are phenotypically males but show presence of sex chromatin.

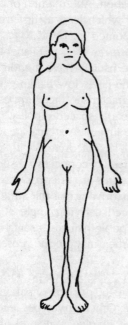

Fig. 85 Turner's syndrome

Approximately one in 1,000 newborn boys has a karyotype which is known to be associated with Klinefelter's syndrome.

Clinical features. The patients with this syndrome have small testes showing hyalinisation of the seminiferous tubules. Secondary sexual characteristics are poorly developed and may be associated with gynecomastia. Many patients are tall and eunuchoid. Mental retardation is a commonly associated feature.

It is frequently reported to be associated with diabetes mellitus, thyroid disorders, peptic ulcers, pulmonary emphysema and hemorrhoids. Acute and chronic leukemias and other cancers are reported more often in association with Klinefelter's syndrome.

Cytogenetics. About 80–90 per cent of all patients with Klinefelter's syndrome have the karyotype 47,XXY. Mosaicism is seen in the remaining 10 per cent, the commonest being 46,XY/47,XXY. The others are 46,XX/47,XXY; 45,X/46,XY/47,XXY; 46,XY/48,XXXY, and 47,XXY/48,XXYY.

Unlike the case of Turner's syndrome, in Klinefelter's syndrome the error is maternal in 64 per cent of cases and paternal in 36 per cent. The error in gametogenesis can occur at either the first or the second meiotic division or at both (seen as rare and more severely abnormal variants of Klinefelter's syndrome with up to four Xs).

47,XYY Males: Males with this karyotype are indistinguishable from normal males on the basis of their phenotype and behaviour. Some correlation has been found between XYY and aggressive, psychopathic or criminal behaviour.

XYY males originate by paternal non-disjunction at the second meiotic division, which produces YY sperm. XXYY and XXXYY males are less common. Such males also probably originate by paternal non-disjunction by a series of nondisjunctional events.

Intersex: An intersex is defined as an individual with ambiguous genitalia. Intersex conditions are

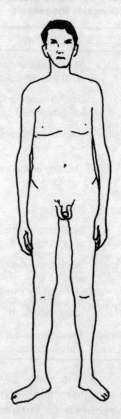

Fig. 86 Klinefelter's syndrome

Table 23: Types, Basis and Features of Hermaphrodites

Type	Basis	Features
True hermaphrodite	Paternally derived X chromosome carries the SRY gene which is responsible for conversion of a gonad or part of the gonadal tissue into testis	Karyotype 46,XX, or a mosaic with 46,XX/46,XY or 45,X/46,XY, or sometimes a chimera with 46,XX 46,XY cell lines; gonadal tissue of both sexes: ovary and testis, or ovo-testis
Male Pseudohermaphrodite	Defects in testosterone synthesis and metabolism due to a variety of enzyme deficiencies; defects in androgen action due to (a) 5α reductase enzyme deficiency leading to lack of conversion of testosterone into dihydro-testosterone, and (b) testosterone receptor defect	Karyotype 46,XY; with testis; incomplete masculinisation — small phallus, with or without undescended testis, male or female internal genitalia
Female pseudohermaphrodite	Congenital adrenal hyperplasia resulting in excessive androgen production; maternal androgen exposure; androgen secreting tumour	Karyotype 46,XX; with ovary; masculinisation of external genitalia — partially fused labia majora, clitoral enlargement

not always due to aberrations of sex chromosomes. They can also be due to single mutant genes. The various types of intersex seen clinically are true hermaphroditism and pseudohermaphroditism. Table 23 gives features of hermaphrodites. The great majority of true hermaphrodites are 46,XX but some are 46,XX/46,XY chimeras or are 46,XY and have only testicular tissue. Female pseudohermaphrodites are 46,XX and have only ovarian tissue. Male pseudohermaphroditism is due to testicular feminisation, which is probably an X-linked disorder and is characterised by unresponsiveness of target organ to testosterone, possibly due to its inability to convert it to its active form, dihydrotestosterone. Phenotypically, the person may have been reared as a male or a female. Female pseudohermaphroditism is commonly due to congenital adrenal hyperplasia. Several distinct genetic and clinical forms of congenital adrenal hyperplasia are seen, inherited as an autosomal recessivetrait. Each disorder is characterised by a block in a specific step in cortisol biosynthesis, resulting in increased secretion of ACTH and hyperplasia of adrenal glands, which leads to masculinisation of female

fetuses. Affected female children have major anomalies in the genitalia which makes it difficult to identify the child as a female. In males the same genotype produces premature virilisation, but there is no difficulty in identifying the sex. Other forms of **female pseudohermaphroditism** may be due to presence of excessive amounts of male or female sex hormones in the fetal circulation. The excessive hormones reach the fetal circulation from the maternal circulation. The mother has higher levels of hormones either due to overproduction or due to therapeutic administration.

Causes of Chromosomal Aberrations: The exact genetic and environmental factors which lead to chromosomal aberrations are not known. What is observed is that some factors predispose to chromosomal aberrations. Late maternal age is a common factor observed in the majority of cases of Down's syndrome but is of less significance in other trisomies. Radiation, viruses, autoimmune diseases and specific genes have been held responsible for non-disjunction or other chromosomal aberrations.

The factors mentioned above are operative for sex chromosomal anomalies also. The basis of all numerical anomalies of sex chromosomes is non-disjunction. The non-disjunctional event occurs at either the first or the second meiotic division in one of the parents during gametogenesis. The non-disjunction occurring in early divisions of the zygote leads to mosaicism.

A study of the gene for the Xg blood group and other X-linked marker genes of the parents and the abnormal child, is useful in finding out in which parent the non-disjunctional event took place.

Mendelian Disorders with Cytogenic Effects: There are several single-gene syndromes in which there is characteristic cytogenetic abnormality. The most common is the fragile X syndrome which is X-linked. The other known disorders are ataxia telangiectasia, Bloom syndrome, Fanconi anemia, Roberts syndrome and xeroderma pigmentosum. All of these are autosomal recessive traits. These disorders have a specific chromosomal defect. They have an underlying molecular defect in chromosome replication or repair. In fragile X syndrome and Bloom syndrome there is sister-chromatid exchange.

All these syndromes are associated with chromosome breakage and increased risk of cancer. It is hoped that further correlation between decreased ability to replicate and/or repair DNA and increased incidence of cancer will reveal the relationship between mutagenesis and carcinogenesis.

Fragile X Syndrome: This is the common cause of mental retardation in males and is characterised by mental retardation, macroorchidism, increased head circumference, large ears and chin. It is associated with a fragile site on the long arm of X chromosome as observed during laboratory culture under conditions of thymidime deprivation. Affected males are mentally retarded; carrier females show mild retardation. CCG triplets occur 6–50 times in a normal individual, 50–230 times in an individual who is premutant. There is an expansion of premutant state from the female to the next generation, but not from the male, to frank mutation of more than 230 repetition of CGG nucleotides.

SUMMARY

Chromosomes may be abnormal either in number or in structure.

Numerical abnormalities are 'euploid' when exact multiples of a chromosome set occur in a cell, or 'aneuploid' when one or more chromosome is more or less than the set.
Structural abnormalities are:
1) Deletion: The elimination of a part of chromosome following a chromosomal break.
2) Ring chromosome: Following terminal breaks, the chromosomal ends join each other.
3) Translocation: This occurs due to breaks in two non-homologous chromosomes and the attachment of broken pieces to the wrong chromosome. A mutual 'wrong' exchange is called reciprocal translocation.
4) Isochromosome: A duplication-deletion anomaly due to transverse split of a metaphase chromosome instead of a longitudinal one. Results in metacentric chromosomes in which their two limbs carry identical gene loci.
5) Inversion: Following two breaks within a chromosome, the segment in between gets reversed and reattached in the same chromosome. The gene loci in the fragment get 'inverted' in sequence. An inversion may include the centromere ('pericentric)' or exclude it — 'paracentric.).
6) Duplication: The representation of a portion or fragment of a chromosome more than twice in a zygotic or more than once in a gametic. Usually occurs due to 'unequal crossing over' in meiosis. It can also occur during gametogenesis in a carrier of translocation, of inversion or of ring chromosome.

Microdeletion: This is a subtype of chromosome deletion that can be observed only using high resolution banding or tools of molecular genetics like FISH. Microdeletion involves deletion of a few contiguous genes.

Mosaicism: Two or more different karyotypes in an individual derived from a single zygote is called mosaicism. Causes could be non-disjunction or structural chromosomal anomaly in early embryonic development.

Chimerism: Two or more different karyotypes, in an individual, derived from separate zygotes is called chimerism. Common causes include sharing of placenta by dizygotic twins.

Numerical abnormalities are:
1) Polyploidy: An euploidy in which an exact multiple other than diploid of a full set of chromosomes of a gamete occurs in a nucleus.
2) Trisomy: An aneuploidy in which one extra chromosome occurs in a nucleus. Examples of trisomy are Down's syndrome (trisomy 21), Klinefelter's syndrome (trisomy XXY).
3) Monosomy: An aneuploidy in which there is one chromosome less than the species specific or 2 number. Example of monosomy is Turner's syndrome (monosomy X).
Radiation, viruses, some drugs and chemicals, autoimmune disease and late maternal age predispose to chromosomal anomalies. The basis of all numerical sex chromosome anomalies is non-disjunction, i.e., a failure of separation or detachment from each other, of the paired homologous chromosomes, either at the first or second meiotic division.
Fragile X syndrome : Due to an X-linked single gene syndrome. It is the most common cause of mental retardation in males.

BIOCHEMICAL GENETICS

Introduction

The chemistry of most living systems centres round the DNA and the wide array of proteins which it codes for. The DNA–protein interactions and interdependence form the basis of such phenomena as cell growth and differentiation, structural and metabolic transformations within cells, and individual variations in responses to drugs. Since all proteins, whether structural or enzymatic are inherited, it follows that any gene mutations are likely to be reflected in the altered structure or in the altered enzyme-dependent metabolic functions.

The study of Biochemical genetics covers inborn errors of metabolism, the inheritance of normal and abnormal hemoglobins in their embryonic, fetal and adult stages, and pharmacogenetics, i.e., the study of genetic variations in responses to various drugs. It also includes the study of factors influencing the inheritance of various blood groups and the immunoglobulins. In view of their outstanding importance in medicine, they are discussed in detail here.

INBORN ERRORS OF METABOLISM

Garrod first put forth the idea that metabolic processes in living organisms proceed in steps. Each step is governed by one enzyme. **Beadle** and **Tatum** further developed the concept of **one gene-one enzyme**, i.e., each enzyme is the product of one gene. A gene defect leads to a specific total or partial enzyme defect, which in turn leads to a metabolic block, producing pathologic consequences.

An inborn error of metabolism is defined as a genetically determined biochemical disorder in which a specific enzyme defect produces a **metabolic block** that may have pathological consequences. Some characteristic examples are phenylketonuria, alkaptonuria, albinism and galactosemia. Table 24 describes uses some of these errors, their chief clinical manifestations, specific enzyme defect, mode of inheritance, carrier detection and antenatal diagnosis. Such disorders can be classified into those of:

1) **Amino acid metabolism**, e.g., phenylketonuria, alkaptonuria and albinism.
2) **Lipid metabolism**, e.g., Tay-Sachs disease (GM_2 gangliosidosis, infantile amaurotic familial idiocy), Niemann-Pick disease (a sphingomyelin lipidosis).
3) **Mucopolysaccharide metabolism,** e.g., Hurler's syndrome, Hunter's syndrome and other mucopolysaccharidoses.
4) **Purine and pyrimidine metabolism**, e.g., Lesch-Nyhan syndrome.
5) **Copper metabolism**, e.g., Wilson's disease (hepatolenticular degeneration).
6) **Amino acid transport**, e.g., cystinuria. Most of these disorders are inherited as autosomal recessives. Some of them are X-linked, e.g., glucose-6-phosphate dehydrogenase (G6PD) variants, hypoxanthineguanine phosphoribosyl transferase (HGPRT) deficiency (Lesch-Nyhan syndrome), the type of glycogen storage disease associated with phosphorylase kinase deficiency and pseudohypoparathyroidism (an X-linked dominant).
7) **Urea cycle disorders**, e.g., ornithine transcarbamoylase deficiency.
8) **Carbohydrate metabolism**, e.g., galactosemia and glycogen storage diseases like McArdle's diseases and Pompe's disease.
9) **Steroid metabolism**, e.g., congenital adrenal hyperplasia, testicular feminisation.
10) **Lipoprotein metabolism**, e.g., familial hypercholesterolemia.
11) **Porphyrin metabolism**, e.g., Hepatic porphyrias like acute intermittent porphyria, hereditary caproporphyria, porphyria variegata and erythropoietic porphyrias like congenital erythropoietic porphyria.
12) **Organic acid disorders,** e.g., methylmalonic acidemia, propionic acidemia.
13) **Thyroid hormone biosynthesis defect,** e.g., Congenital thyroxine deficiency.

Table 24 : Summary of Genetically Determined Biochemical Disorders

Disorder	Chief Clinical Manifestations	Specific Defective Enzyme/Protein	Inheritance	Heterozygote Detection	Prenatal Diagnosis in Cultured Amniotic Fluid Cells
Acatalasia	Oral gangrene; may be entirely normal	Catalase	Autosomal recessive	Low activity of catalase in some but not all types	—
Albinism	Absence of pigmentation in skin and eyes, visual disorders	Tyrosinase (in one common type)	Heterogeneous; usually autosomal recessive but autosomal dominant and X-linked types exist	—	—
Cystinuria	Aminoaciduria, renal lithiasis	Not known; affects transport of cys, lys, arg and orn	Type 1 autosomal recessive; Types II, III incompletely recessive	In Types II and III, increased urinary excretion of cys, lys, arg and orn	—
Galactosemia	Hepatosplenomegaly, cirrhosis of liver, cataract, mental retardation	Galactose-1-phosphate uridyl transferase	Autosomal recessive; milder Duarte variant is allelic	Reduced enzyme activity	Absent enzyme activity
Gaucher's disease	Hepatosplenomegaly, neurological problems, anemia, thrombocytopenia	Glucocerebrosidase	Autosomal recessive; two or more major types	Reduced activity of ß-glucosidase in cultured fibroblasts	Absent enzyme activity
Glucose-6-phosphate dehydrogenase variants	Hemolytic anemia in response to certain foods and drugs	Glucose-6-phosphate dehydrogenase	X-linked; numerous variants	Electrophoretic variants; variants with altered enzyme activity	Theoretically possible
GM$_2$ gangliosidosis (Tay-Sachs disease)	Degenerative neurological changes, cherry-red spot on macula, severe physical and mental retardation; onset 4 to 6 months of age, death 2 to 4	Hexosaminidase A	Autosomal recessive	Reduced level of hexosaminidase A	Absence of hexosaminidase A

Table 24 : (Continued)

Disorder	Chief Clinical Manifestations	Specific Defective Enzyme/Protein	Inheritance	Heterozygote Detection	Prenatal Diagnosis in Cultured Amniotic Fluid Cells
	years				
Hemoglobinopathies	Anemia secondary manifestations depend upon nature of hemoglobin abnormality	Constituent polypeptide of hemoglobin β or α chain	Autosomal clinical manifestations usually recessive; numerous variants	Usually by electrophoresis	—
Isoniazid inactivation, slow	Neurological problem	Acetyltransferase	Autosomal recessive	—	—
Mucopolysaccharidoses (Hurler's syndrome Type I)	Gargoyle facies, mental retardation, hepatosplenomegaly, hearing defect, corneal clouding, cardiovascular problems, dwarfism	Not known; produces mucopolysaccharide accumulation	Autosomal recessive	Excessive storage of certain mucopolysaccharides in cultured fibroblasts	Excessive storage of certain mucopolysaccharides
(Hunter's syndrome Type II)	Similar to Hurler's though corneal clouding is rare	Not known; produces mucopolysaccharide accumulation	X-linked	Excessive storage of certain mucopolysaccharides in cultured fibroblasts	Excessive storage of certain mucopolysaccharides
Niemann-Pick disease	Hepatomegaly, splenomegaly, severe central nervous system damage, cherryred spot on macula	Sphingomyelinase	Autosomal recessive	Potentially by assay of sphingomyelinase in cultured fibroblasts	Absence of sphingomyelinase
Pentosuria	Excretion of a reducing substance in urine, but no symptoms of diabetes mellitus	Xylitol dehydrogenase	Autosomal recessive	Intermediate level of xylitol dehydrogenase; abnormal response to loading test	—
Phenylketonuria	Mental retardation microcephaly diluted pigmentation	Phenylalanine hydroxylase	Autosomal recessive	Plasma phe and phe/tyr ratio above normal	—

Table 24 : (Continued)

Disorder	Chief Clinical Manifestations	Specific Defective Enzyme/Protein	Inheritance	Heterozygote Detection	Prenatal Diagnosis in Cultured Amniotic Fluid Cells
Porphyria, acute intermittent	Episodes of abdominal pain, neurological problems, excessive urinary excretion of δ -amino levulinic acid (ALA)	Excessive production of hepatic ALA synthetase	Autosomal recessive	Patients are usually heterozygous	—
Wilson's disease	Cirrhosis of liver, Kayser-Fleisher ring in cornea, neurological problems	Not known; affects copper metabolism	Autosomal recessive	Decreased serum ceruloplasmin and serum Cu in some but not all heterozygotes	—

14) **Paroxysmal disorders,** e.g., Zellweger's syndrome, adrenoleukodystrophy.

15) **Serum protein α, antitrypsin deficiency.**

16) **Complement deficiency**, e.g., Hereditary angioneurotic edema.

17) **End organ insensitivity,** e.g., Vitamin D resistant rickets.

A large number of biochemical defects, which produce inborn errors of metabolism, are now being detected. Usually the mutation in the gene, which codes for the normal enzyme, involves substitution of a single amino acid. Clinically the picture is diverse, ranging in severity from relatively mild, harmless disorders to the lethal.

The clinical picture is the result of disturbances brought about by the **metabolic block** which leads to:

1) **Accumulation of a precursor** just preceding the step where there is a block. The accumulated precursor itself can have toxic effects, or with alternate minor pathways, may lead to production of toxic metabolites.

2) **Stoppage of subsequent steps in the metabolism.** Whenever a feedback mechanism is involved in the control of metabolism, such deficiency would lead to overproduction of the stimulating agent.

Phenylketonuria (Fig. 87) is a typical example. Clinically the child is found to have severe mental retardation; many untreated patients have TQ less than 20. Because of tyrosine deficiency arising from metabolic block, there is reduction in melanin formation. Affected children have blonde hair and blue eyes; regions of the brain which are normally pigmented such as the substantia nigra, may also lack pigment.

In most of these disorders, it is difficult to provide any substitute for the deficient enzyme. The principal treatment is to cut off from the diet those articles of food which are rich in the substance which the patient cannot metabolise, so that these toxic substances will not accumulate. For phenylketonuria, removal of phenylalanine from the diet constitutes an effective treatment. It has been suggested that **newborns** should be screened for conditions like phenylketonuria, since phenylketonuric children are deceptively normal at birth as the maternal enzyme substitutes the missing enzyme during intrauterine development. Treatment is most effective when the diagnosis is made soon after birth and measures instituted immediately. If the child is given phenylalanine even for some time, **irreversible mental retardation** occurs because of accumulation of toxic

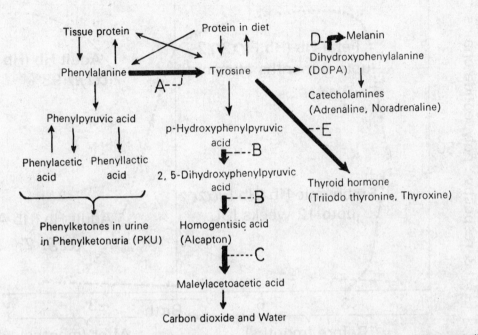

Fig. 87 Phenylalanine and tyrosine metabolism. Sites of enzyme block A, B, C, D and E and their consequences indicated.

metabolites of phenylala-nine in the brain. The condition can be diagnosed by tests, which detect phenylpyruvic acid in the urine (ferric chloride test) or excess of phenylala-nine in the blood (**Guthrie test**).

In a number of genetic disorders resulting from a mutant gene, a particular protein is either not synthesised at all or, although synthesised, is defective. For example in **hemophilia** there is a deficiency of functionally active antihemophilic globulin which is required for normal coagulation of blood. In most patients with hemophilia, antihe-mophilic globulin is synthesised but is not active, the factor being replaced by a functionally inactive but antigenically similar factor.

Hemoglobins

Hemoglobin is a tetramer with a molecular weight of 64500 Daltons. It consists of 2 α and 2 non-α globin polypeptide chains, each of which has a covalently bound hem group. Each of the four hem groups is made up of an iron atom bound within a protoporphyrin IX ring.

In human beings, 6 different **globin polypeptide** chains are known. They are called α,β,γ,δ,ε and ζ. Each chain consists of a specific sequence of amino acids linked by peptide bonds. The α chain has 141 amino acids, while the β,γ,δ and the ε chains have 146. The ε,γ and δ chains are more like β than like α-chains, differing from β at 36, 39 and 10 positions respectively. The two globins ε and ζ are found in **embryonic erythrocytes** and while the ζ sequence is incompletely known, it appears to be an analogue of the α chain.

HbA ($\alpha_2\beta_2$) is usually 92 per cent of the total hemoglobin in normal adults. HbA$_2$ ($\alpha_2\delta_2$) is about 2.5 per cent. HbA$_{1C}$ differs from HbA by the post-translation addition of a glucose at NH$_2$-terminus of the β chain α_2 (β–N–glucose)$_2$. It is usually about 5 per cent. It is related to the intercellular concentration of glucose and the red cell lifespan.

HbA ($\alpha_2\gamma_2$) makes up the bulk of hemoglobin (50–85%) in newborns. It declines rapidly after birth, to become 10 to 15 per cent by 4 months of age (Fig. 88).

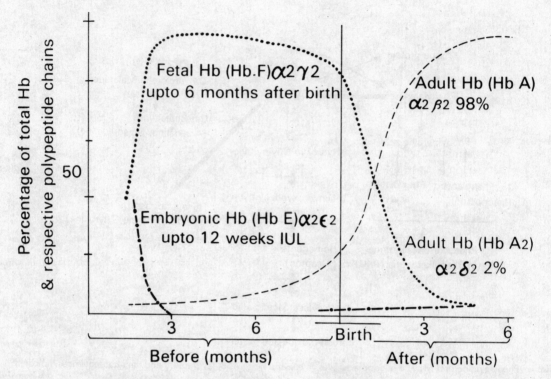

Fig. 88 Normal hemoglobins in prenatal and postnatal life.

Hemoglobins Gower 1 ($\zeta_2\gamma_2$), Gower II ($\alpha_2\epsilon_2$) and Portland ($\zeta_2\gamma_2$) are embryonic hemoglobins found in fetuses before 7 to 10 weeks of gestation. At 4 to 5 weeks of intrauterine life, a simultaneous decrease of ζ and ϵ-chain production and an increase in π and γ chain production takes place.

Hemoglobins H and Barts are tetramers of $\beta-$ and γ-chains respectively. They function very poorly in oxygen transport.

The globin genes are expressed at different times and in different relative amounts during human development.

Genetics of Hemoglobins: In humans there are nine different genetic loci which code for the six globin genes. In addition there are at least three pseudogenes, which have sequences similar to other globin genes, but which differ in having some altered sequences which prevent their expression and therefore the production of functional globin chains.

Fig. 89 represents schematically the various globin genes and their products.

Since in an individual a diploid set of chromosomes exists, there are 4α and 2β loci in all. The relative numbers of α and β loci are important in understanding the different inheritance patterns of α and β-thalassemias. The β-like genes (ϵ, G^γ, A^γ, δ) are β located on chromosome 11.

The α-gene complex contains two α loci, two ζ loci and at least one pseudo $-\alpha$ locus ($\psi\alpha$); and is found on chromosome 16.

Hemoglobinopathies: These are a group of disorders characterised by some abnormality of the hemoglobin molecule.

It has been estimated that about 250 thousand children are born every year in the world with some disorder of the structure or synthesis of hemoglobin. This group of disorders is known as hemoglobinopathies. Its study has also helped

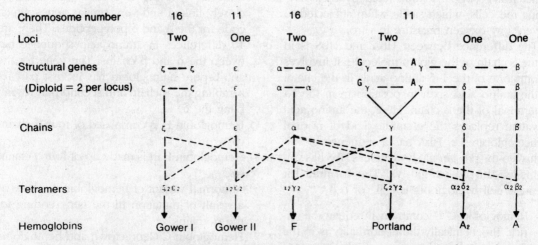

Fig. 89   Scheme to show the various normal and abnormal hemoglobin loci and their products. Two loci for ζ on chromosome 16. Two loci for α on chromosome 16. One locus for ε on chromosome 11. Two loci for γ, i.e., Gγ and Aγ on chromosome 11. One locus for δ on chromosome 11. One locus for ß on chromosome 11.

geneticists to understand the pathology of inherited disease at the individual, cellular and molecular levels.

Abnormal Hemoglobins: These are produced by mutations in α,β,γ,δ,ε and ζ genes, i.e., genes which determine the amino acid sequence of the globin portion of the hemoglobin molecule. Several hundred abnormal hemoglobin variants have been detected by now. Table 25 shows the normal and some of the abnormal hemoglobins and their formulae.

The varieties of mutations responsible for Hb variants are deletion, insertion, frame-shift, point and fusion polypeptides. In deletion one or more of the amino acids of one of the globin chains is missing. In insertion, globin chains are longer than normal. In point mutation and frame-shift mutation variants, the globin chain is either elongated or shortened. In fusion, polypeptides type of variants are due to unequal crossing over in meiosis.

Many of the hemoglobin variants are harmless. They do not interfere with normal function. They are usually identified incidentally in the course of electrophoretic surveys of hemoglobin in a population. The structural variants of hemoglobin identified by electrophoretic techniques represent only a small number of variants which can be theoretically predicted to exist. This is because only a third of possible Hb mutations can produce an altered charge in the hemoglobin molecule to become detectable by electrophoresis.

There are some hemoglobin variants which interfere with normal function and structure of hemoglobin molecule. Any mutation interfering with the structure of globin subunits or inclose proximity of the hem pocket of the chain or interchain contact areas produces an unstable hemoglobin molecule which gets precipitated in the RBC, damaging the cell membrane and resulting in hemolysis. If the mutation interferes with the normal oxygen transport function, it can increase or decrease oxygen affinity. It can alter the hemoglobin molecule which can remain stable in its reduced form known as methemoglobin.

1) Sickle cell hemoglobin (HbS). It was the first abnormal hemoglobin to be detected electrophoretically and is the most important clinically. The patient's red cells become grossly abnormal in shape (**sickled**) under low oxygen tension. Fig. 90 shows the important clinical features of sickle cell disease, which is common in equatorial Africa, the Mediterranean region and in India. Parents of affected children are usually normal clinically but their

heterozygosity is demonstrated by their having red cells, which sickle when subjected to very low oxygen pressure in vitro.

The difference between HbA and HbS is in the ß chain of the globin molecule. It involves only one of the 146 amino acids in the chain, the amino acid sixth in position from the N-terminal of the ß chain. Here, the amino acid valine replaces the glutamic acid of normal hemoglobin, i.e. HbA has a sequence of val-his-leu-thr-pro-*glu*-glu-lys whereas HbS has val-his-leu-thr-pro-*val*-glu-lys. The formula for sickle cell hemoglobin is $\alpha_2\beta_2^{\,s}$ or $\alpha_2\beta_2^{\,s(val)}$.

2) Hemoglobin C is common in equatorial Africa. Biochemically the abnormality is in the ß chain, and involves precisely the same position in the amino acid sequence as is involved in sickle cell hemoglobin. In HbC, lysine replaces the glutamic acid of HbA at the sixth amino acid from the N-terminal.

3) Hemoglobin Lepore is an abnormal hemoglobin in which the α chain is normal but the non-α chain has portions of the N-terminal portion of a normal δ, and the C-terminal portion of a normal β chain. The possible mode of origin of Lepore hemoglobin is from

Table 25: Examples of Normal and Abnormal Hemoglobins

Hemoglobins	Formulae
Normal	
HbA	$\alpha_2\beta_2$
HbA$_2$	$\alpha_2\delta_2$
HbF	$\alpha_2\gamma_2^{\,136gly}$ $\alpha_2\gamma_2^{\,136ala}$
Gower I	$\zeta_2\epsilon_2$
Gower II (Embryonic)	$\alpha_2\epsilon_2$
Variants	
HbS	$\alpha_2\beta_2^{\,s}(\alpha_2\beta_2^{\,6glu\square val})$
HbC	$\alpha_2\beta_2^{\,c}(\alpha_2\beta_2^{\,6glu\square lys})$
HbLepore	$\alpha_2\delta-\beta_2$
Hb Hopkins-2	$\alpha_2Ho\text{-}2\beta_2$ $(\alpha_2^{\,112\ his\ \square\ asp}\beta_2)$
HbH	β_4

unequal crossing over between the two closely linked and very similar genes which code for the β and δ polypeptides. There are 10 differences in amino acid sequence between the δ and β chains. The gene for the anti-Lepore hemoglobin has its first part resembling the ß chain and second part resembling the δ.

4) Hemoglobin H is composed of four β chains (β_4)

5) Hemoglobin Bart is made up of four γ chains (α_4)

6) Abnormal variant of hemoglobin A$_2$ arises as a result of mutation in the gene coding for the α chains.

7) Hemoglobin C Georgetown and hemoglobin C Harlem are two abnormal hemoglobins where two separate amino acids are substituted in the same polypeptide chain. Possibly this arises as a result of a second mutation in the ß^s allele or intragenic crossing over during meiosis between two ß genes carrying mutations at different sites.

8) Hemoglobin Gun Hill $(\alpha_2\beta_2^{\,93-97}$ deletion) has lost five amino acids in the ß chain and hemoglobin Freiburg $(\alpha_2\beta_2^{\,23}$ deletion) has lost one amino acid in the β chain. These deletions possibly arise as a result of abnormal pairing and intragenic crossing over during meiosis.

9) Hemoglobin Constant Spring has a α chain of 172 amino acids instead of the usual 141, possibly a result of mutation of the codon which terminates the chain; so that the polypeptide continues to add amino acids till the next termination codon halts it.

10) Hereditary persistence of high fetal hemoglobin. In this rare condition, the homozygote has no normal adult hemoglobin HbA or HbA$_2$. No abnormalities are detected clinically. In affected persons, the β and δ loci fail to be switched on and the γ locus remains functional in postnatal life. The gene for HbF appears to be closely linked with or allelic to the β gene.

11) Thalassemias (Cooley's anemia, Mediterra-

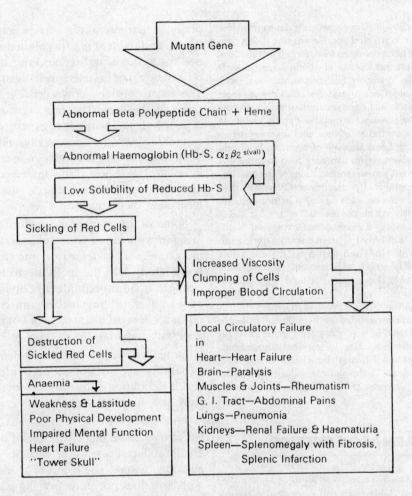

Fig. 90 Scheme to show the formation of sickle cell hemoglobin and its consequences.

nean anemia) are a group of hereditary disorders characterised by red blood cells having target cell appearance. The abnormality is due to decreased synthesis of a particular globin chain. The defect may involve β chains, δ chains, β and δ chains, or α chains and hence the names β thalassemia, δ thalassemia and so on. Clinically there are two forms, a severe form, thalassemia major (homozygous), and a mild form, thalassemia minor or thalassemia trait (heterozygous).

The pathophysiology is similar in all forms of thalassemia. There is an imbalance of α or β chain production. This results in accumulation of free α or β chains in the RBC precursors. These chains are insoluble and hence they get precipitated, resulting in the hemolysis of RBCs. This causes hemolytic anemia and compensatory hyperplasia of the bone marrow.

Family studies suggest that the β thalassemia gene is either allelic to the β chain gene or closely linked to it, where perhaps the β thalassemia mutation affects the operator gene.

SUMMARY

Biochemical genetics: Study of genes governing biochemical processes — inborn errors of metabolism, hemoglobinopathies, immunoglobinopathies, and pharmacogenetics.

Inborn error of metabolism: Genetically determined biochemical disorder in which a specific enzyme defect produces a metabolic block resulting in abnormal metabolism. Disorder can affect metabolism of amino acids (phenylketonuria), lipids, mucopolysaccharides, purines, pyrimidines, copper, etc. Clinical manifestation results from (a) a metabolic block leading to accumulation of a precursor, (b) stoppage of subsequent metabolic steps leading to deficiency of an essential substance, and (c) overproduction of stimulating agent because of negative feedback. Screening of newborn population may help to intervene very early to prevent gross manifestations of the disease.

Normal hemoglobin: It is a tetramer of 2α and 2 non-α globin polypeptide chains, each having a hem group. Six different globin polypeptide chains exist α, β, γ, δ, ϵ and ζ. Nine genetic loci code of 6 globin genes, expressed at different times and in different relative amounts during human development. HbA (a_2b_2) HbA$_2$ (a_2d_2) are adult hemoglobins, HbF (a_2g_2) is fetal hemoglobin. Hemoglobins Gower I (z_2e_2), Gower II (a_2e_2) and Portland (z_2g_2) are embryonic hemoglobins.

Hemoglobinopathies: It is a group of disorders characterised by some abnormality of the hemoglobin molecule produced by mutation in α, β, γ, δ, ϵ and ζ genes. Several hundred abnormal hemoglobins are known. Commonly encountered are sickle cell hemoglobin (HbS). Hemoglobin C, Hemoglobin Lepore. Thalassemias are due to decreased synthesis of any particular globin chain, viz., β, δ, β and δ or α chains.

PHARMACOGENETICS

Pharmacogenetics is a special branch of biochemical genetics that deals with the genetically determined variations in drug responses.

There is a normal variation in response to all the drugs in a given population. Such a continuous variation is explained on the basis of polygenic inheritance or combination of genetic and environmental factors. But in response to some drugs, there is discontinuous variation, with sharp distinctions between different degrees of response. Usually, discontinuous variation has a genetic basis.

The specific genes may affect the metabolism of drugs, precipitate the clinical presentation of certain genetic diseases or increase the frequency of certain side effects.

Genes Affecting Drug Metabolism: Usually when a drug is introduced into the body either orally or parenterally it passes into the blood stream and thereby gets distributed into the various tissue fluids and tissues. The drug is either broken down or excreted unchanged by the body. The actual breaking down process usually takes place in the liver. The process varies with the type of drug. Some drugs are oxidised to carbondioxide to be thrown out during expiration. Some are excreted by kidneys into urine or by liver into bile. Some drugs undergo biochemical modifications which increase their solubility facilitating their excretion.

Some of the important modifications are conjugation with carbohydrate glucuronic acid (e.g., morphine and codeine) or introduction of an acetyl group into the molecule-acetylation (e.g., isoniazid, sulphonamides). Polymorphism in genes affecting drug metabolism can have significant effect on the activity of enzymes that are necessary for drugs.

Drugs known to show well-defined genetic variability are hydrogen peroxide, isoniazid, succinylcholine, primaquine, some anti-coagulants and anesthetic agents.

Hydrogen peroxide. Acatalasemia or acatalasia is a rare recessive trait characterised by absence or greatly reduced activity of catalase in the blood and other tissues. The blood of an individual with acatalasia does not show frothing with H_2O_2, nor does it turn red; instead it turns brownish-black.

Isoniazid. This is a drug used in the treatment of tuberculosis. Based on the rate of metabolism of isoniazid, a population can be classified into rapid inactivators (homozygous or heterozygous for a dominant gene producing isoniazid inactivating enzyme) and slow inactivators (homozygous for the recessive gene). Slow inactivation of this drug is because of lack of the hepatic enzyme acetyltransferase, the enzyme that normally acetylates isoniazid as one step in its metabolism.

Propranolol. It is a β-blocker commonly used in the treatment of hypertension and angina. Some individuals having lower activity of enzyme cytochrome F-450 system involved in its metabolism show increased frequency of side effects at usual doses.

Ethanol. Individuals show varied responses to ethanol. This is due to polymorphism in the enzyme alcohol dehydrogenase. Those persons who metabolise alcohol faster show rapid production of byproducts of ethanol and its increased clinical effects.

Succinylcholine. This is a drug made up of two molecules of acetylcholine and is metabolised by the enzyme serum pseudocholinesterase. It is used as a muscle relaxant in anesthesia and in electroconvulsive therapy. Normally the effect of the drug — paralysis of all muscles including those of respiration — is transient. However, about 1 in 2000 patients has an **abnormal pseudocholinesterase** or no enzyme at all and in such individuals the paralysis lasts for an unduly long time. Such highly sensitive response to succinylcholine is inherited as an **autosomal recessive trait**.

The activity of cholinesterase in the plasma is determined by two codominant alleles, known as E_1^u and E_1^a. (E_1 signifies the first esterase locus to be described; the superscripts u and a denote genes responsible respectively for the usual and atypical forms of the enzyme). Cholinesterase alteration occurs in persons who are **homozygous for the mutant allele** E_1^a; the enzyme produced by $E_1^a E_1^a$ homozygotes is qualitatively altered and has lower activity than the usual type. The E_1 locus is on chromosome 1. A third allele E_1^s (silent) has been postulated. Either $E_1^a E_1^a$ or $E_1^a E_1^s$ can produce the atypical phenotype, and $E_1^s E_1^s$ produces no activity at all. A fourth allele at the E_1 locus E_1^f, produces a type of cholinesterase in which the enzyme is usually resistant to inhibition by sodium fluoride. A locus on chromosome 16 determining cholinesterase activity, E_2 accounts for a serum cholinesterase isozyme that is detectable only by electrophoresis.

Primaquine. This drug is used for malaria. It is known to be capable of inducing hemoloytic anemia in some patients. The cause of primaquine sensitivity is deficiency in the red cells of the enzyme glucose-6-phosphate dehydrogenase (G6PD). Persons with G6PD deficiency are sensitive to other drugs like phenacetin, nitrofurantoin, some sulphonamides and acetylsalicylic acid.

Sensitive individuals also develop hemolytic crisis after eating fava beans (favism). G6PD deficiency is inherited as an X-linked recessive trait.

The specific biochemical role of G6PD is in the hexosemonophosphate shunt pathway, which is the minor pathway for red cell glycolysis. Ninety per cent of red cell glycolysis takes place through the anerobic pathway. It is only when some drugs are taken that this minor shunt pathway is stressed. When an infection or some other precipitating factor is present, greater number of drugs can cause hemolysis, e.g., acetylsalicylic acid.

Though G6PD deficiency is more common in males, it is possible for females to inherit two abnormal alleles and thus get affected.

Anticoagulants. Coumarin anticoagulants are needed in much higher dosage than normal, in some individuals who have increased resistance to the effects of the drug. The trait is inherited as an autosomal dominant trait.

Anesthetic Agents. Agents like halothane and succinylcholine bring about a rare complication of anesthesia — malignant hyperpyrexia — in some individuals. The basic defect in this disorder appears to be a reduced uptake and binding of calcium ions to the sarcoplasmic reticulum. This trait is inherited as an autosomal dominant, with a frequency of 1 in 10,000.

To determine whether a person has inherited the gene for this particular disorder, a muscle biopsy can be carried out to assess an abnormal contraction in response to caffeine or other stimulatory agents. The gene for malignant hyperthermia has been mapped on chromosome 19.

HLA. Some individuals show abnormal response to some drugs (e.g., Gold therapy) because of the presence of specific HLA haplotype.

There are some hereditary disorders where the drug response is altered. For example, barbiturates can precipitate an attack of porphyria; sulphonamides can cause severe hemolysis in individuals with hemoglobinopathies such as hemoglobin H, hemoglobin Zurich; chlorthiazide, a diuretic, can precipitate gout in susceptible individuals.

Taste sensitivity to phenylthiocarbamide (PTC) shows genetic polymorphism. Non-tasters are homozygous for the recessive allele.

Clinical Importance of Pharmacogenetics: A clinician has to bear in mind the fact that genes can alter the therapeutic response to drugs or that drugs may precipitate clinical manifestations of genetic disease. Family history is an useful indicator. In general drug metabolism, process of absorption, distribution, binding to receptors and degradation have a genetic basis.

Ecogenetics: This is an extension of the study of pharmacogenetics. It includes genetically determined differences in susceptibility to the action of physical, chemical and infectious agents present in the environment. This variation can be determined either by single gene or by polygenic and/or multifactorial inheritance. Compounds which are used in industry like organophosphates, aromatic amines, benzpyrenes considered as carcinogens for cancers of the bladder, lungs, etc. The varied susceptibility of common diseases in the population is now ascribed to genetically determined differences in response to environmental agents.

SUMMARY

Pharmacogenetics deals with genetically determined variations in drug response. Individuals with well-defined genetic variability respond abnormally to drugs such as hydrogen peroxide, isoniazid, succinylcholine, primaquine, coumarin (anticoagulant), anesthetic agents like halothane. The abnormal response is based on a genetically governed trait which results in quantitative and/or qualitative defect in the enzyme needed for the metabolism of a given drug.

MODELS OF THE GENETIC BASIS OF DISEASE

Recent advances in genetics and medicine have shown a link between genetic factors and common diseases prevalent in a population. Cancer is discussed here as representative of common diseases affecting the physical body and schizophrenia as a psychiatric disorder affecting the mind.

Cancer: Cancer is an abnormal growth arising from any body cell. It is characterised by uncontrolled cell proliferation resulting in a mass known as a neoplasm or tumour. A malignant tumour can invade adjacent tissues and also spread to distant sites in the body either through lymph or blood. Cancers arising in mesenchymal tissues are known as sarcomas, those originating from epithelial cells as carcinomas, and those characterised by proliferation of hemopoietic or lymphoid tissue are termed leukemias and lymphomas respectively. Cancer can develop irrespective of age, sex, race or country. Overall the incidence of cancer remains the same world over, year after year. Some noticeable features are increasing incidence of cancer with age and selective high incidence of some cancers in one country or race which are balanced by low incidence of some other cancers.

Genetic Basis of Cancer: Recent theories have proposed that cancer has a genetic basis. Though there is no significant evidence from familial patterns of cancer incidence, it seems that there must be some genetic component in certain people which makes them susceptible to developing cancer. It has been shown that cancer is a result of mutation in somatic cells and its progression also involves expression of a series of genes. The carcinogenic agents like viruses, ionising radiation, etc. also operate by bringing about mutation of genes controlling cell proliferation, differentiation and normal functioning. When a normal gene is altered, uncontrolled growth is initiated and a cancer develops. In an individual, somatic mutation in a progenitor normal cell produces cloned cells having identical genetic, chromosomal cytologic, structural and functional features. Each cancer represents a unique clone.

Cancer Genes: Two types of genes are belived to be responsible for causing cancer, namely, oncogenes and tumour suppressor genes.

Oncogenes play a facilitatory role and tumour suppressor genes play an inhibitory role.

Oncogenes are mutated forms of normal genes called protooncogenes that are involved in the control of cell proliferation and differentiation. About 50 human oncogenes and their normal protooncogenes have been identified by experimental DNA transfer studies. The oncogenes can transform a non-tumourigenic mouse cell line in culture to generate foci of cells with tumourigenic properties. A majority of human oncogenes are viral oncogenes. Many protooncogenes are related to specific RNA tumour viruses. Protooncogenes have been conserved in evolution. For example, the protooncogene H-*ras* and its corresponding protein have been found in organisms as far apart on the evolutionary scale as humans and yeast. This leads to the theory that these proteins have essential biological roles.

Oncogenes have a dominant effect at the cellular level. When it gets activated, a single mutant allele is capable of changing the phenotype of a cell from normal to malignant. *Ras* point mutations (which is only a single base pair alteration in its counterpart protooncogene) are present in many cancers. Experimentally it has been shown that *ras* genes are the target of known carcinogens, a finding which lends support to the theory that mutated *ras* genes play a role in the development of many cancers.

Besides point mutations, chromosomal translocations can activate protooncogenes. For example, chronic myelogenous leukemia (CML) shows 9, 22 translocation. Gene amplification is another mode whereby amplified DNA segments include extra copies of protooncogenes with effects on cell growth. For example, N-*myc* protooncogene is amplified up to 200 times in 40 per cent of neuroblastomas. This mechanism of amplification is more likely to be related to tumour progression. Therefore though protooncogenes get converted to oncogenes, this conversion probably involves more than single mutation.

Tumour suppressor genes normally block abnormal growth but they are recessive in nature. Inactivation of tumour suppressor genes by mutation or some mechanism results in the loss of regulation of cell growth, differentiation and other basic functions. Tumour suppressor genes are implicated in several types of cancers which show Mendelian inheritance. Examples are retinoblastoma, Wilm's tumour, familial polyposis coli, neurofibromatosis, etc. Each of these exhibits autosomal dominant traits but it has been observed that loss or alteration of both copies of the responsible tumour suppressor genes is required for expression of cancer. This observation has given rise to a theory that a single functional copy of a tumour suppressor can balance dominant gene whereby a normal cellular phenotype results. When a cell which has only one tumour suppressor allele and that, by chance, gets mutated then it loses its ability to suppress tumour development. Tumour suppressor genes also play a role in inhibition of progression of several common non-inheritable forms of cancer, like colo-rectal cancer.

Familial Cancer: Cancer is a very common disease randomly affecting 20 per cent of the human population the world over. However when it is found that some cancers have a higher incidence in relatives of patients than in the general population and are specific in relation to site, tissue involved and microscopic features, they are called familial cancers.

Chromosomal Factors and Cancer: It has been shown that ataxia telangiectasia, Fanconi anemia, Bloom syndrome and xeroderma pigmentosa, four chromosomal instability syndromes, are associated with increased risk of blood cancers. Therefore the autosomal recessive genes that are defective in chromosomal instability syndromes can be equated with cancer genes. It has also been observed that, in some cases a protooncogene is activated by chromosomal trans-location. Examples: 8, 14 translocation in Burkitt lymphomas and 9, 22 in chronic myelogenous leukemia.

Cancer is a disease which has existed in the biological kingdom since its origin. In fact, it has been suggested that organised life began from a cancerous broth. Mankind has been trying to find its cause and cure since time immemorial. After all the theories of extrinsic causes — carcinogens leading to cancer, research has now focused on genes. Researchers are revealing various possibilities of inception and progression at the genetic level. Perhaps subsequent advances will show that cancer is neither environment-induced nor genetically-based nor a multifactorially-produced phenomenon but an integral part of ontogeny and phylogeny.

Psychiatric Disorders: As early as in the early twentieth century family studies had drawn medical attention to the fact that there is some genetic influence on major psychiatric disorders. Four basic methods have been used to study the genetic influence on psychiatric disorders. These are, family studies by pedigree analysis and interviews, twin studies and prospective studies of high risk individuals. In the last group, long term comparison of disease prevalence in persons at increased risk and in low-risk controls are carried out. Here, as a representative of psychiatric disorders, schizophrenia is discussed.

Schizophrenia: It is a disorder, a form of psychosis, where the patient loses touch with the realities of the environment. The disorder is seen all over the world and its prevalence rate varies from country to country. The varying rates are accounted for by the differing availability of medical facilities and non-uniformity of criteria selected for diagnosis of schizophrenia.

Evidence from family studies and adoption studies has shown that schizophrenia has a genetic basis. On an average there is increased risk of schizophrenia among first-degree relatives of index cases of about four per cent over controls. Monozygotic twins show concordance for schizophrenia upto 15 to 85 per cent. A large study of adoptees has shown that close biologic relatives of schizophrenic proband have higher percentage of schizophrenia as compared to adopted relatives.

The exact mode of inheritance of schizophrenia is not known. It is difficult to carry out direct genotypic studies and hence some inherited physical and laboratory markers like monoamine oxidase activity, dopamine receptor concentration, size of lateral ventricles of brain and neurophysiological marker of abnormal smooth pursuit eye movements are used to get some information on the patterns of inheritance. It has also been observed that in some cases of schizophrenia there is a partial trisomy of the long arm of chromosome 5. The linkage studies in them have revealed that schizophrenia trait segregates as a dominant one. Other cases in which such a linkage to chromosome 5 is not seen suggest that there is genetic heterogeneity even in families with an apparently dominant mode of transmission.

It is likely that schizophrenia and all other behavioural disorders are multifactorially governed but the exact character of those factors and the nature of their influence are likely to remain a medical enigma for some time yet.

SUMMARY

Cancer: All cells have a coded genetic programme of development, growth, differentiation and death in response to physical, chemical and biological signals. Cancer results when normal control over growth is lost, and a cell is free to proliferate indefinitely.

The basic mechanism of all cancers is mutation — somatic or germ line. Usually mutation of genes in somatic cells accumulate over years, until a cell loses a critical number of mechanisms which control growth. Mutation of the germ cells would result in inheritance of pedisposition to cancer.

Cancer is a result of interaction of inherited genetic factors and environmental influences. New insights into the fundamental role of DNA changes in carcinogenesis, would hopefully lead to prevention and treatment of cancers.

Schizophrenia: A psychiatric illness with an onset usually in early adult life. It is characterised by personality and emotional changes, withdrawal from reality and is associated with hallucinations and delusions.

Environmental factors play a significant role in the pathogenesis of schizophrenia. The prevalence of schizophrenia in close relatives could be partly genetic and partly due to sharing a common environment. The genetic contribution in schizophrenia is polygenic.

11 CLINICAL GENETICS

Clinical genetics is the art and science of applying the principles of genetics in day to day practice at an individual level. It involves communicating with the patient/parents through elicitation of history, physical examination and necessary investigations. These methods help the geneticists to guide the patient and the family along an appropriate path. Such an approach is also called genetic counselling. Genetic counselling is an established discipline of providing to the lay people an insight into their problems and the possible measures that modern medicine can offer.

APPROACH TO A PATIENT

It is a difficult task for a physician to determine whether the disease with which the patient is afflicted is genetic in origin. Towards this end, accurate diagnostic steps become imperative. With advances in specific diagnostic laboratory tests, it is now possible to make correct diagnosis of a number of genetic diseases.

Usually, under the following circumstances, the primary physician who suspects that the patient may have a genetic disorder, refers the case to a genetic centre.

1) An abnormal fetus detected in intrauterine life by ultrasonography.
2) A stillborn infant.
3) A child with mental retardation or delayed physical and mental milestones.
4) An infant, a child or an adult with a single or multiple malformations.
5) When it is suspected that the disease is either an inherited metabolic disorder or a single gene disorder or a chromosomal disorder.

6) When a couple have a history of recurrent miscarriages.
7) When there is consanguinity in marriage.
8) Need for preconceptional counselling and risk factor counselling for advanced maternal age or other potential risk factors.
9) When there is family history of genetic disease for person at risk for genetic conditions including presymptomatic diagnosis.
10) Where there is history of exposure to teratogens.

Diagnosis of a Genetic Disorder

As with any other disease, a thorough history and physical examination are essential. A detailed history about the individual's prenatal period, labour, delivery, documentation of family relationships, i.e., charting the pedigree are useful. In pedigree charts, the gender of each individual and the relationship between individuals should be indicated using standard pedigree symbols. The family history should include that of first degree relatives of an index case. In patients with X-linked recessive disorders history of the male relatives on the mother's side of the family becomes important. The age of each member should be recorded along with the history of presence or absence of disease. The ethnic origin of the family is relevant as many diseases vary in incidence among different ethnic groups. History of consanguinity is important and should be recorded. All records of miscarriages and stillbirths should be made.

In the clinical examination, attention should be paid to physical variations or minor abnormalities which can provide clues to diagnosis. Family members may be evaluated for the presence or absence of a genetic disease.

Following physical examination, relevant routine laboratory tests such as blood examination, ECG, imaging studies, special molecular cytogenetic studies and molecular biochemical tests are carried out. Routine tests usually allow record of physical features, like cardiac anomalies or musculoskeletal deformities. Biochemical tests like enzyme level permit establishment of diagnosis and extent of severity of diseases.

Chromosomal analysis helps to establish diagnosis in cases such as failure to thrive, developmental delay, multiple malformation, sexual dysmorphism, mental retardation, etc. Specific recombinant DNA tests can allow the detection of mutation and establish a diagnosis.

After establishing diagnosis depending on the disease the necessary specific and supportive management is offered. This is the first step in genetic counselling. The subsequent steps can be inferred from the definition of genetic counselling given in 1975 by the American Society of Human Genetics:

Genetic counselling is a communication process which deals with the human problems associated with the occurrence of genetic disorder in a family. This process involves an attempt by one or more appropriately trained persons to help the individual or family to:

1) comprehend the medical facts including the diagnosis, probable course of the disorder, and the available management,

2) appreciate the way heredity contributes to the disorder and the risk of recurrence in specified relatives,

3) understand the alternatives for dealing with the risk of recurrence,

4) choose a course of action which seems to them appropriate in their view of their risk, their family goals and their ethical and religious standards and act in accordance with that decision and

5) make the best possible adjustment to the disorder in an affected family member and/or to the risk of recurrence of that disorder.

PRENATAL DIAGNOSIS

Prenatal diagnosis forms an important facet of clinical genetics. This is especially so as the size of the family is diminishing on the one hand, while simultaneously sophisticated advanced expensive medical care helps increase the life span of individuals with genetic disease. There is compromised quality of life. This creates quite a stressful situation for the patient, family members and the society.

The purpose of prenatal diagnosis is therefore not only to detect abnormalities in fetal life and allow termination of pregnancy when the fetus is found to have a defect but also to allow couples at the risk of having abnormal children to make an informed decision, and undergo counselling to reduce their anxieties.

Prenatal diagnosis includes both screening and diagnostic tests. A popular screening test used for prenatal diagnosis is an assay of maternal serum alpha-fetoprotein (AFP) at 15 weeks of gestation. An abnormal result calls for further testing. The diagnostic tests can be for two purposes.

a. analysis of fetal tissues, e.g., amniocentesis, chorionic villus sampling (CVS), cordocentesis and in vitro fertilisation diagnosis.

b. visualisation of fetus, e.g., ultrasonography.

1) Transabdominal amniocentesis (Fig. 91)

Transabdominal amniocentesis in combination with ultrasonography is the most widely used technique for prenatal diagnosis.

Amniocentesis is performed at 15 to 17 weeks of gestation. About 20–30 cc of amniotic fluid is withdrawn transabdominally by a needle put under the guidance of ultrasonography to avoid injury to placenta and fetus. Amniotic fluid contains live amniocytes shed by the fetus. Cytogenetic and biochemical tests are carried out on them.

Indications for prenatal diagnosis by amniocentesis include maternal age more than 35 years, history of previous child or any of the parents having chromosomal anomaly, family history of genetic defect which can be diagnosed by biochemical method or DNA analysis.

The risks involved in amniocentesis are fetal death, amnionitis, fetal puncture, amniotic fluid leakage and maternal vaginal bleeding.

2) Chorionic villus sampling (CVS)

This is performed by aspiration of fetal chorionic villi either transabdominally or transcervically around 9 to 12 weeks of gestation. This provides diagnosis earlier than through amniocentesis. This is useful if early termination of pregnancy is the desired option.

CVS provides diagnostic results in 99 per cent of cases. However, if there is mosaicism in the placenta but not in fetus, as found in 1 to 2 per cent of cases, the results of this test lead to confusion in diagnosis. This calls for amniocentesis. The CVS procedure is relatively safe. There is some risk of fetal loss or development of limb defects.

3) Cordocentesis or percutaneous umbilical blood sampling (PUBS).

This is now preferred over fetoscopy which is risky. The blood sample is obtained by puncture of umbilical cord under ultrasonographic guidance after 16 weeks of gestation. This sample allows a rapid cytogenetic and/or hematologic analysis. The risk to the fetus is about one per cent.

4) Ultrasonography

Technological advances in real time ultrasonography have made this an important non-invasive tool in prenatal diagnosis.

Ultrasonography is useful in (1) verifying whether the fetus is alive, (2) determining gestational age by measurement of the fetal head size, (3) diagnosing multiple gestations, (4) determining placental and fetal positions, (5) detecting gross fetal malformation such as anencephaly or placental malformation such as a hydatid mole, (6) performing effective amniocentesis CVS and PUBS, and (7) detecting a specific condition at risk such as a short limb skeletal dysplasia.

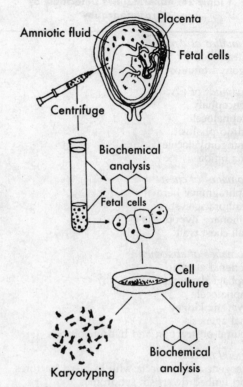

Fig. 91 Schematic representation of amniocentesis. Usually the procedure is carried out at about the sixteenth week of pregnancy

The sensitivity of ultrasonography is about 30 to 50 per cent but it is higher for neural tube defects.

5) Alpha-fetoprotein measurement in amniotic fluid and maternal serum

The amniotic alpha-fetoprotein level is elevated when the fetus has a neural tube defect and provides a reliable prenatal test for the same. Maternal serum alpha-fetoprotein levels can also prenatally detect fetuses with various abnormalities including neural tube defects with Down's syndrome. It is a non-invasive procedure having no risk. However, its sensitivity for detecting neural tube defects is lower than that of amniotic alpha-fetoprotein levels.

The older techniques infrequently used are:

6) Radiography

Besides a plain X-ray, amniography and feto

Table 26: Abnormalities Detectable by Ultrasonography

Anomalies of Amnion
Hydramnios
Oligohydramnios

Anomalies of CNS
Anencephaly
Encephalocele
Hydrocephalus
Meningomyelocele
Spina bifida

Anomalies of chest
Diaphragmatic hernia
Intrathoracic cyst
Pulmonary hypoplasia
Small chest wall

Anomalies of abdomen
Duodenal atresia
Esophageal atresia
Omphalocele
Polycystic kidney
Renal agenesis
Urethral obstruction and hydronephrosis

General body
Osteogenesis imperfecta with in utero fractures
Short limbed dwarfism syndromes

graphy are also carried out. Amniography is a visualisation of the fetus by introducing water soluble contrast dye into the amnion. Some of this contrast material is swallowed by the fetus and thus its gastrointestinal tract is outlined. This helps to diagnose gastrointestinal atresias and diaphragmatic hernias.

Fetography employs an oil soluble contrast material which adheres to the fetal vernix caseosa and permits visualisation of the fetal outline. It is useful in the recognition of limb length anomalies or other major malformations which are externally manifested.

7) Use of fetoscope

This is not used in everyday practice. The technique allows collection of fetal blood by inserting a needle into the umbilical vessels under direct vision, as well as direct visualisation of the fetus. It permits detection of external malformations. The blood sample allows prenatal detection of a number of disorders such as hemophilia and Duchenne muscular dystrophy which are not detectable in cell culture, but are noticeably expressed in blood even in a 16 week fetus.

8) Placentocentesis

The placentocentesis technique is for obtaining a fetal blood sample by inserting a needle into the placenta. This is usually performed at 18 weeks of gestation. This procedure is not commonly done as it carries the hazards of several serious complications.

Newer diagnostic techniques

They are (1) preimplantation diagnostic approaches like in vitro fertilisation and polar body diagnosis, and (2) diagnosis of fetal cells obtained from the mother's circulation. Since each of these methods involves the analysis of DNA from a single cell or very few cells, each utilises polymerase chain reaction to amplify DNA. These techniques are under trial.

Treatment of Genetic Disease

The vast majority of **unifactorial disorders** are serious, and are incurable; a few are treatable. The principal approach to the control of genetic disease is, therefore, prevention through genetic counselling, with prenatal diagnosis and selective abortion, where possible.

Table 27 gives possible modes of management of some genetic disorders.

1) When an **enzyme block** is responsible for the disorder, the defective enzyme or protein may be replaced, its substrate restricted, or the deficient product replaced. The **replacement** of deficient coenzyme may be carried out in some disorders. However, most of the enzymes which are involved in hereditary disorders, are not identifiable. The majority of the enzymes work within cells and so even if enzymes were identified, injection of the enzymes would not be effective. Transplantation of tissue possessing normal enzyme activity is a dream of the future. In mucopolysaccharidoses, infusion of normal plasma or leucocytes helps to a certain extent.

2) **Drugs** help in certain diseases. For example, chelating agents such as penicillamine

Table 27: Examples of Various Methods for Managing Genetic Disease

Therapy	Disorder
Replacement of deficient protein	
antihemophilic globulin	Hemophilia
Replacement of deficient vitamin	
vitamin D	vitamin D resistant rickets
Replacement of deficient product	
cortisone	adrenogenital syndrome
thyroxine	congenital cretinism
Substrate restriction in diet	
phenylalanine	phenylketonuria
carbohydrate	galactosemia
Drug therapy	
insulin	diabetes mellitus
Preventive therapy	
avoidance of certain	G6PD deficiency
drugs Injection of	porphyria
Rh gamma	Rh incompatibility
globulin	
Removal of diseased tissues	
splenectomy	hereditary spherocytosis

increase the urinary excretion of copper, and so are proving beneficial in the treatment of patients with Wilson's disease (Hepatolenticular degeneration).

When mutation of a control gene concerned with synthesis of a specific enzyme results in switching off the enzyme synthesis, drug therapy might be effective in inducing enzyme synthesis. For example in congenital non-hemolytic jaundice, small doses of phenobarbitone can induce synthesis of the enzyme glucuronyl transferase.

3) **Genetic engineering by viral therapy.** It has been suggested that since Shope papilloma virus of rabbits induces the synthesis of the enzyme arginase without having any adverse effect when injected into humans, it may form an effective treatment for argininemia.

4) **Preventive therapy.** Avoidance of harmful drugs by individuals with hereditary disorders such as porphyria or G6PD deficiency, or prophylaxis for preventing sensitisation by Rh-antigen are important examples.

5) **Surgical removal of diseased tissue.** Colectomy in polyposis coli, and splenectomy in hereditary spherocytosis are important examples of this mode of treatment.

6) **Transplant.** Bone marrow transplant is the treatment of choice for a variety of immune deficiency disorders, including severe combined immunodeficiency of any type. Some good results are obtained in patients of Beta thalassemia. Reports indicate usefulness of bone marrow transplant in lysosomal storage diseases. It reduces the enlargement of the liver, spleen and the heart that occurs in certain storage diseases such as Hurler syndrome and Gaucher disease.

Liver transplant is probably the only treatment of choice for some metabolic liver diseases.

7) **Gene transfer therapy.** This is a potential mode of therapy which may be converted into an actual reality in near future thanks to Recombinant DNA technology. It is hoped that by transferring functional genes to the patient, a permanent correction of reversible features of abnormal phenotype will take place. Gene transfer is desirable at the level of somatic cells only and not at germline level as it would risk introducing new mutations.

Medical Intervention and Genetic Diseases: It is possible that improvements in medical treatment can result in an increase in genetic load in future generations. It may also be possible that successful gene therapy would reduce abnormalities. Some medical advances such as antibiotics and insulin have made a significant impact on the health of the population. Considering the high cost and unpredictability of genetic therapy and the physical debility that occurs as a result, the desirability of its administration as compared to natural selection is open to question.

SUMMARY

Clinical genetics deals with the application of principle of genetics at an individual patient/family level for the diagnosis and management of a disorder. The steps taken for establishing a diagnosis of genetic disorder are history-taking, clinical examination, relevant routine laboratory tests and special cytological and molecular laboratory tests.

Prenatal Diagnosis of Genetic Disease:
   Procedures: 1) Transabdominal amniocentesis — amniotic fluid aspirated through abdominal wall. Cytological and biochemical study of amniotic fluid permits detection of gross anomaly. Procedure carried out at about 16 weeks of gestation. 2) Radiography. 3) Ultrasonography — to determine (a) viability of fetus (b) gestational age (c) multiple gestations (d) placental and fetal positions (e) gross fetal malformations. 4) Fetoscopy. 5) Placentocentesis. 6) Chorion Villus Sampling. 7) Cordocentesis or Percutaneous Umbilical Blood Sampling.

Treatment of Genetic Disease:
1) Replacement of deficient enzyme, protein, etc.
2) Drugs
3) Viral therapy
4) Prevention — avoiding harmful drugs
5) Surgical removal of diseased tissue
6) Transplantation of normal tissue
7) Gene transfer therapy.

   Genetic screening of the newborn is carried out to detect inborn errors of metabolism by examination of maternal blood, cord blood, blood and urine of newborn.

GENETIC COUNSELLING

Modern medicine, increasing affluence and effective community health measures, have produced a change in the spectrum of incidence of human disease. Problems of malnutrition and infective disorders have receded, giving place to an increased awareness of genetic or inherited diseases. Today, a **medical geneticist** — a physician specialising in the study of genetic disorders — is called upon to give advice to an individual, to families and even to entire governments on matters pertaining to the causation, incidence and risks of recurrence of inherited defects. Radiation hazards, newer drugs including the anti-cancer compounds and the means of biological warfare like mutant viral strains, would all fall within the purview of the **genetic counsellor**. The specific fields of activity in preventing, diagnosing and treating genetic problems are outlined in the text. The time is not far, when a medical geneticist could be the key figure in all teaching medical institutions in this country.

Genetic counselling deals with the problem of giving advice to families having, or likely to have children with genetic disorders.

The causes of diseases can range from the purely genetic to the entirely environmental (Table 28). With the control of microbial and deficiency diseases, the physician now more often encounters hereditary disorders and congenital abnormalities in practice.

Table 28: Causation of Human Diseases

Genetic	Genetic and Environmental	Environmental
Inborn errors of metabolism, e.g., phenylketonuria, galactosemia Duchenne muscular dystrophy	Pyloric stenosis, club-foot congenital dislocation of hip, diabetes mellitus	Tuberculosis, lead poisoning, pellagra, accidental trauma
Rarer, simple Mendelian (unifactorial inheritance high risk of recurrence	Commoner, genetics multifactorial, Low risk of recurrence	

Surveys have indicated, that at least one in fifty newborns, has a major congenital abnormality about one in hundred has a unifactorial disorder and about one in two hundred has a major chromosomal abnormality. The physician not only faces the problems of diagnosing and treating these disorders but is also called upon to guide on issues such as

1) The risk of recurrence of a hereditary disease in a family;
2) The risks attending the progeny from consanguineous marriages;
3) Genetic basis in cases of abnormal sexual development, infertility, recurrent abortion and congenital malformations;
4) Child adoption;
5) Cases of disputed paternity;
6) Risks of acquiring common diseases; and
7) Detection of carrier.

1. The Risk of Recurrence of a Hereditary Disease in a Family: The physician first establishes a precise diagnosis through clinical examination and investigation. He informs the parents about the prognosis and the possible modes of treatment. He explains to the parents the risk of recurrence. The decision whether or not to accept the risk is left to the parents.

Determining the risk: In conditions where the mode of inheritance is simple (autosomal dominant, recessive, or X-linked) it must be emphasised that chance has no memory, i.e., if the risk of inheritance is 1 in 4 it holds good with every offspring irrespective of whether other offspring are affected.

a. *Autosomal dominant disorders.* For a person heterozygous for an autosomal dominant gene, the chances of any of his children being similarly affected are 50 per cent.

b. *Autosomal recessive disorders.* When both parents are heterozygotes, the chance of their having an affected child is 1 in 4. Of the three unaffected siblings of the affected child, two have a chance of being heterozygous and therefore carriers. The probability of having an affected child is the product of the probabilities of parents being carriers, multiplied by 1/4, i.e., if two cousins of an affected individual marry each other the risk of each child of theirs being affected is 1/4 × 1/4 × 1/4 (cousins have 1/4 genes in common; see Table 10) or 1 in 64.

c. *X-linked disorders.* The carrier of an X-linked disorder is invariably a female. She transmits the gene to half her daughters who become carriers, and to half her sons, who get affected. In severe X-linked disorders, the affected males usually do not live long enough to beget children. If an affected male does have children, his sons are not affected, but all his daughters become carriers.

If a woman has only one son affected, it can be due to a new mutation in the ovum. Under such circumstances, mutation is unlikely to recur and so her future children are unlikely to be affected. However, it is difficult to recognise a carrier, and to prove with certainty that a woman is not a carrier because of the inactivation of the X-chromosome.

It is important to distinguish between an autosomal recessive trait and an X-linked trait. In autosomal recessive inheritance, the normal sister of an affected male, even if she is a carrier, is unlikely to have affected children as the chances of her marrying another carrier are less when the trait is rare. In an X-linked trait, the sister of an affected male (because of their mother being a carrier) has 50 per cent chances of being a carrier and therefore the chances of any of her sons being affected are 1 in 4. The demonstration by appropriate tests that both the parents of an affected individual are carriers of the mutant gene, indicates that the trait is autosomal recessive, and not X-linked.

d. *Sporadic case of a hereditary abnormality.* When normal parents have a child with a

Table 29: Recurrence Risk of Down's syndrome due to various Chromosomal Aberrations

Karyotypes			Chance of Recurrence%
Patient	Father	Mother	
Trisomy-21	normal	normal	1
Translocation 21/21	carrier	normal	100
	normal	carrier	100
D/D	normal	carrier	10
	carrier	normal	5
21/22	normal	carrier	7
	carrier	normal	<3

rare congenital abnormality and there is no history of anyone else being similarly affected on either side of the family, the following must be considered to calculate the risk of the same abnormality affecting future children:

i. To rule out the possibility of the effect of a **teratogenic agent**. The chances that the abnormality will recur in future children will depend on the particular cause.

ii. To find out the possibility of a **new mutation** in the gametes of one of the parents. If mutation is for an autosomal dominant trait, it will be manifested in the offspring. If both parents are normal and the autosomal dominant trait is fully penetrant, a new mutation is a likely cause. In that case, the chance of recurrence in subsequent children is very small.

iii. In an autosomal recessive disorder, the demonstration of **heterozygosity** in the parents by appropriate tests would confirm the basis. The **consanguineous marriage** of parents would offer supporting evidence.

iv. *Known X-linked recessive disorder*. Female children with normal sex chromosomes are not affected by an X-linked recessive disorder. The distinction should be made from an autosomal recessive disorder. The distinction is made on the basis of clinical examination as well as on the relative incidence of two forms of the disease. The distinction may not be drawn, in order to know the chances of further children being affected, but to advise the sister of an affected male as to whether her children would be similarly affected.

v. A number of syndromes are associated with specific chromosomal abnormalities, which tend to be sporadic with no one else in the family being affected. The examples of such syndromes are **Down's syndrome**, the **13-trisomy syndrome**, the **18-trisomy syndrome**, and the **cri du chat syndrome**. When abnormalities involve more than one system, e.g., nervous system, cardiovascular system and others, it is advisable to study the chromosomes of the affected child and of the parents, in order to find out if one of the parents carries a translocation. If the parents have normal chromosomes, chances are that the future children would not be affected by the same abnormality (Table 29).

vi. For a multifactorial trait, the cases occur sporadically and the risk of recurrence is low.

During genetic counselling, the phenomenon of **genetic heterogeneity** should be kept in mind.

2. The Risks Attending Progeny from Consanguineous Marriages: For normal parents the actual risks are small, though studies have shown that among the offspring of consanguineous marriages, there is an increased postnatal mortality rate and an increased frequency of congenital abnormalities and mental retardation.

However, if there is history of a disorder such as **phenylketonuria** in the family, the chance of first cousins carrying the same gene is 1 in 3; thus the chance of two cousins having an affected offspring is much more than in the case of unrelated parents. For example, if a person, with a phenylketonuric father, gets married to his first cousin from the father's side, the chance of their having an affected child is about 1 in 12 whereas the chance of two unrelated persons having an affected child is about 1 in 10,000. The above calculations are arrived at as follows. The person under consideration would be a **carrier**. The chance of his or her cousin being a carrier would be 1/3, the chance of the cousin's parent being a carrier being 2/3. The chance of any child of such a cousin marriage being affected would be $1 \times 1/3 \times 1/4 = 1/12$. Since the frequency of carriers of phenylketonuria in the general population is about 1 in 50, the chance that two unrelated persons will have an affected child is $1/50 \times 1/50 \times 1/4 = 1/10,000$.

Marriages between cousins carry not only an increased risk of producing a child homozygous for a detrimental recessive gene, but also of producing a child with a disorder due to more than one gene. There is also some evidence that the death rate in childhood, apart from known genetic or congenital conditions, is also raised. However, for the individual couple (in the absence of any history of recessive, or possibly recessive defects in the family) the increased risk is a very small one in absolute terms. Where a high rate of first-cousin marriages has been a long-established tradition in a community, it is self-evident that the vast majority of such marriages produce healthy normal children. There is also some evidence that pregnancy toxemia is less frequent when the parents are consanguineous.

3. Genetic Basis in some Disorders: In cases of delayed and **abnormal sexual development, infertility, recurrent abortion** and in individuals with congenital malformations, chromosomal studies help genetic counselling.

Chromosomal studies can reveal or rule out (*i*) **Turner's syndrome** in cases of delayed or abnormal sexual development in females; (*ii*) **Klinefelter's syndrome** or mosaicism in males when there is no apparent endocrinological or anatomical cause for sterility; (*iii*) translocation in one of the parents in cases of spontaneous abortion where the cause is not found; (*iv*) **Down's syndrome** in individuals with congenital malformations.

4. Problems of Child Adoption: Adoption agencies often want to know the risk of inherited disorders occurring in a child, when there is a history of some hereditary disorder in the child's background. The probabilities are calculated in a manner similar to the one discussed earlier under risk of recurrence of hereditary diseases in a family. The main difficulties are encountered when there is a family history of a disease, which is not recognisable clinically or biochemically in the earlier years of the child's life, e.g., Marfan's syndrome, Huntington's chorea.

5. Cases of Disputed Paternity: DNA fingerprinting would be the ideal method in such cases. However, in developing countries, the lack of adequate infrastructure and the costs are prohibitive for DNA fingerprinting. Hence, analysis of various types of blood groups is still being followed.

Paternity cannot be proved with certainty, but it can be disproved without doubt. If the child has a blood group substance which could not have resulted from either of the parents, then the putative father is not the true father. Equally, if the child lacks a blood group which a putative father would positively transmit to all his offsprings, then the putative father cannot be the true father.

6. Risks of Acquiring Common Diseases: Some of the common conditions such as cleft lip, cleft palate, idiopathic epilepsy, pyloric stenosis, idiopathic scoliosis, spina bifida, early onset of diabetes mellitus, etc., have no simple mode of inheritance. Some of these conditions are heterogeneous and include a number of etiologically different disorders; others are either due to many genes or due to the effect of environment. In such conditions only **empiric risks of recurrence** can be given. An **empiric risk** is defined as the probability of occurrence of a specified event based upon prior experience and observations rather than on prediction by a general theory. Empiric risks are calculated by estimating the frequency of the condition in the relatives of the affected persons.

In **multifactorial disorders**, the rate of recurrence in first-degree relatives is equal to the square root of the prevalence in the general population. As the prevalence frequency of most of the multifactorial disorders is between 1 in 500 and 1 in 2,000, the recurrence rate usually ranges from two to five per cent.

7. Detection of Carriers: This is an important facet of genetic counselling as detection of carriers would remove uncertainty associated with various hereditary disorders. It is not possible at present to detect carriers in all conditions and with a high degree of certainty. The following methods are utilised for detecting carrier states:

i. Presence of some **clinical manifestation**, e.g., X-linked ocular albinism.

ii. Demonstrating **linkage** between a hereditary disorder and one of the marker traits, e.g., linkage between one form of congenital cataract and the Duffy blood group locus.

iii. Demonstration of detectable **biochemical**

Table 30: Carrier Detection Tests in X-linked Disorders

Disorder	Abnormality
Anhidrotic ectodermal dysplasia	Sweat pore count reduced
Becker muscular dystrophy	Serum creatine kinase raised
Congenital agammaglo-bulinemia	*in vitro* immunoglobulin synthesis by lympho-cytes reduced
Duchenne muscular dystrophy	Serum creatine kinase raised
Diabetes insipidus	Urinary concentration reduced
G6PD deficiency	Erythrocyte G6PD reduced
Hemophilia A	Factor VIII reduced
Hemophilia B	Factor IX reduced
Hypogammaglobu-linemia	IgG level reduced
Ocular albinism	Patchy depigmentation of retina and iris
Retinitis pigmentosa	Peripheral pigmentary changes in retina Abnormal ERG or Fluroescein angiography
Vit D-resistant rickets (hypophosphatemia)	Serum phosphorus reduced
X-linked ichthyosis	Corneal opacities present, Steroid sulphatase reduced

abnormalities in carriers, e.g., low levels of enzyme in acatalasia, elevated serum levels of creatine kinase in carriers of Duchenne muscular dystrophy.

Table 30 gives X-linked disorders where a carrier can be detected. **Carrier detection** is important when X-linked conditions are under consideration. Carrier detection is less significant in rare autosomal recessive traits. With common diseases due to recessive traits, detecting carriers can be useful, as such an individual can be warned of the risk of having affected children if he/she were to marry another carrier.

Genetic Screening: Genetic screening is the identification of individuals with a genetic disease, genetic predisposition to a disease or a genotype that increases the risk of having a child with a genetic disease. Identifying individuals with a genetic disease can permit management of disease better and curtail its complications, e.g., phenylketonuria or Down's syndrome. When individuals with a genetic predisposition to a disease are identified, then screening and advice can prevent or delay the development of disease or help plan life accordingly, e.g., Huntington's chorea. When couples or individuals can be identified having increased risk of bearing children with a genetic disease, they can select appropriate reproductive options of either not having children or by carrying prenatal diagnosis and termination of affected pregnancies.

Genetic screening is presently carried out for very few diseases. If the disease is very common, then screening for the same is done at the population level. For known family history of uncommon severe genetic disease, screening is done within the families. The screening is carried out for those diseases which impair quality of life of the affected individual and causes increased stress for the family. Also, when there is a possibility of beneficial intervention, genetic screening is carried out.

The screening test should be sensitive, specific and economical. A sensitive test correctly identifies proportion of individuals affected with the disease or genotype. False negatives are produced when individuals affected with the disease or genotype have any negative test. A good test gives a low frequency of false negatives. Specificity is defined as the proportion of those individuals who are not affected with the disease or genotype have a negative test. False positives are false results of tests when individuals not having the disease have a positive test.

Future of Genetic Screening: It is expected that in future when sufficiently large number of genotypes can be identified every individual will be able to know which disease producing trait he or

Table 31: Frequencies of some Metabolic Disorders and Conditions Detected by Screening of the Newborn

Disorder or condition	Fre-quency	Screening involved
Phenylketonuria	1 : 13,000	Newborn blood
Galactosemia	1 : 50,000	"
Maple syrup urine disease	1 : 170,000	"
Homocystinuria	1 : 200,000	"
Hereditary tyrosinemia	Very low	"
Cystinuria	1 : 8,000	Newborn urine
Iminoglycinuria	1 : 12,000	"
Histidinemia	1 : 20,000	"
Hartnup disease	1 : 25,000	"
Methylmalonic aciduria	1 : 50,000	"
Cystathioninuria	1 : 70,000	"
Argininosuccinic aciduria	1 : 90,000	"
Hyperglycemia nonketonic	1 : 180,000	"
Hyperprolinemia	1 : 200,000	"

she has. The screening of future will determine the individual genetic predisposition to a given disease rather then identify normal or abnormal people at the population level.

Genetic Screening of the Newborn: Genetic screening of the newborn is mainly carried out to detect **inborn errors of metabolism**. The aim is the earliest possible recognition of defects in order to execute timely intervention to prevent the more serious consequences of a disorder. The screening is carried out by examination of prenatal (maternal) blood, cord blood, newborn's blood, and newborn's urine. In addition to tests for classical inborn errors of metabolism like phenylketonuria, genetic screening of the newborn is also carried out for genetic disorders such as congenital hypothyroidism, hemoglobinopathies, a-antitrypsin deficiency, cystic fibrosis, Duchenne muscular dystrophy, hyperlipidemia,

adenosine deaminase deficiency and congenital adrenal hyperplasia.

Table 31 gives frequencies of some metabolic disorders and conditions detected by screening the newborn's blood and urine. With such low frequencies of the various disorders, the **expense** and **effort** involved in carrying out genetic screening as a routine procedure, remains a debatable issue. Although the screening tests are sensitive, they do give false negative results at times, so that a negative result from screening does not necessarily exclude the presence of the disorder.

Eugenics: This is the science of improving a species through selective breeding. Modern medical genetics has not focused on this area. Genetic counselling is a communication process that is non-directive and non-judgmental. The individuals, couples (and parents) are given factual knowledge whereby they can make an informed personal choice.

SUMMARY

Genetic counselling refers to giving scientific advice under the following circumstances:
1) Risk of recurrence, in a family, of a hereditary disease — autosomal dominant 50 per cent to 100 per cent; autosomal recessive 1 in 4; X-linked disorder in male: male progeny — nil; female progeny — 100 per cent carrier; X-linked disorders in female: male progeny — 50 per cent, female progeny — carrier 50 per cent.
2) Risk attending the progeny from consanguineous marriages; normal parents — small; parents with a history of a disorder — the risk increases manifold in recessive disorders.
3) Determining genetic basis in cases of abnormal sexual development, infertility, recurrent abortion and congenital-malformations.
4) Problem of child adoption — determining the risk of inherited disorders in child.
5) Cases of disputed paternity — paternity can be often disproved on the basis of blood groups of child and putative father.
6) Risks of acquiring common disease — in conditions due to many genes or due to effect of environment, only an empiric risk of recurrence is given.
7) Detection of carriers based on some clinical manifestations or demonstrations of detectable biochemical abnormalities.

12 LABORATORY GENETICS

The molecular geneticists in the later half of the twentieth century have unravelled the mystery of the essential complex molecule governing heredity, namely DNA. They have explored the DNA molecules in their laboratories to analyse them, synthesise them, amplify them, map them on chromosomes, have made libraries of them. In future, people will have their entire genetic background chart available to them. Perhaps the anatomy of the genome will become as integral to the study of medicine as gross anatomy is today. Geneticists hope to identify the genes responsible for malformations, biochemical abnormalities, and various diseases affecting mankind. They will treat the disease either by modifying the faulty genes or by providing an ample production of the right kind of proteins and other gene products.

Some of the basic elements of molecular genetics are given below. These will help the student.

RECOMBINANT DNA TECHNOLOGY

Basic Principles
Principles of DNA Cloning: (Fig. 92) For generating DNA in large quantities by cloning the following steps have to be taken.

1) Isolation of DNA sequence of interest.
2) Obtaining multiple copies of it in an organism, usually a bacterium.
3) Isolation of pure DNA in large quantities.

The ability to generate as many copies, i.e., clone of a particular sequence is the heart of recombinant technology. The name recombinant DNA refers to a new combination of DNA created in the laboratory between DNA sequence of interest from one organism, and other DNA molecules capable of indefinite duplication from another organisms.

Isolation of DNA Sequence of Interest: Some bacteria produce restriction endonuclease enzymes that cut the double-stranded DNA at specific sequence of nucleotides. More than 300 different restriction enzymes have been isolated and they are named according to the organism from which they are derived, e.g., Eco RI is from *E coli* and was the first restriction enzyme isolated. This enzyme recognises the specific six base pair sequence.

$$5' \, G \, A \, A \, T \, T \, C \, 3'$$

$$3' \, C \, T \, T \, A \, A \, G \, 5'$$

As can be seen from the above example, recognition units by restriction endonuclease enzymes are short, about 4 to 6 nucleotides in length, which is usually palindromic, i.e., with the same sequence of nucleotides on the two complementary strands of DNA if read in one direction of polarity, e.g., $5'$ to $3'$.

Continuing with the Eco RI example, this enzyme recognises the specific six base pair sequence and wherever it occurs in a double stranded DNA molecule, it cleaves DNA at that site on each strand between the G and the adjacent A. This generates two fragments, each with a five bases, single stranded DNA overhung at the end. Such sticky ends are useful for subsequent construction of

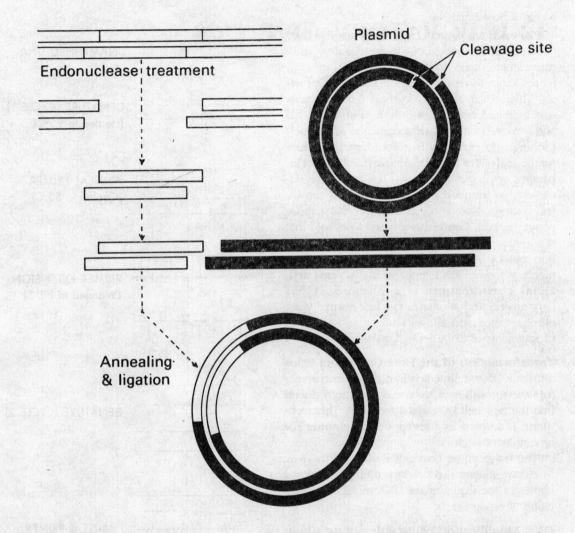

Fig. 92 Recombinant DNA cloning: DNA fragment, containing a gene of interest, is added to the plasmid DNA which is cleaved and therefore becomes linearised. The mixture is annealed and ligated to produce a series of circularised recombinant plasmid DNA molecules.

recombinant DNA molecules. DNA from any source when treated with the same restriction endonuclease enzyme, produces DNA fragments with identical complementary sticky ends.

Any two molecules which are generated by the same restriction endonuclease enzymes can be joined together by interaction of their complementary sticky ends followed by completion of the phospodiester backbones on each strand by an enzyme called DNA ligase. The union of two DNA fragments produces recombinant DNA molecule,

one end derived from one DNA source and the other from a different source.

Vectors: A vector is a carrier of a DNA molecule that is used in the cloning process. A vector can replicate autonomously in a host like bacteria or yeast cells and can be isolated subsequently in a pure form for analysis. This allows production of multiple copies of a particular DNA sequence of interest. The four main types of vectors are plasmids, bacteriophages, cosmids and yeast artificial chromosomes (YACS). All these replicate within a host organism.

Plasmids are naturally found in bacteria. They have double stranded DNA molecules and replicate extrachromosomally in bacteria. They confer resistance to various antibiotics and heavy metals. Their advantage as vectors is that they possess a limited number of unique restriction sites and carry resistance against particular antibiotics. Cloning into plasmids is a standard procedure for the analysis of short DNA molecules. **Bacteriophages** or phages are viruses having a large linear double stranded DNA molecule and can infect bacteria. Commonly used phage is bacteriophage lambda. **Cosmid** is a type of plasmid that has minimum vector DNA necessary for propagation thereby allowing insertion of the large fragments of foreign DNA, upto 50 kb. A **yeast artificial chromosome** is a plasmid. It has centromeres and telomeres just like normal yeast chromosomes and allows cloning and isolation of fragments of DNA up to 1,000 kb in length.

Transformation of the Host Organism: Once a foreign DNA fragment is introduced into a vector, the recombinant vector is then introduced into the host cell by various methods. This technique is known as transformation cloning for recombinant vectors.

The transformed host cell is allowed to grow in culture medium to produce multiple identical copies of the recombinant DNA molecule, i.e., a clone is produced.

DNA Amplification using Polymerase Chain Reaction (PCR) (Fig 93): The cloning procedure described so far is time consuming and requires large amount of purified DNA **over several micrograms**. A newer approach to make copies of DNA is polymerase chain reaction (PCR). Essentially PCR is an artificial means of replicating short DNA sequences (several kilobases) quickly so that millions of copies of the sequences are made.

The procedure requires four components:

1) Two primers, each of 15 to 20 bases of DNA each — oligonucleotides which correspond to the DNA sequences immediately adjacent to

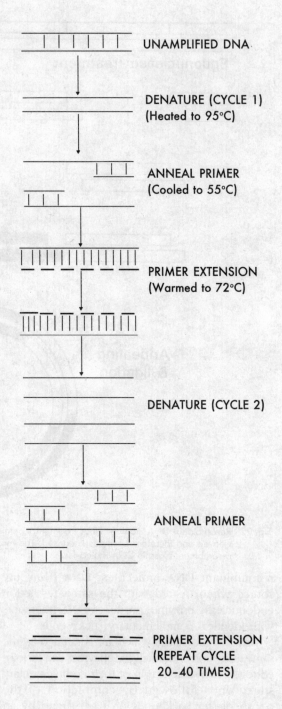

Fig. 93 Polymerase chain reaction

the sequence of interest. These oligonucleotide primers are usually synthesised in the laboratory.

2) DNA polymerase. This enzyme, usually derived from the bacterium thermus aquaticus, is required for DNA replication, known as primer extension in PCR.

3) Free DNA bases.

4) Small quantity of genomic DNA sequence of interest.

The PCR Process: The genomic DNA is first denatured by heating to a high temperature (around 95 degrees) so that DNA becomes single-stranded. This DNA is then exposed to large quantities of primers which hybridise or anneal to the complementary bases in the genomic DNA, when the temperature is reduced to 35 to 65 degree celsius. The DNA is then heated to an intermediate temperature of 70 to 75 degree celsius. Extending from primer sequence, a new DNA is synthesised by DNA polymerase the in presence of a large number of free DNA bases. The newly synthesised DNA is double strand. It is heated again leading to denaturing. The heating – cooling cycle is then repeated. The newly synthesised DNA serves as a template for synthesis. As the heating – cooling cycles are repeated, the primer bounded DNA is amplified geometrically. The number of copies doubles in each cycle. That is why the process is called a chain reaction. When the cycles are repeated 20 to 30 times it produce millions of copies of original DNA. Since each heating – cooling cycle requires only a few minutes, DNA can be amplified to make millions of copies in only a few hours.

PCR has advantages over older techniques.

1) It can be used with extremely small quantities of DNA, a single cell can be enough.

2) As it does not require genetic cloning it is faster. The genetic diagnosis of sickle cell disease which used to take a week or more using older techniques, now can be done in a single day.

3) It gives large quantities of pure DNA so it is not necessary to use radioactive probes to detect specific DNA sequences.

Disadvantages of PCR: 1) Primer synthesis requires knowledge of DNA sequence flanking the DNA of interest. When no sequence information is available other technique has to be used.

2) Extreme sensitivity of PCR makes it susceptible to contamination in the laboratory.

In general, since PCR is very fast, efficient, convenient, versatile and easy to use, it is now used extensively for diagnosis in forensic medicine and evolutionary genetics.

DNA Libraries: A collection of recombinant DNA molecules generated from a specific source is called a DNA library. If it is a clone of genomic DNA then it is referred to as genomic library and if DNA is cloned using mRNA as template then it represents complementary DNA or cDNA and hence called cDNA libraries.

Such a collection forming a library is done so that theoretically it contains all the sequences found in the original source. A DNA library using plasmids as vector would require several hundred thousand clones to be large enough to contain the whole of the human genome. If YACS are used as vectors with DNA digested by infrequently cutting restriction enzymes, it would mean creating 13 to 14 thousand clones for the whole human genome. Now genomic libraries have been created where clones from individual chromosomes are separately available.

Availability of such clones allows isolation of a particular gene or other DNA sequences in large quantities for further study. Complementary DNA libraries have advantage over genomic libraries because the clone represents a direct coding sequence without introns or other non-coding sequences found in genomic DNA. It also allows use of particular mRNA to enrich selective gene source. For example, a cDNA library prepared from RBC provides excellent cloning source to isolate globin gene cDNAs or a liver muscle cDNA library would provides a good source of clones of genes known to be expressed selectively in those tissues.

Methods of DNA and RNA Analysis: An analysis of DNA or RNA commonly involves detection of homologous sequences by using a probe which searches specific sequence and marks them out in such a way that the same can be readily observed and analysed in diagnostic or research laboratory.

In a genomic DNA sample that contains a total of several million DNA fragments, the problem arises as to how to find and analyse the specific DNA segment one is interested in. Similarly, how to detect a particular mRNA and measure its quantity in RNA sample from a tissue in which the desired mRNA may be present in very small amount, becomes a problem. To solve this problem, nucleic acid hybridisation technique is used in which single stranded nucleic acid are used which when mixed with specific probes form hybrid selectively with a complementary sequence. The probes used are tagged for subsequent detection.

DNA probes can be random genomic DNA sequences, specific gene cDNA sequences and DNA sequence produced synthetically based on amino acid sequence of a given protein. The probe can be radioactively labelled. The sites where a radioactively labelled probe hybridises with complementary DNA sequence in a nitrocellulose filter is localised by autoradiography. Probes can also be labelled fluorescently. Though less sensitive, this method is preferred because no radioactive isotopes are used.

Southern Blotting: This technique devised by E.M. Southern, uses gel electrophoresis and specific probes. The DNA sample is treated with restriction enzyme that makes sequence-specific cuts. The resulting fragments are subjected to electrophoresis on an agarose gel. This separates the DNA restriction fragments by size, the smaller running faster than the larger ones. The DNA fragments in the gel are then denatured with alkali, making them single stranded and rendering them capable of hybridising with complementary DNA sequences. The single stranded DNA molecules are then transferred from the gel to a piece of nitrocellulose or nylon filter by blotting and capillarity. To identify one or more fragments of interest among the millions, a specific labelled probe and filter are incubated together in solution under conditions that favour formation of double stranded DNA molecules. Afterwards the filter with its bound radioactive probe is exposed to show the position of the one or more fragments with which the probe is hybridised.

Northern Blotting: This technique is the counterpart of the Southern blotting technique for analysis of RNA samples. It allows determination of the size and quantity of the mRNA from a gene under consideration in a sample of RNA.

mRNA cannot be cleaved by restriction enzymes. However, RNA transcripts themselves are of different lengths depending on the size of the transcribing gene. So purified mRNA obtained from a particular cell type is separated according to size by agarose gel electrophoresis and transferred to nitrocellulose filter. The filter is then incubated with a denatured, labelled probe, which hybridises to a specific RNA transcript. After exposure to X-ray, one or more bands are seen showing the position and abundance of the specific transcript under consideration.

Polymerase Chain Reaction for DNA and RNA Analysis: As elaborated earlier, PCR is a very powerful technique for selective and rapid amplification of DNA. It can be employed for RNA by using a single stranded cDNA synthesised from the mRNA of interest.

DNA Sequence Analysis: The purified DNA segment obtained either by cloning or amplified by PCR can be studied further to determine its nucleotide sequence. The common approach is to use chemical analogs of nucleotides to inhibit the enzyme DNA polymerase as it synthesises the complementary strand to the original template to be sequenced. DNA synthesis is primed by a short oligonucleotide; DNA polymerase proceeds along the template sequence, incorporating either ^{32}P or ^{35}S labelled nucleotides into the newly synthesised sequences. Four inhibitory analogs which compete with their respective deoxynucleotides are used. For example, in a reaction to define the location of A (adenine) residues, an A analog is used, and DNA synthesis of individual molecules stops when A analog substitutes regular A in the chain. So in newly synthesized strands some stop at first A, some at second A and so on. Studies of this strand give details of the positioning of A. Similar studies with the other 3 bases are carried out. The reaction is further studied on electrophoretic gel which yields a ladder of DNA sequences and is read as radioactive bands. The total study gives the nucleotide sequence of the DNA under study.

Screening for Mutations in the Sequence: A sequencing of gene can be carried out to identify mutation within it. However, since many of the genes in humans are long it becomes a very difficult task. So selective techniques like denaturing gradient gel electrophoresis (DGGE), single stranded conformational polymorphism (SSCP) and chemical cleavage mismatch facilitate screening for mutations.

In DGGE, any of the DNA is matched with the identical sequence of DNA probe and the two form a homoduplex. Any mismatches of the DNA being screened with the DNA probe forms heteroduplex. This can be detected by a specialised technique.

In SSCP, altered sequence of DNA is observed as altered three-dimensional structure under specific laboratory process. Chemical cleavage mismatch method is available for cytosine and thymine. By selective chemical process, it picks up mismatches for cytosine and thymine on both the strands. Indirectly this permits detection of mismatches of adenine and guanine through their complementary nucleotides on the opposite strands.

Protein Analysis: A study of the protein levels helps in understanding normal and abnormal gene function, and also the effect of the abnormal gene on the alteration of protein structure which has produced the phenotypic effect.

Some of the methods of carrying out protein analysis are Western blotting, amino acid sequencing and reverse genetics.

Western Blotting: This name is given to keep in tune with Southern and Northern blotting. The method helps find out the size and amount of altered proteins in cell extracts from diseased individuals. The proteins are separated by gel electrophoresis, transferred to nitrocellulose filter and then incubated with antisera specific for the protein under study. The antigen–antibody reaction can be detected by the second tagged antibody against the first. The tagging can be done histochemically or by fluorescent or radioactive substance.

Amino Acid Sequencing: Amino acid sequencing can be an important primary requirement in search for the gene for a particular protein. A sequence of amino acids of a small portion of protein gives information of nucleotide sequence of the corresponding portion of the gene coding for the protein. Knowledge of the nucleotide sequence permits synthesis of oligonucleotide probes to screen genomic or cDNA libraries.

In this technique a purified protein is caeaved into a number of large peptide fragments. The peptide fragments are isolated and sequence of 15 to 30 amino acids from the amino terminal of each fragment is determined through ready-made available sequenators.

Reverse Genetics: When no identifiable protein or enzyme abnormality is detected, the finding of linked DNA sequence polymorphisms will lead to isolation and cloning of the structural gene. This allows recognition of its protein product. This process is called reverse genetics.

SUMMARY

Recombinant DNA Technology
Restriction enzymes recognise certain segments of nucleotides in any source of DNA and cleaves the DNA at those sites. The fragments are made to recombined with a suitable vector—plasmids, bacteriophages, cosmids or yeast artificial chromosome. The vector is then introduced into suitable host cells. The host cells multiply in a culture medium to produce clones of DNA molecules.
PCR

PCR is a means of making millions of copies of a short DNA sequence in a short span of time. Heating and cooling cycles are used to denature DNA, anneal to a primer and produce new copies of DNA. PCR is used for assessing genetic variation, diagnosing genetic diseases and for forensic purposes.

DNA Libraries

A collection of recombinant DNA molecules generated from a specific source constitutes a DNA library. If the clone is from a nucleus it is called genomic library but if the clone is produced by the action of reverse transcriptase on mRNA, it is called complementary DNA or cDNA library.

Methods of DNA Analysis: Southern Blotting Technique

The DNA sample is treated with restriction enzymes. The digested material is subjected to electrophoresis. The DNA fragments are denatured by alkali. These single stranded DNAs are made to hybridise with known complementary DNA sequences.

Methods of RNA Analysis: Northern Blotting Technique

mRNA is obtained from a particular cell, separated by electrophoresis and then transferred to a nitrocellulose filter. This is hybridised with a known, labelled probe.

DNA Sequencing

DNA sequencing can be accomplished using chemical analogues of nucleotides like dideoxynucleotides. These chemicals are incorporated into the DNA chain. The chemicals have one missing hydroxyl group and therefore they terminate the DNA chain. Thus, they mark the position of specific bases.

Protein Analysis: Western Blotting Technique

Protein extract from an individual is separated by electrophoresis, transferred to nitrocellulose filter and incubated with specific antisera. The reaction can be detected by a second antibody produced against the first antibody.

Amino Acid Sequencing

Purified protein extract is cleaved into peptide fragments. The peptide fragments are isolated and the first 15 to 30 amino acids from the amino terminal are determined through readymade sequenators.

GENE MAP

Gene mapping is done at two levels. Chromosomal mapping involves techniques to assign a gene or DNA sequence to a specific chromosome or a particular region of the chromosome. DNA mapping involves analysis for mapping, at DNA level, the detailed structures of the gene.

Chromosome Mapping

The following direct and indirect methods are used for chromosomal mapping:

Family Studies and Linkage: Initially, mapping of chromosomes for various genes was totally based on available family studies in large pedigrees carried to determine the modes of inheritance. X-linked traits could be mapped on the X chromosome because of their unique pattern of transmission. A few autosomal traits could be mapped on individual chromosomes because of their co-transmission through meiosis with other well known autosomal genes. When family studies show linkage between loci, both the loci must reside on the same chromosome. The frequency of recombination between linked markers gives measurement of genetic distance and can be used to place the two linked loci in a linear order.

Genetic Dosage: This is another indirect method of studying the location of genes on specific chromosomes. This principle is based on the assumption that the amount of protein product specific for a given gene is directly proportional to the number of copies that the gene presents in an individual or a cell. So a person with trisomy will have increased protein product level whereas a person with deletion will have decreased protein product level. For example, a cell with trisomy for chromosome 21 exhibits an enzyme level of superoxide dimutase one and half times that in normal cell and three times as much with monosomy 21. Red cell acid phosphatase gene was assigned to chromosome 2 in a similar manner.

Direct methods of chromosomal mapping are somatic cell hybridisation and in situ hybridisation.

Somatic Cell Hybridisation (Fig. 94): Somatic cell hybridisation is a common method of gene localisation. When mouse and human cells are grown in the same culture under specific condi-

particular gene or DNA sequence.

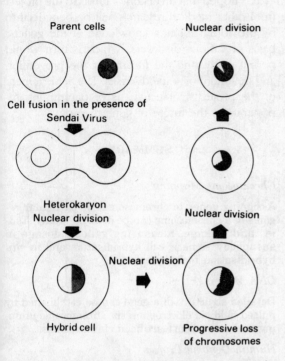

Parent cells

Nuclear division

Cell fusion in the presence of Sendai Virus

Heterokaryon
Nuclear division

Nuclear division

Nuclear division

Hybrid cell

Progressive loss of chromosomes

Fig. 94 Scheme showing cell hybridisation and subsequent selective loss of chromosomes from the hybrid cells.

tions, they fuse together to form hybrid cells. This is somatic cell hybridisation method. The mouse and human hybrid cell contains 86 chromosomes; 46 of human and 40 of mouse. These cells are then cloned. The hybrid cells begin to lose some of human chromosomes as they undergo cell division. Eventually cells remain having a full set of mouse chromosomes and only a single or few human chromosomes. The cells are karyotyped to determine which human chromosomes remain. These sets of cells are studied to know which chromosome contains which genes. This is done by several methods like study of gene products or use of labelled probe containing DNA of interest using Southern blotting or PCR tech-niques. At times translocations occur in which a part of a single human chromosome gets attached to one of the mouse chromosome. This allows mapping of a gene on a specific segment of a chromo-some. Similarly, other structural abnor-malities allow more specific chromosomal mapping of a

In Situ Hybridisation: Single stranded radio-labelled DNA sequences are incubated under special conditions with chromosomes prepared by usual method. The DNA strand hybridises with homologous DNA sequence in the genome. This permits mapping of single copy genes or DNA sequences on the chromosomes by exposure of the preparation to X-ray film. Labelling can also be done by non-radioactivity, i.e., by fluorescent in situ hybridisation.

DNA Mapping: Advanced laboratory techniques like pulsed field gel electrophoresis, chromosome jumping or linking and yeast artificial chromosome clones allow detailed gene mapping at DNA level.

Pulsed field gel electrophoresis allows construction of physical maps of relatively large stretches of DNA. Chromosome jumping or linking permits mapping of markers which directionally are hundreds of kilobases apart. Yeast artificial chromosome clones permit a large segment of genomic DNA to be cloned. This facilitates analysis of major genomic rearrangements.

Positional Cloning: Closing in on the gene: The technique of the cloning of a gene localised to a particular region of chromosome, without any prior knowledge of the product of the gene, is known as positional cloning.

In this technique, a polymorphic marker, closely linked to the disease gene under consideration, is selected. The technique of proceeding towards the gene is called chromo-some walking. DNA from the marker is used as a probe to pick out partially overlapping segments of DNA from a genomic library. These partially overlapping DNA segments are used to walk along the chromosome until the disease gene is reached. Because the disease gene can be on either side of the marker, chromosome walking typically proceeds in both directions away from the marker. To determine whether one has reached the gene of interest the following tests are used: cross-species hybridisation, identification of unmeth-ylated CG islands, linkage analysis in the newly isolated DNA segments as marker, mutation screening in affected individuals and tests of gene expression.

Candidate Genes: Candidate genes are those genes whose known protein product makes them likely candidates for the disease in question. A selective study of these genes helps to hasten the identification and mapping of these genes. Examples are identification of fibrillin gene on chromosome 15 responsible for Marfan syndrome, without exhaustive physical mapping and cloning. In general, the gene hunting process is expedited significantly by candidate genes.

All the techniques mentioned for gene mapping have enabled mapping of a large number of genes which are held responsible for major diseases.

The Human Genome Project

This project is a major international collaborative venture to map and sequence the entire human genome. This is a herculean task. The haploid human genome contains 50,000 to 100,000 genes and about 3,000,000,000 base pairs. The project has funding of 3 billion dollars over a period of 15 years. The USA, France, Japan and the UK are investing huge sums of public and charitable funds in the projects. This is being undertaken by the Human Genome Organization (HUGO). Annual workshops are held at which the data is pooled and individual chromosome maps are compiled. The results are published and are widely available.

It is hoped that diversion of funds to the project from other medical research will be beneficial to by providing humans knowledge of the genetic basis of various disorders. Which is turn would permit cultivating the means for the prevention and treatment of some diseases. The achievement of the project's, objectives is of paramount importance to the future of gene therapy.

SUMMARY

Chromosome Mapping

Assigning genes to chromosomes or particular regions of a chromosome can be done by family studies and linkage, measuring genetic dosage in aneuploidy, somatic cell hybridisation and in situ hybridisation techniques.

DNA Mapping

Detailed structure of a gene can be established by pulsed field gel electrophoresis, chromosome jumping and using yeast artificial chromosomes.

Human Genome Project

The project is to map and sequence the entire human genome. A haploid genome has 50,000 to 100,000 genes and 3,000,000 base pairs. It is hoped that the project would provide knowledge of the genetic basis of various disorders and thereby the means for prevention and treatment of at least some of these diseases.

APPENDIX
A Map of the Human Genome

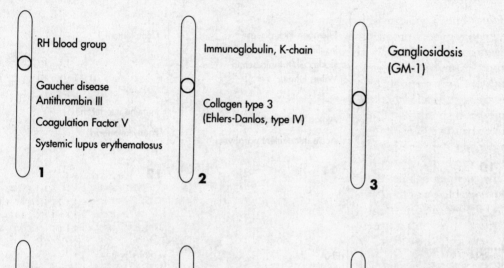

RH blood group

Gaucher disease
Antithrombin III

Coagulation Factor V

Systemic lupus erythematosus

1

Immunoglobulin, K-chain

Collagen type 3
(Ehlers-Danlos, type IV)

2

Gangliosidosis
(GM-1)

3

Huntington disease
Harler syndrome

Coagulation factor XI

4

Complement 6,7,9

Familial polyposis coli
Coagulation factor XII

5

Complement 2,4
Hemochromatosis
HLA
Congenital adrenal
hyperplasia (Type I)

6

Craniosynostosis

Collagen type 1(α_2 chain)
Cystic fibrosis

7

Congenital adrenal
hyperplasia (Type 2)

8

α-interferon
Galactosemia

Friedreich ataxia

Nail patella syndrome

Complement 5
Xeroderma pigmentosa
ABO blood group

9

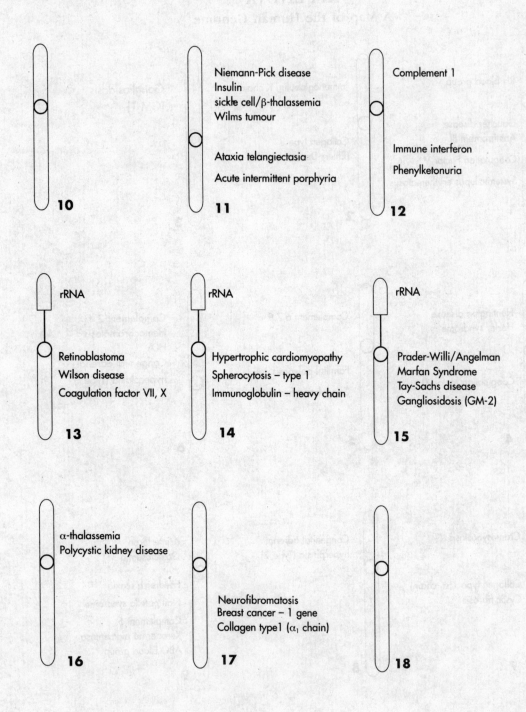

10

Niemann-Pick disease
Insulin
sickle cell/β-thalassemia
Wilms tumour

Ataxia telangiectasia

Acute intermittent porphyria

11

Complement 1

Immune interferon

Phenylketonuria

12

rRNA

Retinoblastoma
Wilson disease
Coagulation factor VII, X

13

rRNA

Hypertrophic cardiomyopathy
Spherocytosis – type 1
Immunoglobulin – heavy chain

14

rRNA

Prader-Willi/Angelman
Marfan Syndrome
Tay-Sachs disease
Gangliosidosis (GM-2)

15

α-thalassemia
Polycystic kidney disease

16

Neurofibromatosis
Breast cancer – 1 gene
Collagen type1 (α₁ chain)

17

18

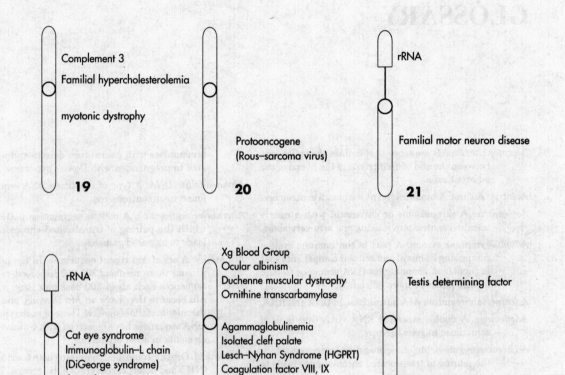

19
Complement 3
Familial hypercholesterolemia

myotonic dystrophy

20
Protooncogene
(Rous–sarcoma virus)

21
rRNA

Familial motor neuron disease

22
rRNA

Cat eye syndrome
Immunoglobulin–L chain
(DiGeorge syndrome)
Acoustic neuroma

X
Xg Blood Group
Ocular albinism
Duchenne muscular dystrophy
Ornithine transcarbamylase

Agammaglobulinemia
Isolated cleft palate
Lesch–Nyhan Syndrome (HGPRT)
Coagulation factor VIII, IX
Hunter Syndrome
Fragile X Syndrome
G - 6PD deficiency
Colour blindness

Y
Testis determining factor

GLOSSARY

Acceptor site: An AG sequence that defines the splice site between the end of an intron and the 5ᴵ end of the adjacent exon.

Acentric: A chromosomal fragment without a centromere.

Acrocentric: A chromosome or chromatid with a nearly terminal centromere making one arm very short.

Adaptive immune system: A part of the immune system comprising humoral and cellular components that is capable of changing its DNA sequence to bind foreign particles more efficiently.

Adenine: (abbreviation A) A purine base in DNA and RNA.

Adenovirus: A double stranded RNA virus that is used sometimes in gene therapy.

Adjacent segregation: Meiotic segregation patterns in which the pairing of translocated chromosomes leads to unbalanced gametes.

Affinity: The binding power of an antibody with an antigen. Low affinity means poor binding and high affinity means precise binding.

AIDS: Acquired Immuno Deficiency Syndrome.

Albinism: A condition characterised by congenital absence of pigmentation resulting in pale, milky skin, light hair and pink eyes.

Alleles, Allelomorphs: One or more alternative forms of a gene found at the same locus on homologous chromosomes in an individual and/or in a population of individuals. Alleles segregate at meiosis; a child thus usually receives only one of each pair of alleles from each parent. See also *Multiple alleles* and *Isoalleles.*

Allele-specific oligonucleotide: A short specific DNA sequence usually 18–20 nucleotides, that can hybridise with the selected DNA sequence, used in DNA diagnosis of mutation.

Allograft, Homograft: A tissue graft from a donor to a host with a different genotype, host and donor being members of the same species.

Allotypes: Genetically determined differences in antigens.

Alpha-fetoprotein: An albumin-like protein produced by the fetus. Its titre in the amniotic fluid increases in pregnancies with neural tube defects and is lowered in pregnancies with Down's syndrome.

Alpha-satellite DNA: A type of repetitive DNA sequence found near centromeres.

Alternative segregation: A meiotic segregation pattern in which the pairing of translocated chromosomes leads to balanced gametes.

Alu family: A set of Alu repeat sequences. In the human genome there are about 300,000 dispersed, related sequences each about 300 base pair long, named Alu because they have an Alu cleavage site near the middle of the sequence. These or such repeated DNA sequences have homology with transposable elements in other organisms.

Amino acid: Organic compound containing both basic amino (NH_2) and acidic carboxyl (COOH) groups. There are over twenty amino acids universally found. Amino acids are polymerised to form proteins.

Amniocentesis: Aspiration of amniotic fluid, by a syringe and needle, from the amniotic cavity through the abdominal wall and the uterus. The term is also applied to the entire procedure of antenatal diagnosis by culture and analysis of amniotic fluid cells.

Amorph: A gene having no effect; an apparently inactive gene.

Amplification: In molecular biology, it refers to the production of multiple copies of a sequence of DNA.

Anaphase: Stage of mitosis or meiosis when daughter chromosomes are separating from the equatorial plate towards the opposite poles of the spindle.

Aneuploid: A chromosome number which is more or less than an exact multiple of the haploid number, e.g., $2N-1$ or $2N+1$ where N is the haploid number of chromosomes.

Antibody, Immunoglobulin: A specific complex protein produced in response to the introduction of a specific antigen into an animal and reacting specifically with that antigen.

Anticipation: The apparent tendency for some diseases to begin at an earlier age and to increase in severity with each succeeding generation; apparently this has no biological basis.

Anticodon: A triple in the tRNA complementary to an mRNA codon (see *codon*).

Antigen: A substance which elicits antibody formation by immune competent cells and reacts specifically with the antibody so produced.

Antigen presenting cell: A cell that engulfs foreign material, digests it and then displays the foreign antigens on its cell surface for recognition by T lymphocytes.

Antisense oligonucleotide: A short oligonucleotide synthesised to bind to a particular RNA or DNA sequence to block its expression.

Antisense strand of DNA: The non-coding DNA strand. It is complementary to mRNA and serves as the template for RNA. It is also called the transcribed strand.

Apoptosis: Programmed involution or cell death of a developing tissue or organ of the body.

Ascertainment: The finding and selection of families with hereditary disorders.

Association: The occurrence of two or more phenotypic characteristics in kindred members or a population in a frequency greater than would be predicted on the basis of chance.

Assortative mating, Non-random mating: The preferential selection of a mate with a particular genotype. Preference for a mate of the same genotype is positive assortative mating; preference for a mate of a different genotype is negative assortative mating.

Assortment, genic and chromosomal: The random distribution to the gametes of different combinations of genes and chromosomes. Each 2*N* individual has a paternal and a maternal set of chromosomes forming *N* homologous pairs. At anaphase of the first meiotic division, one member of each chromosome pair passes to each pole, and thus the gametes contain one chromosome of each type, but this chromosome may be either of paternal or maternal origin. Thus, non-allelic genes assort independently to the gametes. Exception: linked genes.

Autograft: A graft from the host's own tissues.

Autoimmunity: Immunity to self seen in certain conditions in which an individual forms antibodies against one or more of his own antigens.

Autosome: Any chromosome other than the sex chromosomes. In humans there are 22 pairs of autosomes.

B cells: Small lymphocytes (bursa-equivalent cells) derived from precursors in the bone marrow sensitive to bacterial and viral antigens, and transformed by antigenic stimulation into plasma cells which produce humoral antibodies.

Backcross, Test cross: A mating of a heterozygote with a recessive homozygote (T/t x t/t) in which the progeny (1/2 T/t, 1/2 t/t) reveals the genotype of the heterozygous parent. The double backcross mating (T/t R/r x t/t r/r) is the most useful mating for linkage analysis.

Bacteriophage: A virus which infects bacteria.

Banding: The techniques of staining chromosomes in a characteristic pattern of cross bands, thus allowing identification of each individual chromosome pair. Giemsa banding (G banding) and quinacrine fluorescence banding (Q banding) are the best available techniques.

Barr body, Sex chromatin: The condensed single X chromosome seen adjacent to the nuclear membrane in the nuclei of somatic cells of female mammals; named for M.L. Barr, who first described this body, thus demonstrating sexual dimorphism in somatic cells.

Base: Any one of the five nitrogenous bases in the nucleic acid molecules A = adenine; T = thymine; U = uracil; C = cytosine; G = guanine.

Base analog: A type of mutagen which can mimic the chemical behaviour of one of the four DNA bases.

Base pair substitution: A type of mutation where one base pair in DNA is replaced by another.

Base pairing: Adenine forms a base pair with thymine in DNA and with uracil in mRNA; similarly guanine pairs with cytosine in both DNA and RNA. This specificity of base pairing is fundamental to DNA replication, and to its transcription into mRNA for protein synthesis.

bp: Abbreviation of base pair.

Benign trait: A variant trait having no clinical significance.

Benign tumour: Aeoplasm which unlike a malignant one, does not invade surrounding tissues or spread to other parts of the body.

Bivalent: A pair of homologous chromosomes as seen during metaphase of the first meiotic division.

Blood group: Genetically determined red cell antigens.

Breakpoint: The location on a chromosome at which a translocation has taken place.

Burden: In clinical genetics the term burden refers to the total impact of a genetic disorder on the patient, his family and the society as a whole.

c: Abbreviation of cytosine.

CA repeat: A short dinucleotide sequence present as tandem repeats at multiple sites in the human genome producing microsatellite polymorphisms.

c-banding: A type of chromosome staining that demarcates the constitutive heterochromatin present at and around the centromeres.

Candidate gene: A gene known to be located in the region of interest and likely to be responsible for a genetic disease, as hinted by the protein produced by the gene.

5ᴵ cap: Methylated guanine nucleotide added to the 5ᴵ end of a growing mRNA molecule by an unusual 5ᴵ to 5ᴵ triphosphate linkage, needed for normal processing, stability and translation of mRNA.

Cap site: The site of initiation of transcription.

Carcinogen: A substance that can supposedly produce cancer.

Carcinogenesis: The process of cancer development.

Carrier: An individual heterozygous for a single recessive abnormal gene which is not expressed phenotypically, though it may be detected by appropriate laboratory tests.

CAT box or CCAAT box: A conserved non-coding sequence of DNA found about 75 to 80 base pairs upstream from the transcriptase initiation site of many genes and presumed to be promoter in nature.

cDNA: Complementary DNA or copy DNA synthesised through enzyme reverse transcriptase in the laboratory from a specific mRNA obtained from cells. This DNA corresponds only to the coding sequence (exons).

cDNA library: A collection of copies of the expressed messenger RNA.

Cell adhesion molecule: Present on the cell wall that takes part in the interaction of T cells and their targets.

Cell cycle: An alternating sequence of cell division and interphase (rest or non-division) in the life of cell.

Cellular immune system: T cell component of immune system mainly active during transplantation immunity (rejection) and delayed hypersensitivity.

centi Morgan (cM): A unit used to measure map distance based on phenomenon of linkage. It is named after Thomas Hunt Morgan. One map unit refers to one per cent chances of recombination taking place during meiosis.

Centric fusion: Fusion of the long arms of two non-homologous acrocentric chromosomes at the centromere. Also known as Robertsonian translocation.

Centriole: One of the pair of organelles which form the points of focus of the spindle during cell division. Centrioles are short cylinders containing nine pairs of peripheral microtubules disposed about a central cavity. The centrioles lie together at right angles to each other outside the nuclear membrane at prophase, and replicate and migrate during cell division to opposite poles of the cell.

Centromere, Kinetochore, or Primary constriction: The small mass of heterochromatin within a chromosome by which the chromatids are held together, and by which a chromosome becomes attached to the spindle during cell division.

CG island: Unmethylated CG sequences found near the 5ᴵ end of some genes.

Chiasma: The cross configuration of chromatids of homologous chromosomes during the diplotene stage of the first meiotic division.

Chimera: An individual containing cells derived from different zygotes. In human genetics the term is used with reference to blood group chimerism, in which dizygotic twins exchange hematopoietic stem cells in utero and continue to form blood cells of both types; or to 'whole-body' chimerism, in which two separate zygotes are fused into one individual.

Chorionic villus sampling (CVS): A prenatal diagnostic procedure carried out under ultrasound control to obtain chorion frondosum, usually performed around 10–12 weeks of gestation, either transcervically or transabdominally.

Chromatid: One of the two daughter strands of a duplicated chromosome which are joined by a single centromere. Each is destined to form one chromosome in the daughter cell — one half of a replicated chromosome.

Chromatin: The nucleoprotein fibres the chromosomes are composed of.

Chromatin loop: A unit of DNA coil of about 100 kb in size comprising a group of solenoids.

Chromatin opener: A regulatory element that can decondense or open regions of chromatin.

Chromomere: A densely coiled region of chromatin on a chromosome. Chromomeres give the extended chromosome a headed appearance.

Chromosomes: DNA-histone threads residing in the nucleus of a cell. They carry genetic information. Invisible as distinct entities during interphase, they become prominent during metaphase of cell division.

Chromosomal aberration: An abnormality of chromosome number and/or structure.

Chromosome abnormalities: A group of genetic diseases which have bases in microscopically observable alternation of chromosome number or structure.

Chromosome banding: The process of applying specific stains to chromosome which produce characteristic staining patterns called bands.

Chromosome breakage: A break in chromosome that increases in the presence of clastogens (klastos = broken).

Chromosome disorder: Any clinical condition caused by an abnormal chromosomal constitution.

Chromosome instability syndrome: A disease characterised by a significant number of chromosome breaks or exchanges, for example, Bloom syndrome.

Chromosome specific library: A collection of DNA fragments from a single chromosome.

Chromosome walking: A molecular cloning process in which overlapping clones are used to progress along a chromosome towards a gene of interest by sequential sequences of clones carrying overlapping sequences of DNA.

Cistron: The smallest structural and functional unit of genetic material (DNA) which specifies the formation of a particular polypeptide chain. The structural gene as usually conceived is synonymous with the cistron.

Class switching: A normal change in antibody class from IgM to IgG in an immune response.

Clastogen: Any substance that can induce breaks in chromosomes, e.g., radiation klastos = broken).

Clone: A group of genetically identical cells derived from a single cell by repeated mitosis.

Codominance: When both alleles are fully expressed in the heterozygote.

Codon: A triplet of three successive bases in a DNA or RNA molecule specifying a single amino acid.

Coefficient of inbreeding (F): This represents the probability that an individual has received both alleles of a pair from a common ancestral source or the proportion of loci at which he is homozygous. For example, offspring of a first cousin marriage. For any gene the father has, the chance that the mother also has the same, is one-eighth. For any gene the father gives to his child, the chance that the mother has the same gene and will transmit it is $1/2 \times 1/8$ = 1/16. This is the coefficient of inbreeding for the child of a first cousin marriage. It indicates that the offspring has a 1/16 chance of being homozygous at any given locus, or that he is homozygous at 1/16 of his loci.

Coefficient of relationship: Represents the probability that the two persons have inherited a certain gene from a common ancestor, or the proportion of all their genes that have been inherited from common ancestors.

Colcemid or colchicine: A drug that arrests cell division in metaphase by immobilising spindles thereby rendering chromosomes easily discernible microscopically.

Colinearity: The parallel relationship between DNA and a protein, in which the sequence of bases of DNA specifies the sequence of amino acids of the protein.

Complement system: A group of serum proteins, a part of immune system coded by gene is class III MHC region which can help destroy invading organisms. They get activated to participate in the overall immune response to bring about the destruction of cellular antigens.

Complementary base pairing or Watson-Crick pairing: A fundamental process of adenosine pairing only with thymine and guanine with cytosine.

Complementation: It is the ability of two different genetic defects to correct for one another, thus establishing that the defects are not in the same gene, e.g., when two persons, each homozygous for a recessive defect, produce children without the defect. The term is more commonly applied to the complementation test, in which two mutant cell lines grown together mutually correct one another's biochemical defect or in which a somatic cell hybrid made from two genetically defective cells lacks the defects of the parent lines.

Compound: A heterozygous individual (or genotype) who possesses two different mutant alleles (not 'wild' or 'normal') at one particular locus on homologous chromosomes.

Concordant: Twins are said to be concordant for a given trait if both exhibit the trait.

Congenital: Any abnormality, genetic or otherwise present at birth.

Congenital trait: Trait present at birth, not necessarily genetic.

Consanguinity, Blood relationship, Genetic relationship: Consanguineous individuals have at least one common ancestor in the preceding few generations.

Consensus sequences: A sequence of DNA bases commonly seen at a definite position. Example: a GGGCGGG sequence promoter element found at the 5' side of gene in eukaryote involved in the control of gene expression or sequence found near donor and acceptor splice sites.

Conservation: Preservation of similar DNA sequences in different organisms. Conserved sequences are usually found in functional genes.

Constitutional or constitutive DNA: DNA found in normal cells of the body in contrast to that in cancer cells.

Contiguous gene syndrome: A disorder seen as a result of microdeletion of chromosomal DNA involving two or more contiguous loci. Also known as segmental aneusomy.

Cordocentesis: See percutaneous umbilical blood sampling (PUBS).

Cosmid: A hybrid of bacteriophage and plasmid, capable of accepting largest possible insert of DNA (40–50 kb) in comparison to either phage or plasmids.

Costimulatory molecule: A cell surface molecule that participates in the binding of T cell receptor to MHC-antigen complexes.

Coupling: In a heterozygote for two loci, both non-allelic genes of interest at different loci on the same chromosome are said to be linked in coupling or in *cis* configuration.

Cross: Mating between organisms in genetic studies.

Cross reacting material (CRM): Immunologically detected protein or enzymes produced by a mutant gene. Being functionally inactive, it reacts antigenetically with the antibody against the unaltered protein.

Cross-reaction: An antibody binding itself to an antigen other than the one for which it was specifically stimulated. Such antigens are usually very similar to the original antibody generating antigen.

Crossover, Crossing over, Recombination: The exchange of genetic material between homologous chromosomes. The chiasmata seen at diplotene are the physical evidence of crossing over.

Cryptic splice site: A site where intron-exon splicing may occur when the normal splice site is altered by mutation. It results in abnormal splicing of mRNA.

Cytogenetics: The science that combines the methods and findings of cytology and genetics, concerned mainly with the chromosomes and their correlations with the phenotype.

Cytokine: A growth factor that causes cells to proliferate. Example interleukins.

Cytokinesis: Cytoplasmic division occurring during cell division.

Cytosine: A pyrimidine base constituent of DNA and RNA.

Cytotoxic T lymphocyte or Killer lymphocyte: A part of the cellular immune system concerned with killing when infected vertebrate cells present a complex of MHC class I molecule and foreign peptide of microorganism.

Degeneracy of the code, Degenerate code: The genetic code is said to be degenerate because more than one nucleotide triplet codes for the same amino acid.

Deletion: The loss of a segment of the genetic material from a chromosome, a form of chromosomal aberration.

Derivative chromosome: An altered chromosome as a result of translocation.

Dermatoglyphics: The study of the patterns of the ridged skin on the palms, fingers, soles and toes.

Dicentric: A structurally abnormal chromosome with two centromeres.

Dictyotene: The interphase-like stage in which the oocyte persists from the late fetal life until ovulation. During this stage, the oocyte has not yet completed the prophase of meiosis I.

Dideoxy method: A technique of sequencing DNA in which dideoxynucleotides, which terminate replication, are incorporated into replicating DNA strands.

Diploid: The double state of all chromosomes in normal somatic cells (Symbol: 2N).

Direct diagnosis: The direct diagnosis of disease by examination of mutation itself when a DNA base mutation is suspected in patients.

Discordant: Twins are said to be discordant with respect to a trait, if one shows the trait and the other does not.

Dispermy: Fertilisation of a duplicated egg nucleus, or egg and polar body, by two sperms. This event can produce a rare type of chimera in which two separate zygotes fuse to form a single individual.

Dispersal repetitive DNA: A class of repeated DNA sequences in which single repeats are found to be scattered throughout the genome. Compare with tandem repeats.

Dizygotic, Dizygous, Fraternal: Type of twins produced by the fertilisation of two different ova by two different sperms. Dizygotic twins are no more similar genetically than are brothers and sisters.

DNA, Deoxyribose nucleic acid: The nucleic acid of the chromosomes, which carries the genetic code. Also found in the mitochondria.

DNA fingerprint: A pattern of hypervariable tandem DNA repeats of a core sequence which is unique to an individual. Since there are great number of polymorphisms available, combined genotypes are useful in identifying individuals for forensic purposes.

DNA library: It is collection of DNA cloned into vehicles such as phage or plasmid.

DNA looping: The formation of looped structures in DNA. It permits the interaction of various regulatory elements.

DNA polymerase: An enzyme which synthesises a new DNA

strand using a previously synthesised DNA strand as a template during DNA replication and repair.

DNA repair: A process in which bases which are incorrectly introduced in the DNA sequence are altered to produce the original correct sequence.

Dominant: A trait which is expressed in individuals even when they are heterozygous for a particular gene.

Donor site: GT sequence that demarcates the splice site at the 5' end of an intron.

Dosage compensation: The genetic mechanism by which the two X chromosomes of the normal female are rendered quantitatively identical, in their effect, to the one X chromosome of the normal male. See Lyon hypothesis.

Dosage mapping: A technique for mapping genes on chromosomes with the help of excess or deficient gene product measurement correlated with a chromosomal duplication or deletion.

Drift, Random genetic drift: Fluctuations in gene frequencies which tend to occur in small isolated populations.

Duplication: A type of chromosomal aberration in which part of a chromosome is duplicated.

Dysmorphism: Morphological developmental abnormality, as seen in many syndromes of genetic or environmental origin.

Electrophoresis, denaturing gradient gel (DGGE) (Denaturing gradient gel electrophoresis): A laboratory technique to detect mutation in DNA. In this method a radiolabelled single stranded DNA probe is mixed with a double stranded DNA that is being screened, which is heated to make it single stranded. This mixture is electrophoresed on a denaturing gradient gel. DNA which matches with the sequence of the DNA probe forms a homoduplex, which under the denaturing conditions of the gel remains hybridised. Any mismatches of DNA being screened with the DNA probe results in the formation of a heteroduplex which as it runs down the denaturing gradient of the gel separate out as a single strand at a certain point forming a branched structure having decreased mobility. This results in an altered position compared to the homoduplex which can be detected on an autoradiograph.

Empiric risk: Computation of probability that a given trait will occur or recur in a family based on past experience rather than based on knowledge of the causative mechanism.

Endogamy, Inbreeding: Mating within the group.

Enhancer: Regulatory DNA sequence that interacts with promoters to increase the transcription of genes.

Epistasis: Interaction between products of two genes situated at different loci, where one gene masks or prevents the expression of another gene at a different locus. (Dominance is the term used when one gene masks one of its own alleles, i.e., another gene at the same locus).

Euchromatin: Chromatin which shows the staining behaviour characteristic of the majority of the chromosomal complement. It is uncoiled during interphase and condenses during mitosis, reaching a maximum density at metaphase.

Eukaryote: An organism in which the cells have a nucleus with a nuclear membrane.

Euploid: It is a polyploid chromosomal number that is an exact multiple of the haploid number. It can be normal ($2N$) or abnormal ($3N$, $4N$...).

Exons (Extrons): Parts of a gene (cistron) involved in protein synthesis by transcribing active mRNA.

Expressivity: The extent to which a gene is expressed in individuals. A trait with varying expressivity shows variation in degree of expression from mild to severe.

Extended repeat: A type of mutation in which a tandem trinucleotide repeat increases in number.

F: See coefficient of inbreeding.

Family: Parents and children. See also Kindred.

F1, F one, First filial generation: The first generation progeny of a mating 'P', which stands for parental generation.

False negative: The result of a test or screening whereby an affected individual is incorrectly diagnosed as being unaffected by the disease under consideration.

False positive: The result of a test or screening whereby an unaffected individual is incorrectly diagnosed as being affected by the disease under consideration.

Fetoscopy: A procedure for direct visualisation of the fetus used for prenatal diagnosis.

Fingerprint: The pattern of the ridged skin on the distal phalanx of a finger.

Fingerprint technique: A method of combining electrophoresis and chromatography to separate the components of a protein such as hemoglobin.

First-degree relatives: Closest relatives, i.e., parents, offspring and siblings.

Fitness (Darwinian, biological): The relative ability of an organism to survive and transmit its genes to the next generation. It is determined by the number of offspring who reach reproductive age. Fitness is unity (or 100 per cent) if a person has at least two such offspring.

Flow cytometry or Fluorescent activated cell sorting (FACS): A laboratory technique in which chromosomes are stained with a fluorescent dye which selectively binds to DNA. The differences in the fluorescence of the various chromosomes allow them to be individually sorted out by a special laser.

Fluorescent in situ hybridisation (FISH): A laboratory technique in which probes of single stranded DNA sequence with a fluorescent label are hybridised with its complementary target sequence in the chromosomes allowing them to be visualised under ultraviolet light.

Forme fruste: Any extremely mild expression of a genetic trait in an abnormality, disease or syndrome which is of no clinical significance.

Frame-shift mutation: A mutation at the level of DNA base pairs involving a deletion or duplication or insertion that is not an exact multiple of three base pairs and so the reading frame of the gene changes.

Fusion gene: A gene resulting from a combination of two genes or parts of two genes.

G bands: The dark and light cross-bands formed on chromosomes after treatment with trypsin and Giemsa stain.

Gamete: A haploid germ cell (sperm or ovum).

Gene: A segment of a DNA molecule coded for the synthesis of a polypeptide.

Gene(s) in common: Genes which are inherited by two individuals from a common ancestral source.

Gene family: A group of genes containing exons of similar DNA sequence indicating that the genes have evolved from a single common ancestral gene by duplication and subsequent divergence. These genes may or may not be located in the same chromosome region.

Gene flow: Gradual diffusion of genes from one population to another by migration and miscegenation (interracial breeding).

Gene frequency: The proportion of chromosomes that contain a specific gene in a given population.

Gene map: A representation of the human karyotype showing the locations of the genes on the chromosomes.

Gene pool: All the genes present at a given locus in a given population.

Gene therapy: Insertion of normal genes into a cell to correct a disease. If it alters all cells of the body, including germline, then it is germline gene therapy. If it only alters somatic cells excluding the germ line then it is called somatic cell gene therapy.

Genetics: The scientific study of heredity.

Genetic code: The base triplets of DNA or mRNA that specify the different amino acids.

Genetic counselling: Providing guidance to the problems related to the occurrence, or the risk of occurrence of a genetic disorder in a family. It also deals with the problems of the risk and the burden of the disorder and the options available for handling them.

Genetic death: Death of an individual without reproducing.

Genetic drift: The random fluctuations of gene frequencies due to sampling errors. While drift occurs in all populations, its effects are most evident in very small populations.

Genetic engineering: Alternation of genes, recombinant DNA techniques.

Genetic lethal: A genetically determined trait in which affected individuals do not reproduce.

Genetic library: A collection of DNA fragments from an organism's total genome. It includes both DNA and non-coding DNA.

Genetic load: The average number of lethal equivalents per individual in population.

Genetic mapping: Determining the order of genes on chromosomes according to recombination frequency. Compare with *Physical mapping*.

Genetic marker: A trait can be used as a genetic marker in studies of cell lines, individuals, families and populations, if (a) it is genetically determined, (b) can be accurately classified, (c) has a simple unequivocal pattern of inheritance and (d) has heritable variations common enough to allow it to be classified as a genetic polymorphism.

Genetic screening: Examining a population to detect individuals at risk of having a specific genetic disorder or of having a child with a specific genetic disorder. Genetic screening tests are normally applied only when some method of treatment or intervention is available.

Genetic trait: Trait determined by genes, not necessarily congenital. It may be manifested any time during life.

Genocopy, Gene mimic, Genetic mimic: See heterogeneity.

Genome: The full set of genes in a gamete or in an individual.

Genotype: The total genetic constitution (genome) of an individual, or more specifically the alleles present at one locus, for a particular trait.

Genotype frequency: The proportion of individuals in a population that carry a specific genotype.

Germline: The cell line that produces gametes.

Gonosome: Sex chromosome, X or Y.

Guanine: A purine base, a structural unit of DNA and RNA.

Haploid: The single set of all chromosomes, found in normal gametes (Symbol IV).

Haplotype: A set of genes from closely linked loci on one chromosome, usually inherited as a unit, e.g., the four gene-loci of the HLA complex on chromosome 6 are very closely linked loci constituting a haplotype, thus each individual has two haplotypes. Within a kindred, the combinations of alleles at these loci are transmitted as units.

Hardy-Weinberg law: If two alleles (A and a) occur in a randomly mating population with the frequency of p and q, respectively, where p + q = 1, then the expected proportions of the three genotypes AA = P^2, Aa = 2pq, and aa = q^2 and remain constant from generation to generation in an infinitely large, in-breeding population. Mutation, selection, migration, and genetic drift can and do disturb the Hardy-Weinberg equilibrium.

Heavy chain: A major structural component of an antibody molecule having a higher molecular weight than the other major component the light chain. There are five types of heavy chains found in the humans, Y, m and E.

Helper T lymphocyte: A part of the immune system. This cell has a receptor on its surface which can bind with the MHC and foreign peptide complex. Such a process stimulates the helper T lymphocyte to secrete cytokines which in turn stimulate B lymphocytes whose cell surface receptors known as immunoglobulins bind to the invading microorganisms.

Hemizygous (hemizygotic): The genotype of a male with regard to an X-linked trait, since males have only one set of X-linked genes.

Hereditary, Heritable, Heredofamilial: Essentially synonymous terms for genetic traits transmissible through parents.

Heritability: A statistical measure of the degree to which a trait is genetically determined.

Heterochromatin: Chromosomal material staining differently from the rest of the chromosomal material in the cell during interphase, e.g., the Barr body. Also referred to as heterochromosome.

Heterochromosome: See *heterochromatin.*

Heterodisomy: When in a cell both the homologous chromosomes are derived from a single parent and none from the other parent, the phenomenon is known as disomy. When both the chromosomes are non-identical homologous chromosomes (because of non-disjunction at meiosis) the disomy is further specified as heterodisomy.

Heterogametic sex: The sex that produces equal numbers of two different gametes. In man, it is the heterogametic male that produces X- and y-bearing sperms. In birds, the female is heterogametic producing X- and Y-bearing ova.

Heterogeneity: The process in which an identical or similar phenotype is produced by a different genetic mechanism. Genocopy and genetic mimic are terms for a genetic trait which is phenotypically similar to, but fundamentally (genetically) distinct from another.

Heteromorphism: Variation in the microscopic appearance of a chromosome.

Heteroplasmy: The presence of different DNA sequence at the same locus, i.e., heterogeneity in DNA composition found often in mitochondrial genes.

Heteroploid: Any chromosome number other than the normal.

Heterozygote, Heterozygous: An individual who possesses two different alleles at one particular locus on homologous chromosomes.

High resolution banding: The technique of staining chromosomes in prophase or prometaphase when they are more extended, than during metaphase. This method yields more bands and greater resolution.

Histocompatibility: Antigenic similarity between the graft and the host. A graft is accepted by the host only if there is histocompatibility, i.e., graft has no antigens which the host does not have.

Histones: Basic protein core around which DNA coils in the chromosome. They are of four types H_1, H_2A or H_2B, H_3 and H_4, rich in basic amino acids (lysine or arginine); and are found throughout the eukaryote evolution.

hnRNA (Precursor RNA): It is the initial, faithful transcript of a gene, containing 'active' and 'inactive' portions.

Holandric inheritance: The pattern of inheritance of genes on the Y chromosome. Only males are affected and the trait is transmitted by affected males to all their sons but to none of their daughters.

Homogametic sex: The sex that produces one type of gamete.

Homograft: See *allograft.*

Homologous chromosomes: Chromosomes that pair during meiosis. Each homologue is a duplicate of one of the chromosomes contributed at syngamy by the mother or the father. Homologous chromosomes contain the same linear sequence of genes and as a consequence, genes as a rule occur in pairs.

Homozygote, Homozygous: As individual who possesses two identical alleles at one particular locus on homologous chromosomes.

Human leucocyte antigen (HLA): The term used for specific group of antigens from major histocompatability complex (MHC).

Hybrid: The progeny of a cross between two genetically different organisms.

Iatrogenic, Iatral: Literally, caused by a physician. The term refers to any condition which results from medical treatment.

Immune competent: Cells capable of producing an antibody in response to an antigenic stimulus.

Immune reaction: The specific reaction between antigen and antibody.

Immunogenetics: The study of the genetic basis of the immune system. It includes studies using a combination of immunologic and genetic techniques, as in the investigation of genetic characteristics detectable only by immune reactions.

Immunoglobulin: See *antibody.*

Immunologic tolerance: The inability to respond to a specific antigen because of previous exposure to that antigen, especially during embryonic life.

Immunological homeostasis: The characteristic condition of a normal adult, who has certain antigens and the ability to react to antigens by producing antibodies, but who does not produce antibodies to his own antigens.

Imprinting: The differing expression of genetic material depending on whether it is inherited from the mother or the father.

In situ hybridisation: Technique used to map genes by molecular hybridisation of a cloned DNA sequence probe labelled by radioactivity or fluorescence directly on a chromosomal preparation on a slide and then studied by X-ray or fluorescence studies to reveal the position of the probe.

In vitro fertilisation (IVF) diagnosis: A form of genetic diagnosis in which DNA from a single blastomere cell obtained by IVF is amplified by PCR so that mutation causing disease can be easily revealed.

Inborn error: A genetically determined biochemical disorder in which a specific enzyme defect produces a metabolic block which may have pathological consequences.

Inbreeding: The mating of closely related individuals. The progeny of close relatives are said to be inbred. In laboratory mice, brother-sister inbreeding over many generations has been used to produce inbred lines.

Incompatibility: The donor and host are incompatible if, because of a genetic difference, the host rejects cells transplanted from the donor. In maternal-fetal incompatibility, the mother forms antibodies against fetal cells which have entered her circulation.

Independent assortment: Mendel's law stating that alleles at different loci on homologous chromosomes are transmitted from generation to generation independent of one another.

Index case: See *proband.*

Indirect diagnosis: A form of genetic diagnosis in which the mutation responsible for the disease is not directly observed. Usually it is diagnosed employing link markers.

Innate immune system: That part of the immune system which operates during initial immune response and it does not change its characteristic response to infections. Compare with *adaptive immune system.*

Insert: A DNA sequence that is introduced into a vector such as a plasmid or cosmid using recombinant DNA technology.

Insertion: A structural abnormality of chromosome in which a part of an arm of one chromosome is inserted into the arm of a non-homologous chromosome.

Interchange: See *translocation.*

Interphase: The major portion of the cell cycle, during which a cell is not undergoing division. The stage between two successive mitotic divisions during which DNA replication occurs.

Introns: Inserts or parts of a gene, alternating with exons, and with them, concerned in transcribing heterogeneous nuclear RNA (hnRNA or precursor RNA).

Inversion: A type of chromosomal aberration in which part of a chromosome is reversed end-to-end. When occurring in one of the arms of a chromosome, the inversion is termed paracentric; when the inverted segment includes the centromere, it is called pericentric.

Isoallele: Allelic genes which are 'normal' and can be distinguished from one another only by their differing phenotypic expression when in combination with a dominant mutant allele.

Isochromosome: A type of chromosomal aberration in which one of the arms of a particular chromosome is duplicated because the centromere divides transversely and not longitudinally during cell division.

The two arms of an isochromosome are therefore of equal length and contain identical genes. This is an example of duplication, and deletion.

Isodisomy: The presence of two identical chromosomes derived from only one parent and none from the other as a result of non-disjunction during meiosis II. Compare with *heterodisomy.*

Isograft: A tissue graft between two individuals who have identical genotypes, as between MZ twins.

Isolate: A segment of a population within which assortative mating occurs.

Isotype: This refers to classes of immunoglobulin molecules IgA, IgE, IgG, IgD, IgM. Each class is determined by the type of heavy chain present in the molecule respectively.

Karyotype: The chromosome set of a somatic cell. A photomicrograph of an individual's chromosomes arranged in a standard fashion.

Kilobase (kb): One thousand DNA base pairs.

Kindred: An extended family group where each one is related, genetically or by marriage, to every other member of the group.

Kinetochore: Centomere, primary constriction of a chromosome.

Lethal equivalent: It is one gene which, if homozygous, would be lethal, or two genes which, if homozygous, would be lethal in half the homozygotes and so on.

Light chain: A major structural component of the antibody molecule, consisting of either a K or a chain. The light chain has a lower molecular weight than the other major component, the heavy chain.

LINEs (Long Interspersed Elements): A class of dispersed repetitive DNA in which each repeat is relatively long, up to 7 kb. Compare with SINEs.

Linkage: Greater association in inheritance of two or more non-allelic genes than is to be expected from independent assortment, because of location of the genes on the same chromosome.

Linkage disequilibrium: When there is non-random association of alleles at linked loci in a population, it leads to linkage disequilibrium.

Linkage equilibrium: When there is random association of alleles at linked loci in a population it creates linkage equilibrium.

Locus: The position or site of a gene on a chromosome. Different alleles are always found at the same position on the chromosome. A complex locus is a group of loci within which, at a time, mutation and recombination can occur at more than one site.

Locus control region: DNA sequences in the 5′ region of the globin gene clusters that is involved in transcription regulation.

LOD score: A statistical score of the relative likelihood of two loci being linked. The LOD score is the logarithm to base 10 of the ratio of the likelihood of linkage at a specific recombination fraction to the likelihood of no linkage. This is used to test genetic marker data in families to determine whether two loci are linked. By convention an LOD score of 3 (odds of 1000; in favour) is taken as proof of linkage and a score of –2 (100:1 against) as proof that loci are not linked.

Lyon hypothesis, Lyonisation: The hypothesis advanced by Mary F. Lyon that in mammals, one or the other of the two X chromosomes of the female is inactivated in embryonic cells and their descendants; and that mammalian females are consequently X chromosome mosaics. See *Barr body, sex chromatin.*

Major gene: Single locus responsible for a trait in contrast to polygenic trait.

Malformation: A primary morphologic defect because of an abnormal development.

Malignant: A tumour that is capable of invading surrounding tissues and metastasising (spreading) to other sites in the body. Compare with benign tumour.

Manifesting heterozygote: A female heterozygous for an X-linked disorder, in whom, because of Lyonisation of the 'normal' X chromosome the trait is expressed clinically with approximately the same degree of severity as in hemizygous affected males.

Mapping a chromosome: Determining the position and order of gene loci on a chromosome, especially by analysing the frequency of recombination between the loci.

Mature transcript: The mRNA after the exons have been spliced out. Before splicing the mRNA is referred to as a primary transcript.

Map unit, Map distance: The measure of distance separating loci on a chromosome as inferred from the recombination fraction.

Megabase (mb): One million base pairs.

Meiosis: The special type of cell division occurring in the germ cells by which gametes having the haploid chromosome number are produced from diploid cells. Two meiotic divisions occur, first and second (meiosis I and meiosis II). Reduction in number takes place during meiosis I, and further reduction of genetic material during meiosis II.

Memory cells: A class of high-affinity binding B cells. They persist after the immune response of the body is over. It provides a relatively fast specific response in case the memory cells encounter the same microorganisms/foreign antigens.

Mendelisation: The attribute of traits which show simple qualitative patterns of inheritance.

Messenger RNA: The RNA which has a base sequence complementary for a DNA strand, and is formed during 'transcription' to function during 'translation' as a template for synthesis of a polypeptide.

Metacentric: Designating a chromosome with a nearly centrally placed centromere. Also called median.

Metaphase: The stage of a cell division when the contracted chromosomes, each consisting of two chromatids, line up on the equatorial plate following the disappearance of the nuclear membrane.

Metastasis: The spread of malignant cancer cells from one site in the body to another.

Methylation: In genetics, it refers to the addition of methyl groups to cytosine bases, forming 5-methylcytosine. Methylation is done for reducing transcription of genes.

MHC: Abbreviation for the major histocompatibility complex, H-2 in the mouse or HLA in humans.

Microdeletion: A chromosomal deletion too small to be seen under the microscope. See also *contiguous gene syndrome*. Example, DiGeorge syndrome, Prader-Willi syndrome.

Microsatellite: A type of satellite DNA comprising small repeat units usually two, three or four bp, that occur in tandem.

Microsatellite repeat polymorphism: A type of genetic variation in populations consisting of differing numbers of microsatellite repeat units at a locus.

Mimic genes: Different genes with similar phenotypic effects. Also called gene mimics or genocopies.

Minisatellite: A type of satellite DNA that consists of tandem repeat units each about 20–70 bp in length. Variation in the number of minisatellite repeats is the basis of VNTR polymorphism.

Missense: A mutation at the level of base pairs of DNA whereby a codon specific amino acid is changed to specify another amino acid. Compare with *nonsense mutation*.

Mitosis: Somatic cell division resulting in the formation of two daughter cells, each with the same chromosome complement as the parent cell.

Mitotic cycle: The cycle of a cell between two successive mitoses, in which four periods are distinguished: G_1 (Gap 1), S (DNA synthesis), G_2 (Gap 2) and M (Mitosis).

Mobile elements: DNA sequences that are capable of inserting themselves into other locations in the genome.

Modifier gene: A gene that alters the expression of another gene at another locus.

Monoclonal: A group of cells that belong to a single clone, i.e., all cells are derived from the same single ancestral cell.

Monosomy: The state where only one member of a given homologous chromosomal pair is present, e.g., the single X of XO, as in Turner's syndrome. Partial monosomy results when part of a chromosome is deleted so that the portion of the homologous chromosome is monosomic.

Monozygotic, Identical, Monozygous: Twins derived from a single fertilised ovum. Such twins are genetically identical.

Morphogenesis: The process of development of a cell, organ or organism. It is the evolution and development of the form of a cell, organ, or organism.

Mosaic, Mixoploid: An individual composed of cells of different genotype or karyotype derived from a single zygote. Mosaicism is brought about by gene or chromosomal mutation in somatic cells. It does not include different cell types arising by neoplasia or chimerism. Gonadal mosaicism results from a somatic mutation early in embryogenesis so that some or all the germ cells are of a mutant type. A person with a gonadal mosaicism for a dominant trait can have two or more children with that trait without showing it himself. Gonadal mosaicism may also involve chromosomal aberration.

Multifactorial: A trait determined by multiple factors, genetic and non-genetic (environmental), each with only a minor additive effect.

Multiple alleles: The existence of more than two different alleles at a given locus of a chromosome in a population. In a given individual only two of these alleles occur, one derived from each parent.

Multipoint mapping: Type of genetic mapping in which the recombination frequencies of three of more loci are estimated simultaneously.

Mutagen: A substance that induces a mutation.

Mutant: An individual bearing a gene in which a mutation has occurred, that expresses itself in the phenotype of the organism.

Mutation: 1) Process by which a gene or chromosome undergoes a structural change. 2) Modified gene resulting from mutation. 3) By extension, the individual manifesting the mutation, i.e., a mutant. The term is commonly used to describe a change in a single gene-locus (point mutation). A mutation which occurs in the somatic cells (somatic mutation) cannot be transmitted to the next generation.

Mutation rate: The number of mutations of any one particular locus which occur per gamete per generation.

Muton: The smallest unit of DNA which can be involved in a mutation. Since change in a single base pair changes the genetic code, a muton is equivalent to one base pair.

Natural killer cell: A type of lymphocyte that is involved in early phase of non-specific defence against foreign microbes and tumours and whose function is not restricted to MHC.

Neoplasm or tumour: An abnormal growth of cells characterised by unregulated proliferation, abnormal secretions, invasiveness and metastasis.

Non-directiveness: Term used in genetic counselling for that approach in which information is provided to a family but final decision about reproduction is left to the family.

Non-disjunction: The failure of separation of paired chromosomes or of chromatids during cell division, resulting in one daughter cell receiving none of the chromosomes in question. Non-disjunction can occur during a meiotic or mitotic division.

Non-secretor: See *secretor.*

Non-sense mutation: A type of mutation wherein mRNA stop codon is either produced or eliminated. This leads to respectively a premature termination of translation or an elongated protein chain. Compare with mis-sense mutation.

Non-penetrance: Failure of a genetic trait to be evident in a population even though the genotype usually productive of that phenotype, is present. Opposite of expressivity.

Northern blotting: A laboratory blotting technique analogous to southern blotting. It is used for detection of RNA molecules. It is done by electrophoretic separation of RNA with subsequent transfer to a filter which can be clearly localised by hybridisation to a complementary DNA probe.

Nucleoside: A purine or pyrimidine base attached to a 5-carbon sugar (deoxyribose or ribose).

Nucleosome: A globular, repetitive constituent of chromatin fibre, consisting of a histone core, around which is wound a variable length of DNA (about 140 base pairs).

Nucleotide: A nucleoside attached to a phosphate group. A nucleic acid molecule is a polymer of many nucleotide units.

Obligate carrier / heterozygote: An individual who may be clinically unaffected but on the basis of pedigree analysis must carry a mutant allele. Example: parents of a child with an autosomal recessive disorder.

Occurrence risk: The probability that a couple who have not yet produced a child with disease in question will produce a child with a genetic disease. Compare with *recurrence risk.*

Ochre codon: UAA, one of the three stop codons.

Oligonucleotide: DNA sequence made up of a small number of nucleotide bases.

Oncogene: A gene that can transform a normal cell into a cancer cell.

Oogenesis: The process of formation of the female gametes, from primordial germ cells to mature ovum.

Operator gene: A gene which switches on adjacent structural gene(s).

Operon: A postulated unit of gene action, consisting of an operator gene and the closely linked structural gene(s), whose action it controls.

Optimon: A unit of natural selection. Also called *selecton.* 1) The short arm of a chromosome (from the French petit=small). 2) Often used to indicate the frequency of the more common allele of a pair, in the statement of Hardy-Weinberg law.

Palindrome: Any DNA sequence whose complementary sequences is the same if read backwards, e.g., 5'CTAATCGATTAG will have complimentary strand 3'CTAATCGATTAC

Panmixis: Random mating.

Partial trisomy: A chromosomal abnormality in which a portion of the chromosome is present in triplicate. It is produced either by reciprocal translocation or unequal crossing over.

Pedigree: A diagrammatic representation of family history, indicating the affected and normal individuals, gene carriers and their relationship to the propositus.

Penetrance: The frequency of expression of a genotype in a population. When the frequency is less than 100 per cent, the trait is said to exhibit reduced penetrance. See *non-penetrance.*

Percutaneous umbilical blood sampling (PUBS): Cordocentesis. Prenatal fetoscopic diagnostic technique in which fetal blood is obtained for laboratory examination by puncturing the umbilical cord.

Pharmacogenetics: The area of biochemical genetics concerned with responses to drugs and their genetically controlled variations.

Phenocopy: The alteration of the phenotype, by nutrition or the exposure to environmental stress during development, to a form imitating that characteristically produced by a specific gene. Thus rickets due to a dietary lack of Vitamin D would be a phenocopy of vitamin D-resistant rickets. A suntan is a phenocopy of the genetically determined brown skin.

Phenodeviant: A member of a population different significantly in phenotype from the population as a whole.

Phenotype: The appearance (physical, biochemical, and physiological) of an individual, produced by the interaction of environment and the genotype.

Philadelphia chromosome: An aberrant human chromosome. Ph[1] is found in patients suffering from chronic myeloid leukemia. The chromosome is believed to be chromosome 21 or 22 minus a substantial portion of its long arm (22q minus).

Physical mapping: The determination of physical distances between genes using cytogenetic and molecular techniques. Compare with *genetic mapping*, in which recombination frequencies are determined.

Plasma cell: A mature B lymphocyte which can secrete antibodies.

Plasmagenes: Genes situated within the cytoplasm of the cell.

Plasmid: An extrachromosomal complex, small circular double stranded DNA molecule capable of independently replicating in bacteria. The plasmids are used, in molecular biology as cloning vectors in recombinant DNA techniques.

Pleiotropy, Polypheny: The phenomenon of a single gene being responsible for a number of distinct and seemingly unrelated phenotypic effects.

Point mutation: See *mutation*.

Polygenic, Quantitative inheritance: Determined by many genes at different loci,with small additive effects. To be distinguished from multifactorial, in which environmental as well as genetic factors are involved. However, to many geneticists, polygenic and multifactorial are synonymous.

Polymerase chain reaction (PCR): It is a laboratory technique of amplifying (producing) a large number of copies of specific DNA sequence of interest flanked by two oligonucleotide primers. DNA is alternately heated and cooled in the presence of DNA polymerase and free nucleotides so that the specified DNA segment is denatured, hybridised with primers and extended by DNA polymerase. By this technique a short DNA or RNA sequence can be amplified a million times. This permits analysis of a short sequence from very small quantities of DNA or RNA without the necessity of cloning it first.

Polymorphism: The occurrence together, in the same habitat, of two or more discontinuous forms of a trait, in such proportions that the rarest of them cannot be maintained in the population by mutation alone. The existence of two or more genetically different classes in the same interbreeding population, e.g., Rh-positive and Rh-negative humans. The polymorphism may be transient, or the proportions of the different classes may remain the same for many generations. In the latter case, the phenomenon is referred to as balanced polymorphism. Geographic polymorphism is said to exist when the classes are located in different regions. Over forty genetic polymorphisms in serum proteins, red cell antigens and red cell enzymes are known.

Polypeptide: A chain of one or more peptides. Each peptide has two or more amino acids, held together by peptide bonds between the amino group of one and the carboxyl group of the adjoining one. A protein molecule may be composed of a single polypeptide, or of two or more identical or different polypeptides.

Polyploid: Any multiple of the basic haploid chromosome number, other than the diploid, thus $3N$ $4N$ and so on.

Polysome, Polyribosome: A group of ribosomes associated with the same molecule of messenger RNA.

Polyteny: A multi-stranded chromosome in which, following replication, the sister chromatids do not separate.

Poly-A tail: The addition of several adenine nucleotides to the 3[l] end of a primary mRNA transcript.

Population genetics: A branch of genetics that deals with genetical variation and genetical evolution of populations.

Population screening: The testing of a large population for a particular disease.

Positional cloning: The technique of cloning a gene localised to a particular region of chromosome, without any prior knowledge of the product of the gene.

Prenatal diagnosis: Determination of the sex, karyotype or phenotype of a fetus, usually prior to the 20th week of gestation. A variety of techniques, especially amniocentesis and cell culture, is employed.

Primary constriction: See *centromere*.

Primary transcript: The first mRNA molecules transcribed off a gene containing introns as well as exons. A mature mRNA transcript is formed from the primary transcript when the exons are spliced out.

Primer: An oligonucleotide sequence that flanks either side of the DNA to be amplified by PCR.

Primer extension: Part of the PCR process in which DNA polymerase extends the DNA sequence beginning at an oligonucleotide primer.

Proband, Index case: An affected individual (irrespective of sex) through whom the family came to the attention of the investigator is called propositus, if a male proposita if a female; (plurals and propositi and propositae).

Probe: In molecular genetics, it refers to a labelled DNA or RNA sequence used to detect the presence of a complementary sequence, a gene, mRNA transcript or gene product usually through molecular hybridisation of the probe with the target. It can also refer to a reagent which is capable of recognising a desired clone in a mixture of many DNA or RNA sequences.

Promoter: A DNA sequence located at the 5ˡ end of a gene and determines the site of initiation of transcription. RNA polymerase binds to it in order to begin transcription of the DNA into mRNA. It also decides the quantity of mRNA, and the tissue distribution of the same.

Proofreading: The rectification of errors that may have crept in replication, transcription or translation.

Prophase: The first stage of cell division, during which the chromosomes become visible as discrete structures and subsequently thicken and shorten. Prophase of the first meiotic division is further characterised by pairing (synapsis) of homologous chromosomes.

Propositus, Proposita: See *proband.*

Protein electrophoresis: A laboratory technique in which amino acid variations are identified on the basis of charge differences that cause differential mobility of polypeptides through an electrically charged medium.

Proto-oncogene: A normal gene whose protein product is involved in the regulation of cell growth. When altered by a mutational event, a proto-oncogene can become a cancer causing oncogene.

Pseudoalleles: Genes at two closely linked loci concerned with the same function, rarely can be separated by crossing over. Though known in experimental organisms, they have not been demonstrated in man.

Pseudoautosomal region: The distal tip of the Y chromosome short arm which exchanges material with the distal tip of the X chromosome short arm during meiosis in male.

Pseudomosaicism: False indication of fetal mosaicism caused by an artifact in cell culture.

Pulsed field gel electrophoresis: A type of electrophoresis suitable for relatively large DNA fragments >5000. The fragment is moved through a gel by alternating pulses of electricity across fields that are at 90 degrees to one another in orientation.

Purine: The two DNA as well as RNA bases, namely adenine and guanine that consist of double carbon-nitrogen rings.

Pyrimidine: The two DNA bases, namely thymine and cytosine and two RNA bases, namely uracil and cytosine that consist of a single carbon nitrogen ring.

q: 1) The long arm of chromosome. 2) Often used to indicate the frequency of the rarer allele of a pair, as in the statement of the Hardy-Weinberg law.

Q bands: The pattern of bright and dim cross-bands seen on chromosomes under fluorescent light after quinacrine staining.

Quantitative trait: A genetically governed trait that can be measured phenotypically on a continuous scale, e.g., height, weight.

Quasicontinuous variation: The type of variation shown by a multifactorial trait which becomes manifest only on crossing a certain threshold and thus appears to have a discontinuous distribution.

Quasidominant, Quasidominance: The direct transmission, from generation to generation of a recessive trait. This pattern of inheritance is produced by the mating of a recessive homozygote with a heterozygote, so that recessively affected members appear in two successive generations and the frequency of affected persons in the second generation is half that of the first generation.

Random genetic drift: See *Drift.*

Random mating, Panmixis: Selection of a mate without regard to the genotype of the mate. In a randomly mating population, the frequencies of the various matings are determined solely by the frequencies of the genes concerned.

Recessive: A trait which is expressed in homozygotes for a particular gene but not in those who are heterozygous for that gene.

Recombinant: An individual who exhibits a recombination of genes.

Recombinant DNA: Artificially synthesised DNA in which a gene or part of a gene from one organism is inserted into the genome of another.

Recombinase: An enzyme that helps to bring about somatic recombination in B and T lymphocytes.

Recombination: The occurrence of progeny with combinations of genes other than those that occurred in the parents, due to independent assortment or crossing over.

Recon: The smallest unit of DNA capable of recombination, crossing over can occur within the cistron, so that the smallest unit of recombination may be any two successive nucleotides in a codon.

Recurrence risk: The probability that a genetic disorder present in one or more members of a family, will recur in another member of the same or a subsequent generation.

Reduction division: The first meiotic division, where the chromosome number is reduced from diploid to haploid per cell. Also see *meiosis*.

Regulator gene: A gene whose primary function is to control the rate of synthesis of the products of other genes. The regulator gene (rG) controls the synthesis of a protein repressor (R), which inhibits the action of an operator gene (oG) and thus turns off the operon it controls.

Repetitive DNA: DNA sequences found in the genome in multiple copies that are either dispersed or repeated in tandem.

Replication: The duplication of the double stranded DNA molecule.

Replication bubble: A structure formed by coalescence of two adjacent replication forks in the copying of the DNA molecule of a chromosome.

Replication fork: The structure formed at the site of origin of replication of the double stranded DNA molecule of chromosomes.

Replication origin: The point at which replication begins on a DNA in eukaryotes. There are many replication origins in each chromosome.

Replicative segregation: The changes in the proportion of mitochondrial DNA alleles as the mitochondria reproduce.

Repulsion: In a double heterozygote, linkage is said to be in the repulsion phase when the mutant alleles of interest at the two loci are on opposite chromosomes.

Restriction digest: A process in which DNA is cleaved into restriction fragments by restriction enzyme.

Restriction endonuclease: A bacterial enzyme which has the capability of cleaving DNA at a definite DNA sequence called restriction site.

Restriction fragment: A piece of DNA that is cleaved by restriction endonuclease.

Restriction fragment length polymorphism (RFLP): This is polymorphism seen in DNA sequence in population due to presence or absence of a particular restriction site. It is detected by digesting DNA with a restriction endonuclease, electrophoresing the resulting restriction fragments, transferring the fragments to a solid medium (blot) and hybridising the DNA on the blot with a labelled probe.

Restriction site: A DNA sequence that is cleaved by a specific restriction endonuclease.

Restriction site polymorphism: A variation in DNA sequence that is due to the presence or the absence of a restriction site. This type of polymorphism is the basis for most traditional RFLPs.

Retrovirus: A type of RNA virus that can transcribe in reverse its RNA into DNA for insertion into the genome of a host cell. It is a useful vector for gene therapy.

Reverse banding (R-banding): A laboratory technique for producing banding patterns in chromosomes. The chromosomes first are heated in a phosphate buffer which produces dark and light band patterns that are the reverse of those seen in G-banding.

Reverse transcriptase: An enzyme that can transcribe RNA into DNA.

Ribosome: Small spherical structures found in cytoplasm. They are rich in RNA and are the site of translation of mature messenger RNA into amino acid sequences.

Ring chromosome: A structurally abnormal chromosome, in which the ends of both arms break off and get deleted and the remainder of the chromosome becomes a ring by the mutual reunion of its ends.

RNA, Ribonucleic acid: Any of a family of polynucleotides characterised by their component sugar (ribose) and one of their pyrimidines (uracil). RNA molecules are single stranded and have molecular weights lower than that of DNAs. There are four classes of RNAs: messenger RNA, ribosomal RNA transfer RNA and viral RNA.

RNA polymerase: An enzyme that binds to a promoter site and synthesises messenger RNA from a DNA template.

Robertsonian translocation: See *centric fusion*.

Satellite DNA: A class of DNA sequences which separates out on density-gradient centrifugation as a shoulder or satellite to the main peak of DNA. It contains highly repetitive DNA sequences which code for ribosomal and transferRNAs. It constitutes 10 to 15 per cent of the DNA of the human genome.

Secretor: The person who secretes ABO blood group substance into saliva and other body fluids.

Segregation: The separation of allelic genes at meiosis, i.e., during gametogenesis. Since allelic genes occupy the same locus on homologous chromosomes, they pass to different gametes, i.e., they segregate.

Selection: 1) The manner in which kindred are chosen for study, i.e., ascertainment. 2) In population genetics, the operation of forces that determines the relative fitness of a genotype in the population.

Sense strand / Coding strand: The double stranded DNA that has the same 5¹ to 3¹ sense sequences, except that T is substituted by U in mRNA. The coding strand is not transcribed by RNA polymerase.

Sensitivity: The proportion of affected individuals who are correctly identified by a test as true positives.

Sequence anomaly: A primary defect leading to secondary structural changes in sequence of development. Examples: Oligohydramnios sequence, Pierre-obin sequence.

Sex chromatin: See *Barr body.*

Sex chromosomes: Chromosomes responsible for sex determination. (XX in women, XY in men).

Sex-influenced, Sex-conditioned: A trait which is not X-linked in its pattern of inheritance but is expressed differently (either in degree or in frequency) in males and females, e.g., a sex-influenced, autosomal gene may behave as a dominant in males and as a recessive in females. Furthermore in the homozygous female the condition may be expressed to a minor degree, e.g., pattern baldness.

Sex-limited: A trait which is expressed in only one sex, though the gene determining it is not X-linked.

Sex-linkage: Genes carried on the sex chromosomes. Since there are very few Mendelising genes on the Y chromosome, the term is often used synonymously for X-linkage.

Sex-ratio: The relative proportion of males and females of specific age distribution in a population. The primary sex ratio refers to that at fertilisation; the secondary sex ratio refers to that at birth.

Sibship: Group of brothers and/or sisters.

Signal transduction, A process in which biochemical messages are transmitted from a cell surface to the nucleus.

Silent allele: An allele which has no detectable product.

Silent substitution / Silent mutation: A point mutation in a codon that does into alter the amino acid sequence because of the degeneracy of the genetic code.

SINEs (Short Interspersed Elements): A class of dispersed repetitive DNA in which each repeat is relatively short.

Single strand conformation polymorphism (SSCP): A technique for detecting variations in DNA sequence. Single stranded DNA fragments are run through a non-denaturing gel. Because of the differences (conformation) in the three-dimensional structure of single stranded DNA there is differential gel electrophoresis motility under special conditions.

Single-copy DNA: The DNA sequences that occur only once in the genome. Compare with *repetitive DNA.*

Sister chromatid exchange: Exchange of DNA segments between sister chromatids, during mitosis. This occurs very frequently in patients with Bloom's syndrome.

Solenoid: A model of quaternary structure of chromosomes consisting of approximately six nucleosomes.

Somatic cell genetics: The study of genetic phenomena in cultured somatic cells.

Somatic cell hybridisation: A technique of physical gene mapping. Somatic cells of two different species are fused and allowed to undergo cell division. Chromosomes from one species are selectively lost, resulting in clones with only one or a few chromosomes from one of the species, which is used for assigning genes to particular chromosomes.

Somatic hypermutation: The phenomenon of an extreme increase in the mutation rate seen in somatic cells. Commonly observed in B lymphocytes as they achieve increased binding affinity for foreign antigens.

Somatic mutation: See *mutation.*

Somatic recombination: The exchange of genetic material between homologous chromosomes during mitosis in somatic cells which is much rarer than in meiotic recombination.

Southern blot / transfer: A technique devised by E.M. Southern. It consists of transferring DNA fragments that have been separated by agarose gel electrophoresis to a nitrocellulose filter on which specific DNA fragments are then detected by hybridising.

Specificity: The proportion of unaffected individuals who are correctly identified by a test as true negatives. Compare with *sensitivity.*

Spermatogenesis: The process of formation of spermatozoa. It includes both meiosis and spermiogenesis.

Spermiogenesis: The formation of sperm from the spermatids produced during the meiotic divisions of spermatocytes.

Spindle: Microtubular complex seen in the cell during cell division. It extends from centriole to the centromeres of chromosomes. It enables the arrangement of chromosomes on equator at metaphase and their segregation at anaphase.

Splice site mutation: An alteration in DNA sequence of donor or acceptor site or of consensus sites near them. This results in altered intron splicing, such that portions of exons are deleted or portion of introns are included in the mature mRNA transcript.

Sporadic: A trait, occurring in an isolated case within a kindred, which has no known genetic basis.

Stop Codon / Termination Codon: One of the three codons (UAG, UAA and UGA) of mRNA that specify the point at which translation of the mRNA ceases, leading to termination of the synthesis of polypeptide.

Structural gene: See *cistron.*

Submetacentric: A chromosome having centromere located in between the centre and one of its ends.

Syndrome: A group of symptoms and signs that occur together, characterising a disease.

Synteny, Syntenic: Presence together on the same chromosome of two or more gene-loci, whether or not they are close enough together for linkage to be demonstrated.

T cells: Small lymphocytes (thymus-dependent cells) responsible for cell-mediated response to antigens.

Tandem repeat: DNA sequence that occurs in multiple copies located directly next to one another. Compare with dispersed repetitive DNA.

Telocentric: A chromosome with a terminal centromere.

Telophase: The stage of cell division which begins when the daughter chromosomes reach the poles of the dividing cell and lasts until the two daughter cells take on the appearance of interphase cells.

Template: A strand of DNA that serves as the model for replication of a new strand. It also denotes the DNA strand from which mRNA is transcribed.

Teratogen: Any agent that produces or raises the incidence of congenital malformations.

Termination sequence: The DNA sequence that signals the cessation of transcription.

Tetrad / Bivalent: The set of four homologous chromatids (two sister chromatids of each homologous chromosome) seen during the metaphase I of meiosis.

Tetraploid: Having four haploid sets of chromosomes in the nucleus.

Thymine: A pyrimidine base constituent of DNA.

Tissue mosaic: Only specific tissues of the body show mosaicism.

Trait: Any gene-determined characteristic. Although in medicine it has come to be used particularly for

the heterozygous state of a recessive disorder such as sickle-cell anemia, it has a more general meaning in genetics.

Transcription: The formation of messenger RNA against a DNA template.

Transduction: Change in the genetic constitution of an organism (e.g., bacterium) by treatment with DNA from a different strain. (A bacteriophage is used as a vector.)

Transfection: Introduction of foreign DNA sequence into eukaryotic cells in culture. It also refers to the transformation of bacterial cells by infection with phage to produce infectious phage particles.

Transformation: A form of recombination of genetic material in bacteria in which a bacterium incorporates DNA extracted from other bacteria into its own genetic material.

Translation: The formation of a protein directed by a specific messenger RNA molecule.

Translocation: A chromosomal aberration involving transfer of a piece of one chromosome to a nonhomologous chromosome. If two non-homologous chromosomes exchange pieces, the translocation is reciprocal. When an individual or gamete carries neither more nor less than the normal diploid or haploid genetic material, respectively, the situation is referred to as balanced translocation. See also *centric fusion.*

Transposon: See *mobile element.*

Triplet: A unit of three linear successive bases in DNA or RNA which codes for a specific amino acid.

Triploid: A cell having three haploid sets of chromosomes, or an individual made up of such cells.

Triradius: In dermatoglyphics, a point from which the dermal ridge course in three directions at angles of approximately 120 degrees.

Trisomy: The state that is diploid but contains one extra chromosome, homologous with one of the existing pairs, so that one kind of chromosome is present in triplicate, e.g., trisomy 21 (Down's syndrome).

True negative: An individual who is correctly identified by a test as not having a disease.

True positive: An individual who is correctly identified by a test as having a disease.

Tumour: See *neoplasm.*

Tumour suppressor: A gene whose products help to control normal cell growth and proliferation. Any mutations in tumour suppressors can lead to cancer.

Ultrasonography: A procedure to delineate the outline of

various structures using high frequency sound waves. Often used in prenatal diagnosis.

Unifactorial, Mendelising: Inheritance controlled by a single gene pair.

Uniparental disomy: When both the members of two homologous chromosomes are derived from a single parent because of non-disjunction at either meiosis I or meiosis II and hence no chromosomal member of the other parent gets inherited. It can be heterodisomy or isodisomy.

Variable expression: When the same genotype produces varying degree of expression at phenotypic level.

Variable number of tandem repeats (VNTR): A type of polymorphism created by variation in the number of minisatellite repeats in a given chromosome region.

Vector: It is a biological vehicle in the form of phage plasmid, cosmid or YAC which is used to carry DNA insert into a bacterium.

Wild type: Term used especially in experimental genetics to indicate most frequently observed phenotype, or one arbitrarily designated as 'normal'.

Wild type gene: The allele commonly found in nature or arbitrarily designated as 'normal' (often symbolised as +) or normal homozygote (+/+).

Xenograft: Graft from a donor of one species to a host of a different species.

X-inactivation: See *Lyon hypothesis*.

X-inactivation centre: A locus on the X chromosome which is required to signal X inactivation. It includes *XIST* gene.

X-linkage: Genes carried on the X chromosome are said to be X-linked.

Yeast artificial chromosome (YAC): A synthesised yeast chromosome capable of carrying a large DNA insert of around 1000 kb.

Zygote: The diploid cell resulting from the union of the haploid male and female gametes. The term is also used to refer to the organism that develops from the zygote.

Zygosity: The term refers to multiple births in relation to their origin vis-a-vis the zygote, e.g., twins may be either monozygotic or dizygotic. To determine which type a certain twin pair represents is to determine the zygosity of the pair.

BIBLIOGRAPHY

1. Abercombie M., Hickman C.J. and Johnson M.L. 1970. *A Dictionary of Biology*, ELBS, Penguin Books, London.
2. Bullock A. and Stallybrass O. (eds.) 1977. *The Harper Dictionary of Modern Thought*, Harper & Row, New York.
3. Ciba Foundation Symposium 1979. *Human Genetics: Possibilities and Realities*, Excerpta Medica, Amsterdam.
4. Dawkins R. 1982. *The Extended Phenotype*, Oxford University Press, Oxford.
5. Emery A.H., and Rimoin D.L. (eds.) 1983. *Principles and Practice of Medical Genetics*, Volumes 1 & 2, Churchill Livingstone, Edinburgh.
6. Fraser Roberts J.A., and Pembrey M.E. 1983. *An Introduction to Medical Genetics*, Oxford University Press, Oxford.
7. Friedman J.M., Dill F.J., Hayden M.R. and McGillivray B.C. 1992. *Genetics: The National Medical Series for Independent Study*, Harwal Publishing Company, Malvern, Pennsylvania.
8. Goodenough U. 1984. *Genetics*, Holt-Saunders, Philadelphia.
9. *Harrison's Principles of Internal Medicine*, McGraw-Hill, New York, 1994.
10. Jorde L.B., Carey J.C. and White R.L. 1995. *Medical Genetics*, Mosby, Missouri.
11. Krupp M.A. and Chatton M.J. 1984. *Current Medical Diagnosis and Treatment 1984*, Lange Medical Publication, Maruzen Asia, Singapore.
12. Medawar P.B. and Medawar J.S. 1983. *Aristotle to Zoos: A Philosophical Dictionary of Biology*, Harvard University Press, Cambridge.
13. Mueller R.F. and Young I.D. 1995. *Elements of Medical Genetics*, ELBS, Churchill Livingstone.
14. Strickberger M.W. 1976. *Genetics*, Macmillan, New York.
15. Thompson M.W. McInnes R.R. and Willard H.F. 1995. *Genetics in Medicine*, Saunders, Philadelphia.

INDEX